BETRAYAL
—of—
VALOR

AN EXPOSÉ OF A HORRIBLY FLAWED
VETERAN'S ADMINISTRATION

★ ★ ★

ERIC GANG

SUTTON HART PRESS

Betrayal of Valor is published by Sutton Hart Press, llc
Vancouver, Washington

Inquiries: Inquiries@SuttonHart.com
Website: www.suttonhart.com
First Printing: June, 2022
Copyright 2022 by Eric Gang
All rights reserved

ISBN
Hardcover: 9781947779273
Digital: 9781947779280

Library of Congress Number: Pending

Printed in the United States of America
Media and Reviewer Contact: maggie@platformstrategy.com
Copy Editor: Veronica Pamoukaghlian
Layout Design: Jason Enterline

TABLE OF CONTENTS

This book is dedicated to…

all the heroic service personnel of the U.S. military who have come home with injuries of body and mind, and especially those who have been treated with indifference by their government…Strong be your hearts.

FOREWORD

By The Honorable Edward T. Timperlake

In his Second Inaugural Address, President Lincoln uttered the immortal words that became the concise mission statement of the Department of Veterans Affairs: "To care for him who shall have borne the battle and for his widow, and his orphan." Today, too many VA employees have lost sight of that mission, subjecting ill and disabled veterans to unconscionable wait times, incompetent care, and callous, bureaucratic disregard. Thankfully, there are still Americans who believe in a never-ending commitment to our nation's veterans. Among them is Eric Gang, a passionate veterans rights attorney, whose seminal book, *Betrayal of Valor, An exposé of a horribly flawed Veterans Administration*, conveys irrefutable, vividly detailed, hard evidence of betrayal within the Department of Veterans Affairs.

Skillfully written and easy to read, Gang's smart book shines disinfecting sunlight on many—far too many—tragic cases of veterans cast aside by uncaring bureaucrats. In my personal experience, many rank-and-file VA employees are dedicated and decent. The problems lie with the "others"—the incompetents (at times deadly so), the retirement-minded clock watchers, the fraudsters, the outright crooks, and the way-too-many bullying, mean-spirited careerists. The "others" not only endanger but degrade and dispirit valiant former service members. A national service officer of the Disabled American Veterans described their soul-crushing damage to me quite succinctly, yet ominously: "they have ways to get you." These are the villains that undermine the VA today whom Attorney Gang puts dead center in his legal crosshairs with great success.

As an attorney, Mr. Gang knows how to lay out a case. He sets the stage with an overview of the benefits system, followed by a powerful section on the *Physical Impact of War*. Then, as the sympathetic reader yearns for a compassionate response to the deserving veterans' need for care, he delivers the chilling reality of *The Deadly Wait*. Deadly indeed, and most revealing, given how the unofficial mantra of the VA has become "Deny, Delay, Death."

The epic brilliance of *Betrayal of Valor* can be seen in the scope of its chapters, with specifics ripped from the headlines, covering *Dangerous Doctors, Agent Orange and Vietnam Veterans, The Military Sexual Trauma Epidemic, Traumatic Brain Injury, Service-Disabled Veteran-Owned Small Business Fraud, Military Service Substance Abuse, Veteran Homeless*, and *Suicide Among U.S Veterans*.

Myself a combat-disabled Vietnam Veteran, I have also served in the VA, as the first Assistant Secretary of Veterans Affairs for Congressional and Public Affairs and then Public and Intergovernmental Affairs, while the VA transitioned to Cabinet status, becoming The Department of Veterans Affairs. Proud to have served in war and in peace, I take pride, too, in the work done by our team under the late Ed Derwinski, the first DVA Secretary. We accomplished two critically important missions: service-connecting the effects of Agent Orange for Vietnam Veterans and establishing a nationwide network of "vet centers" to address the lingering effects of PTSD.

It is in this capacity that I would urge the DVA to issue Attorney Gang's book free to veterans suffering from PTSD or from exposure to the toxic effects of chemicals on the battlefield. One of the most powerful ways a nation can express gratitude to veterans who are hurting is to show them that our society is still free and open, we still honor our First Amendment, and the Department of Veterans Affairs can take deserved criticism. By distributing Attorney Gang's important, comprehensive book to veterans, the VA will empower them with specific knowledge to successfully fight for earned benefits.

Healing requires more than medication. It requires a restoration of the heart and soul, through intangible measures. Servicemembers who have shared valor and sacrifice get that, and they take comfort from the knowledge that someone with the ability to fight for them also "gets it." For that reason, reading *Betrayal Of Valor*, and sharing the valiant fight Attorney Gang wages, can be a healing experience for those veterans who have felt forgotten.

The Honorable Edward T. Timperlake
Former Assistant Secretary Department of Veterans Affairs
Former Senior Government Officer Department of Veterans Affairs

FOREWORD

By Norm Pattis

"You've got to come listen to Eric Gang," my friend said. "He's amazing." We were in Arizona, at a convention. I am not generally inclined to go to listen to another lawyer. What's he going to say or do that I haven't already thought of or done? I went, nonetheless.

And I fell in love with Attorney Gang. Reading this book made me recall how blown away I was as I watched him in Arizona. His command of the law regarding veteran's rights is encyclopedic. His passion is awe-inspiring. His attention to detail is intimidating. I would not want to see him across the aisle from me in a courtroom. My hunch is that no one outworks him. And he has the track record to prove it.

Eric Gang is a hero among American lawyers. He made me wish I was starting my legal career all over again. I'd work for him for free, simply to be mentored and inspired by his courage, grit, and generosity of spirit.

Of course, Eric would tell you that he isn't the hero. His clients are the heroes and heroines. He's right, in a manner of speaking. He represents veterans, men and women who have risked life and limb in the service of our country. Sadly, their estates, in the case of those who have given their lives, or they themselves, when they have been broken or maimed in the line of duty, need a warrior of their own, someone inspired to tangle with a government far too often callous, distracted, or unconcerned about its commitment to military veterans.

But Eric has a passion for serving veterans that transforms him from just another lawyer in a suit into something dazzling, He is the lawyer I would want standing beside me if my future were on the line. He is passionate, eloquent, learned, and, in ways that defy mere description, charismatic. It's no wonder that clients nationwide trust him.

Betrayal of Valor reflects Eric's strengths. It is no mere compilation of war stories, although you learn about his handling of cases. This is a resource guide. It is at once a roadmap and an overview of the Veterans Administration system, a description of the benefits to which a veteran is entitled and a tool for the perplexed to use when confronted with the all-too-often unresponsive bureaucratic machinery of government. There is a glossary that explains technical terms, and, most impressive of all, at least to me, hundreds of footnotes with citations to further resources you can use to learn more about any of the topics he discusses. Eric would no doubt be quick to tell you that no two cases are alike, but, given the well over 1000 cases he has successfully handled, he's learned enough to know trouble when he sees it, and to have quick and ready access to a strategy necessary to make the government listen.

After listening to Eric, I was introduced to him in the hallway. I expected a towering man, say twenty feet tall with granite fists and shoulders wide enough to carry the world's weight. Instead, I met a quiet, soft-spoken, understated gentleman. I was, and I remain, dumbstruck.

If you've decided to read this book, odds are that is because either you or someone you know needs help. You might find enough information in this volume to solve the problem on your own. But just in case you don't, do not be intimidated by the scholarship, vision, and passion of the man who wrote it. Eric Gang is the real deal, a warrior in service of warriors forgotten or neglected by the government that promised to care for them.

Call him. Something tells me he just might answer his own phone. I will never forget Eric Gang.

Norm Pattis

Author of *Taking Back the Courts, Juries and Justice,* and *In the Trenches*

INTRODUCTION

The Department of Veterans Affairs (VA) does not enjoy the best reputation, and with reason. Every few months, or even weeks, we hear of some egregious misconduct by that organization and the people entrusted with assisting the men and women who have fought for our country as they try to move on with their lives.

One day, we learned veterans were exposed to carcinogenic substances during their service, were never informed about it, and they are not receiving appropriate medical care. Then a whistleblower reveals the VA is systematically denying home loans to veterans who are employed in the legal cannabis industry. Later a major media outlet runs a story about how VA hospitals welcome doctors with a track record of malpractice with open arms. It is no secret that veterans who are at suicide risk do not receive appropriate mental health care, often with fatal consequences. And it can take months to get a doctor's appointment, even if you suffer from a life-threatening condition.

Allegations faced by the VA also include substandard health care and shocking wait times for processing benefits claims. Quite simply, few people, if any, in this country trust the VA to do its job properly. This includes lawmakers. Texas Rep. Beto O'Rourke conducts a survey of the VA's services accessibility in El Paso every year. "We don't trust the VA to tell us how the VA is doing, we trust veterans to tell us how the VA is doing," O'Rourke has commented.

The press has referred to the VA's benefits claims process as a "game of Chutes and Ladders." No matter how many shocking stories a veteran has read about the VA, they are seldom prepared for just how slow and flawed the system truly is. Even after news outlets disseminated countless horror stories, as told by helpless and virtually abandoned veterans and their families, very little seems to have changed over the years.

From hiring a psychiatrist with a history of sanctions related to sexual misconduct to denying benefits to individuals suffering from severe PTSD, the VA has done everything to merit a stellar spot in the podium of America's least efficient government institutions.

There is never a shortage of clients for attorneys looking to represent veterans who feel that America has failed them. In many cases, they come to our firm after exhausting every other possibility. Especially if they are suffering from a serious condition, people seldom view the prospect of complex litigation in a positive light. However, for the courageous men and women who have risked their lives for our nation, this is often the only way to secure appropriate care and assistance.

A Little History

No other country in the world has such an extensive benefits system for military veterans. As far back as the mid-1600s, the Pilgrims of Plymouth Colony enacted legislation to support soldiers that had been disabled during combat.

The first medical facility for veterans came to being in 1811, with the federal government's authorization. Later came pensions, not only for veterans but also for their widows and their children. And after the Civil War, veterans' benefits and related facilities kept expanding.

By the time the first World War began, there was already a complex system in place, made up of three separate agencies, which were consolidated into the Veterans Administration in 1930. Over 50 years passed without many fundamental changes to this structure until, in 1989, it became the "Department of Veterans Affairs" (DVA), which still handles veterans affairs in the U.S. today.

The DVA, or VA, as it is most commonly known, is the second biggest Cabinet-level department in the nation. With a budget exceeding $100 billion, it employs a quarter of a million individuals and manages thousands of facilities nationwide.

Since the passing of the Veterans' Judicial Review Act of 1988, the VA's benefits decisions are open to judicial review. Earlier, veterans could only file an appeal with the Board of Veterans' Appeals. Whatever the Board said was final, and claimants were forced to accept its rulings. The Court of Appeals for Veterans Claims, created in 1989, now handles these types of cases. The VA's poor performance has been under increasing public scrutiny since then.

The VA Benefits System

What is Available to a Disabled Veteran?

The statutes and regulations addressing the benefits available to veterans are contained in Title 38 of the U.S. Code and Title 38 of the Code of Federal Regulations. The Federal appellate decisions come from the U.S. Court of Appeals for Veterans Claims and the U.S. Court of Appeals for the Federal Circuit. Their decisions can be found in West's Veterans Appeals Reporter and Westlaw or LexisNexis.

There are various types of monetary benefits available to veterans and their survivors:

- Service-Connected Disability Benefits ("Compensation")
- Non-Service-Connected Disability Pension Benefits for War-Time Veterans ("Needs Based")
- Service-Connected Death Benefits for Survivors of Deceased War-Time Veterans
- Service-Connected Death Benefits for Survivors of Deceased Veterans ("DIC")

Eligibility

To qualify for these benefits, a claimant has to establish basic eligibility. For veterans' benefits to attach to an individual or his survivor or dependent, he or she must establish the basic threshold of being a veteran. So who is a veteran?

A veteran is a "person who served in the active military naval or air service, and who was discharged or released therefrom under conditions other than dishonorable."[1] Individuals outside of the conventional military are also included, such as commissioned officers in the Public Health Service on full-time duty, commissioned officers of the National Oceanic and Atmospheric Administration or Environmental Science Services Administration on full-time duty, WWII service in the military forces of the Commonwealth of the Philippines, WWII service in the Merchant Marine. The term "active duty" can also cover Reservists or members of the National Guard. Members of the National Guard will be considered to have "active duty" if they were activated for federal purposes under Title 10 of the U.S. Code. Generally, however, those in the Reserves and National Guard have active duty mostly for training purposes, except if they are otherwise deployed.

A person is also considered a veteran if he or she had qualifying "active duty for training."[2] A term of active duty for training will qualify as active military, naval, or air service where the individual "was disabled or died from a disease or injury incurred or aggravated in line of duty."[3] Active duty for training is often undertaken by members of the Reserve. A person is also considered a veteran if he or she had qualifying "inactive duty for training."[4] A qualifying period of inactive duty for training is where the individual was "disabled or died-- (i) from an injury incurred or aggravated in line of duty; or (ii) from an acute myocardial infarction, a cardiac arrest, or a cerebrovascular accident during such training."[5]

The person's discharge must be "under conditions other than dishonorable."[6] A discharge under other than honorable conditions is a bar to receipt of benefits. (There are exceptions, such as "insanity"). Dishonorable conditions include a discharge resulting from willful and persistent misconduct.

- Alcohol and substance abuse
- Exception when alcohol and drugs are secondary to a service-connected condition
- Residuals of venereal disease. The case law supports service connection for residuals of venereal disease

Overview of Criteria for Benefits

Veterans are entitled to compensation for disabilities incurred in or aggravated during active military, naval, or air service.[7] The relevant time period is from the date of enlistment to the date of discharge. The disabilities do not have to be related to military activities. Some examples would include heart conditions or skin conditions with idiopathic causes. This means there does not have to be a relationship between anything the veteran did during service and his disability. In other words, anything that arises during the time period from induction to separation (excluding conditions due to willful misconduct or use of tobacco products, or abuse of drugs and alcohol). The disabilities that can be service connected are not limited to classical war-related injuries, such as bullet wounds or shell fragment wounds. This type of compensation is needed because there is no worker's compensation or long-term disability insurance for individuals who served in the armed forces.

Service-Connected Compensation

The primary VA benefit is service-connected compensation. Compensation benefits are the most important benefits paid by the VA. The Veterans

Administration's bureaucracy is primarily predicated on the disability compensation program. Naturally, the public supports the idea of disability compensation for disabled veterans.

For a specific disability to warrant compensation, it must be shown that it was incurred in or aggravated by active service. There are several factors that the VA considers when analyzing a claim for compensation. The VA system takes into consideration two primary issues when deciding claims: (1) eligibility and (2) entitlement. If a veteran is entitled to service-connected compensation, the VA will then consider (1) the degree of disability, and (2) the effective date for the award of compensation.

Once an individual has achieved the status of "veteran," he must provide the following elements to obtain disability compensation:

- Current disability. This means there must be an active pathology during the pendency of the claim.
- An in-service incident, injury, disease, or event.
- Evidence linking or establishing a nexus between the event in service and the current disability. (This is usually a medical, etiological opinion).

Criterion One: Current Disability

There must always be evidence of a current disability. If the veteran healed or was cured prior to filing his claim, the claim will not survive. Claims for benefits in the VA context are different than claims for monetary damages in a personal injury lawsuit. In a personal injury lawsuit, a person can recover monetary damages for a period of past pain and suffering that may have healed. There is no such concept in the world of VA disability compensation. However, the current disability does not need to be present at the time the claim is granted, only so long as it existed during the pendency of the claim.[8] To prove the current disability criterion, competent "medical" evidence is always required. In the majority of cases, this requires a degree of diagnostic precision by a medical professional who is qualified to render such a diagnosis. However, some conditions, such as personality disorders, congenital defects, and refractive eye error, will not qualify as a current disability. In general, conditions that a veteran is born with will generally not be deemed a current disability for compensation purposes unless a separate disease process is superimposed thereon.

Criterion Two: Something Happened in Service

The second criterion to establish service connection involves whether something happened in service. This is a broad concept. As noted earlier, it does not have to be a specific event linked to combat or official military duties. It means that some event happened during the time period of active duty. This could include exposure to a risk factor for the later development of disease, the exposure to a toxic chemical, the initial manifestations of the early symptoms of a rare disease that is not diagnosed until years after service, or the occurrence of a medically significant event that can lead to chronic health problems after service. An example of this would be a back injury in service that heals in a few weeks; the medical literature indicates that trauma is a risk factor for the later development of osteoarthritis. The VA would likely say that there is no connection between a current back disability and a one-time, acute and transitory back injury that healed without residuals prior to discharge and many years before an actual diagnosis. Although no abnormalities would be seen at the time of discharge, a disease process is started that takes years to manifest in the form of degenerative changes.

Another example is a veteran who gains too much weight during service and is placed in the weight control program due to obesity. He is later discharged at the end of his period of enlistment with no abnormalities, but five years after discharge, he is diagnosed with diabetes mellitus type II. The VA then denies the claim on the grounds that there was no diagnosis of diabetes in service—i.e., no in-service event. In doing so, however, the VA ignores the medically significant event of the development of obesity, which is a known risk factor for type II diabetes.

In establishing whether something happened in service, the VA favors service medical records and personnel records over the veteran's own testimony. If a medically significant event was not recorded in a veteran's medical records, the VA treats it as if it did not happen. This creates problems because young military personnel tend to downplay medical issues, especially psychiatric complaints, and thus seldom resort to medical personnel. In addition, the VA relies heavily on discharge physical exams. If the discharge physical was negative for any complaints or medical concerns, the VA usually interprets that to mean that the veteran did not have any medical problems in service. The VA then implies that any post-service medical problems that manifest were due to intervening, post-service causes.

The VA's reliance on discharge exams also ignores the basic attitude of service personnel who are about to discharge from active duty. If there is a medical problem, this could delay the discharge process. Military personnel know this. As they are anxious to leave and go home, they typically choose not to report the presence of medical symptoms that they may be experiencing at discharge. This results in separation physical exam reports that tend not to show the presence of relevant symptoms. Naturally, this makes proving service connection many years later more difficult. Hence, veterans need good attorneys and advocates.

Case Study

Scenario: Veteran with kidney disease developed during the Korean conflict
Result: Nearly 12 years of back pay awarded for accrued benefits, and service connection for the cause of death and back pay in excess of $190,000

In this illustrative case, the veteran was scheduled to be discharged from Camp Kilmer, New Jersey. He notified his father and a friend that he was getting out, and they made arrangements to go to New Jersey to meet him. The veteran had his separation physical, which included a urine test. The medical corps physician told him that there was protein in his urine and that he needed to stay over and come back the next day for another urine test. The veteran advised his father and friend that he would be delayed in getting out due to protein in his urine. The next day his urine test was negative. The medical corps recorded a negative urine test result and made no record of the initial positive test result.

The veteran got out of the service and went on with his life. Everything went on as normal for many decades. He married and had a family. However, in the 1990s, he began having some trouble with his kidneys. It was found that he had high blood pressure, which the doctors said was a factor in the onset of his kidney disease.

The kidney disease progressed to the point that he needed dialysis. He eventually got on the list for a kidney transplant. But before he could get the transplant, he had to have heart surgery to address some heart issues. Thankfully, the Veteran received a kidney transplant and did fairly well under the circumstances.

He then remembered his discharge exam from the Army in the early 1950s. He remembered that the doctor told him he had protein in his urine. After some research, he learned that protein in the urine could be an early sign of kidney disease. But there was no record of the positive urine test. The veteran looked up his old friend, who met him at Camp Kilmer almost five decades earlier. He remembered the veteran advising him that he had to be held over due to protein in the urine. The veteran got a statement from his friend and filed a claim.

Naturally, the VA denied him on the grounds that there was no proof of anything happening with his kidneys while in service. The Board also denied the veteran. He then appealed to the U.S. Court of Appeals for Veterans Claims, and our firm represented him. We discovered that the Board had not adequately considered the statements of the veteran's friend. We were able to successfully argue for a remand.

When the case was remanded, we discovered that the veteran's separation exam report contained several clues. First, the negative urine test result was marked as a "re-check." We reasoned that there would not have been a "re-check" unless there was an initial positive test result. We also noticed that he had a systolic blood pressure of 135. We suspected that this might have been borderline hypertension in service. We hired a top medical expert.

Our medical expert reviewed the case and found that it would not have been the standard practice to do a re-check of a urine test unless the first test was positive. Establishing this then allowed us to prove that the veteran was telling the truth. The medical expert also found that the veteran had the beginnings of hypertension during service. Hypertension then led to the kidney disease. Based on this, the medical expert concluded that it was at least as likely as not that the veteran's kidney disease was related to service.

The Board had the veteran go to a C&P exam. The C&P examiner partially agreed with our medical expert. The case went back to the Board, where service connection was granted. The case then returned to the regional office to be implemented. However, six weeks after the favorable award—and after our client had been appealing for more than a decade— he died of complications of the kidney disease. His death came as a shock to his surviving wife. He had not even received the money from the VA for his back pay.

We immediately filed to substitute his wife on all his pending claims, including accrued benefits. We also filed to obtain service connection for the cause of death.

We submitted additional arguments to the regional office and obtained and submitted an additional medical expert report regarding the cause of the veteran's death. The result: almost 12 years back pay awarded for accrued benefits and service connection for the cause of death.

Because of the high probability that service medical records may not document what problems a veteran may have had during service, they are often left trying to prove Criterion 2 using what we call lay evidence. Lay evidence is essentially a veteran's statements about what he experienced during service. In some situations, lay evidence will not suffice to establish an in-service event. However, in non-PTSD cases, the VA is required to consider lay evidence and cannot reject it solely because a veteran's testimony is not corroborated by contemporaneous medical records.[9] However, the VA is permitted to weigh the lack of medical records against the lay evidence.

In practice, the VA is reluctant to establish Criterion 2 based on merely what a veteran says, and the absence of corroborating in-service medical records almost always weighs more heavily. Usually, the only time the VA will concede Criterion 2 based on lay evidence alone is if the determinative issue is not an in-service occurrence. In other words, if there is no evidence of a current disability and the VA is planning on denying the claim based on the absence of a current disability, it may concede Criterion 2 based on lay evidence—but only in cases where this would not affect the outcome. The VA will generally not grant a claim based on lay evidence alone.

The In-Service Event Criterion and Special Rules for Combat Veterans

Although lay evidence will likely not be sufficient in most cases to establish Criterion 2, combat veterans have a special advantage in establishing an in-service event. Under 38 U.S.C. § 1154(b), VA is required to accept a veteran's lay statements regarding events of service if:

- The event occurred when he was engaged in combat with the enemy
- It is consistent with the time, place, and circumstances of service
- There is no clear and convincing evidence to the contrary

The idea behind the special combat veteran rule is that under the stress of combat, it is unlikely that all relevant events are being properly recorded in a veteran's personnel file or medical records. Because the use of lay evidence alone to establish Criterion 2 can be so powerful, there has been significant discussion as to what constitutes "combat." The VA General

Counsel observed that combat would constitute an actual fight or encounter with the enemy. The U.S. Court of Appeals for Veterans Claims has noted that the meaning of the phrase "engaged in combat with the enemy" does not require that a veteran have received enemy fire. It is sufficient that a veteran personally participated in events constituting an actual fight or encounter with a military foe or hostile unit or instrumentality. This means that a veteran could have brought fire upon an enemy or merely have been fired upon by the enemy. In other cases, the veteran has been recognized as a combat veteran because he "saw combat on the front line in Korea," and incoming rounds landed near him.[10]

Case Study

Scenario: Vietnam veteran with PTSD unable to prove exposure to combat
Result: Veteran was recognized as combat veteran and won service
    connection for PTSD

This particular veteran served in Vietnam, and his personnel records documented his participation in the Tet Counteroffensive. The veteran claimed he had been exposed to combat, but since he did not have any of the usual combat decorations, such as a Combat Infantryman Badge, the VA determined that he was not a combat veteran. Further, the only proof of his exposure to a PTSD stressor was his own testimony as to what he experienced during his time in Vietnam. As such, the VA denied his claim for PTSD.

The veteran retained our law firm to appeal his Board of Veterans Appeals denial to the U.S. Court of Appeals for Veterans Claims. We were able to overturn the denial and get the claim remanded to the Board to be re-adjudicated. We argued that the veteran's military occupational specialty ("MOS") was that of "cannoneer." This was documented in his personnel file, along with notation that he had participated in the Tet Counteroffensive. We reasoned that if the veteran was performing his job, he was operating and firing artillery at the enemy. We then applied the court's jurisprudence that says that a veteran will be deemed to have engaged in combat if he brought fire upon the enemy—even if he did not receive incoming fire. Thus, functioning as a cannoneer—firing artillery—during the Tet Counteroffensive would satisfy the definition of combat. After almost ten years on appeal, we finally convinced the Board that the veteran was a combat veteran; the Board had to accept the claimant's lay statements about the PTSD stressor. The result: the VA granted service connection for PTSD and awarded the veteran a 100 percent disability rating.

Criterion Three: A Nexus With Service

Once a veteran has established that he has a current disability and that something happened in service, he must connect the current disability to the event from active duty. This is called the nexus requirement. The veteran must prove a nexus with service. In other words, there must be causation between whatever happened in service and a current disability.

There are multiple theories that a veteran can use to prove a nexus. The VA is required to consider all possible theories when adjudicating a claim. A nexus can be established with a direct service connection theory, by presumption, by aggravation, and secondarily. We will address all of them in more detail below.

Direct Service Connection

This theory is the simplest and most direct. A typical example would be someone diagnosed during service with type II diabetes. After separation from service, he files a claim for diabetes. The VA would grant this type of claim easily.

But it gets more complicated when the in-service origins of a problem are less clear. Typically, as a veterans' benefits attorney, cases as easy as the example above would never reach my desk. The VA would grant those claims, and the veteran would not need to hire a lawyer to handle a complicated appeal. When things are not so clear-cut, however, there are three different ways to prove direct service connection:

1. **Delayed Onset Service Connection.** This is where an incident in service caused a veteran to develop a disease many years later. A medical nexus opinion is almost always required for this type of claim.

2. **Chronicity.** Chronic conditions shown in service to be "chronic" can be service connected if they manifest at any later date, no matter how remote, unless there was a clear intervening cause.

3. **Continuity of symptomatology.** Continuity of symptomatology is required only when there is no showing of chronicity in service. If a condition is acute and transitory during service, then a medical nexus opinion will be required. In other words, for chronic diseases that are not shown to be chronic in service, a nexus can be established by showing a continuous chain of symptoms since service. In practice, even with such evidence of continuity of symptomatology, securing a medical nexus opinion is still the best strategy.

Case Study

Scenario: U.S. Army veteran developed severe depression after car accidents that occurred in peacetime service

Result: Service connection granted for Major Depressive Disorder with Psychotic Features resulting in over $455,000 in retroactive pay

The veteran served in the United States Army during peacetime from February 1983 to January 1986, and later in the Reserves. He was stationed in Germany receiving Air Traffic Control training. Upon his discharge, he worked for the United States Postal Service for nine years until he was medically separated from employment.

While in service, he was in two automobile accidents, the first in August 1984 and the second in January 1986. In the first accident, he injured his neck and cervical spine. In the second, a more serious accident, he was the driver of an automobile that flipped over twice, causing him to lose consciousness, sustain a closed head injury and a traumatic brain injury. He developed depression, anxiety, agitation, and a type of psychosis. He filed his first claim for service connection in 1996 after being medically terminated from the USPS. The veteran's claim languished in the appeals system for more than a decade.

After his final denial at the Board of Veterans Appeals, the veteran hired our firm to represent him at the U.S. Court of Appeals for Veterans Claims. We successfully obtained a Joint Motion Remand from the Court. Initially, we had some success and obtained service connection for Major Depressive Disorder, but only at a 50 percent rating effective July 2001. We had submitted additional evidence in the form of the veteran's medical records, which documented a psychiatric hospitalization dating back to 1996. We believed the veteran was entitled to a much higher rating and so we hired a private psychiatrist to evaluate the veteran's records and provide us with an expert report. We also discovered a VA examiner's 1999 diagnosis of service connection for a head injury. By this time, 2014, there had been many advances in the diagnosis of closed head injuries resulting in delayed psychiatric conditions. Our expert wrote a strong report opining the veteran suffered from "late onset organic-based psychosis" due to car accident injuries he sustained while in service.

In a Board decision implemented by the RO in September 2019, we succeeded in obtaining service connection at 100 percent for Major Depressive Disorder with Psychotic Features with an earlier effective date of January 21, 1999.

The Result: Over $455,000.00 in back benefits granted to the veteran after twenty years of fighting the VA.

Presumptive Service Connection

In addition to proving a nexus directly, a veteran can also use legal presumptions to establish one. This means that as a matter of law, certain chronic diseases that become manifest within one year after discharge are presumed to be service connected. In other words, assuming the veteran has a current disability, the nexus with service will be presumed. Notable examples are arteriosclerosis, arthritis, brain hemorrhage, diabetes, leukemia, and psychosis.[11] Other diseases are subject to presumptive service connection when they become manifest within three years. Examples would be tuberculosis and leprosy.[12] And there is a seven-year presumptive period for multiple sclerosis.[13]

Five Established Categories of Presumptive Service Connection

Tropical Diseases. If they manifest within one year after separation.

Examples: cholera, dysentery, malaria, filariasis, yellow fever, blackwater fever, and plague.[14]

POWs: They can obtain presumptive service connection for certain diseases any time they become manifest. These diseases are considered to be common among POWs. They include cirrhosis of the liver, beriberi, peptic ulcers, malnutrition, irritable bowel syndrome, psychosis, anxiety, hypertension, and stroke.[15]

Persian Gulf Veterans. This involves a number of diseases that must be manifest prior to the statutorily-defined date. They include frequently undiagnosed multi-symptom chronic illnesses such as chronic fatigue, fibromyalgia, etc. Objective signs of these conditions include fatigue, headaches, muscle pain, skin problems, and headaches.[16]

Radiation Exposed Veterans. Certain diseases associated with exposure to ionizing radiation are presumptively service connected.[17] Examples: leukemia, various cancers such as those affecting the thyroid, breast, pharynx, esophagus, stomach, small intestine, bone, brain, colon, lung, and urinary tract.

Herbicide Exposure (Agent Orange): If a veteran had service in the Republic of Vietnam during the Vietnam War, he is entitled to service connection if he has any of the diseases on the "list" of diseases shown to be associated with Agent Orange.[18] Examples: Type II diabetes, Hodgkin's disease, multiple myeloma, prostate cancer, some respiratory cancers, and soft tissue sarcoma.

The presumptive diseases must be manifest within the required time period but not necessarily diagnosed.

Aggravation

If a veteran has a pre-existing condition (that is, prior to service) and it is shown that the condition worsened during service, then a presumption of aggravation applies. Once the presumption applies, the burden shifts to the VA to prove that any increase in disability during service is due to the disease's natural progression. The showing that an increase was due to natural progression must be established by "clear and unmistakable" evidence.[19] The clear and unmistakable standard requires the evidence to be beyond debate.

Relevant to the issue of aggravation is a doctrine called the Presumption of Soundness. A veteran is considered in sound condition and fit for duty except for those conditions "noted" at his induction exam. To rebut this presumption, VA must show by clear and unmistakable evidence that the condition pre-existed service and was not aggravated by service.

Secondary Service Connection

A veteran is entitled to service connection for any condition that is approximately the result of, or linked to, a service-connected condition.[20] If the service-connected condition causes or aggravates a second condition, the second condition may be service connected, and compensation may be paid to the degree that the disability was aggravated beyond the baseline, pre-existing level of impairment.[21]

A classic example is a service-connected spine disability that causes chronic pain and eventually depression. The depression could be eligible for service connection on a secondary basis. Another example is service-connected anxiety disorder that aggravates a pre-existing ulcer condition.

Case Study

Scenario: Veteran with service-connected low back condition seeking service connection for PTSD

Result: Secondary service connection for depression, more than $200,000 in retroactive benefits for the client

Another veteran who served on active duty from 1977 to 1979 suffered from a service-connected low back condition. His case was on appeal due to the VA's denial of his claim for service connection for PTSD. He had appealed all the way to the U.S. Court of Appeals for Veterans Claims. He was unable to win his claim on his own. He hired our firm to represent him before the CAVC. His claim for service connection for PTSD was based on an event that happened in boot camp. He claimed that he witnessed a fellow soldier commit suicide. The VA made an attempt to verify the stressor, but its attempts were inadequate. As a result, we were able to make an argument on appeal at the CAVC that the VA failed in its duty to assist the veteran in obtaining evidence to corroborate his PTSD stressor.

To win a non-combat PTSD claim, the stressor (the event that caused the PTSD) must be verified by evidence other than the veteran's own statements. As a result of our arguments, we successfully got the veteran's claim remanded back to the Board to be re-adjudicated. Once the case was back at the Board, we had the opportunity to submit new evidence and argument and raise new theories. The strategic advantage of a CAVC remand is that it gives a veteran a way to keep his claim alive and submit additional arguments or raise new theories but still preserve his retroactive effective date.

Once the case was back at the Board, we realized that the PTSD stressor may never be verified. That meant that the success of the veteran's claim was tenuous, and I was uncomfortable with predicating our entire case on a theory that depended on verifying a stressor. So, we examined his medical records closely and realized that in addition to the PTSD diagnosis, he also carried a diagnosis of depression. We understood that under the CAVC's case law, a claim for one mental disability includes claims for other diagnosed mental conditions within the scope of the claim. As such, we determined that the claim could be recharacterized to include depression. Since we had an existing service-connected condition in place, a low back disorder, we determined that we could link the depression to the service-connected low back disorder. Chronic pain from back disabilities is well known to cause depression.

We obtained a forensic medical expert opinion that linked our client's depression to the pain from the service-connected disability. The Board granted the claim, and we eventually obtained more than $200,000 in retroactive benefits for the client. Had we continued to pursue the claim for PTSD alone on a direct basis, the stressor would likely never have been verified, and the Board would have denied the claim. It was the use of a secondary service connection theory that resulted in a winning outcome.

38 U.S.C. § 1151 Claims

Disability compensation benefits can be achieved based on VA medical negligence. These types of claims are filed under 38 U.S.C. § 1151. A disability caused by VA medical care or vocational rehabilitation may be treated as if it were related to service. Section 1151, however, requires proof of negligence and proof of an actual increase or additional disability as a result of the aforementioned VA treatment. Since these claims are grounded in concepts of medical negligence, a veteran must establish what the standard of medical care is and then prove that the standard was breached in his case, resulting in additional disability. Medical negligence cannot be established without an expert medical opinion.

If a veteran files a claim for compensation based on § 1151, he can also file a civil lawsuit under the Federal Tort Claims Act. In other words, he could file a lawsuit in federal district court to recover money damages for the injuries he incurred as a result of the VA medical malpractice, and he could file a claim for VA compensation. However, there is an offset for any money recovered under the FTCA.

Established in August of 1946, the FTCA is a federal statute that allows private parties to sue the United States government in federal court when a person or entity acting on behalf of the government causes injury. The VA qualifies as an entity acting on behalf of the federal government.

If a veteran secures both a win in a Federal Tort case and Section-1151 benefits related to the same disability, the VA will withhold payment of those benefits until the total amount of the Federal Tort judgment is offset. Thus, there can be no double payment. However, the offset rule applies only when the claimant is an individual. If the estate of a veteran is behind the tort lawsuit, there is no offset requirement. Likewise, a court may, in some cases, prohibit the offset, though this will generally lead to a VA appeal.

THE PSYCHOLOGICAL IMPACT OF WAR

PTSD and Mental Health Issues

Our nation boasts of having the most highly developed military forces in the world. Indeed, the United States military's power has been influential in winning two major world wars in the 20th Century and is credited with influencing the collapse of the Soviet Union during the Cold War. Because of our military's influence around the globe, many young people join the service with patriotic ideals and the expectation that they are serving their country and protecting a way of life. But few young people realize the darker side of serving in a massive military often engaged in multiple foreign conflicts.

Over the many years I have spent as a practicing veterans' benefits attorney, I have heard the anger and the dismay of many veterans who felt that the story the recruiter sold them was quite different from their actual military experience. Recruiters don't tend to mention that around 25 percent of today's veterans are homeless or that an average of 22 veterans commit suicide each day. Here we stand, a country of wealth and civilized society, yet our veterans feel their nation has betrayed them.

The wounds of combat reach far beyond physical injuries and disabilities. Mental health complications like post-traumatic stress disorder (PTSD), depression, anxiety, and substance abuse linger and intensify long after soldiers return home. A wide array of psychological issues, including adjustment disorder, bipolar, panic disorder, chronic pain disorder, schizophrenia, schizoaffective disorder, and delusional disorder, occur among veterans at a significantly higher rate than in the civilian population. Without proper and timely treatment, these debilitating mental health issues persist, can become worse, and make it nearly impossible for many veterans to lead productive and fulfilling lives after service.

With the right counseling, rehabilitation, and medical interventions, veterans can move through these rough spots and go on to reach new milestones in their personal and professional lives. But the VA doesn't make it easy to get this level of treatment.

Veterans must overcome several obstacles when seeking VA benefits to cover mental health complications. First, the VA usually doesn't mention the fact that a veteran's mental health condition makes them eligible to file a claim for benefits. Many veterans don't realize they can obtain coverage for treatment. Second, the claims process is confusing, and the VA spends little time guiding veterans on how to proceed, and sometimes no time at all.

When veterans finally decide to seek benefits, they can feel like the VA is calling them liars as if they were just out for money and hadn't actually experienced trauma during service. And many veterans who are denied benefits the first time around simply give up without an appeal. Veterans come to the conclusion that the VA just wants them to give up. Indeed, the mantra, "Deny, deny; until they die!" is frequently spoken in veterans' circles.

The VA's motto is, "To care for him who shall have borne the battle and for his widow and his orphan." It sounds good—but in reality, many veterans face decades-long battles to collect the benefits they deserve. While there are no easy answers when it comes to the difficulties veterans face in obtaining VA benefits for mental health issues, as a veterans disability attorney who's spent years in the VA claims trenches, I know that many of these frustrations can be avoided with careful planning and expert legal strategies.

Nostalgia, Shell Shock, and Combat Fatigue

Throughout world history, the stress of combat has taken a mental toll on soldiers. Military trauma has been known to cause debilitating psychological damage for centuries, from the battles of ancient Greece to the Afghanistan War. The Greek historian Herodotus described an Athenian warrior who lost his sight for the rest of his life after seeing a comrade killed in the 490 B.C. Battle of Marathon.[22] By the mid-1600s, Swiss doctors referred to mental health issues that developed during battle as "nostalgia," believing that the fatigue, anxiety, depression, and paranoia were due to soldiers' homesickness.[23]

During World War I, soldiers experiencing feelings of helplessness, panic, fear, mutism, insomnia, and the inability to walk or reason were said to have "shell shock."[24] At first, officials thought shock waves from the nearby explosion of artillery shells were causing hidden brain damage, hence the name. But after more and more soldiers exhibited symptoms of shell shock who had never been exposed to artillery fire, doctors began to categorize shell shock as a psychiatric disturbance rather than a physical injury.[25] As of December 1914, four percent of enlisted men and up to 10 percent of British officers were reported as suffering from "nervous and mental shock."[26]

During World War II and the Korean War, "combat fatigue" and "battle fatigue" replaced the "shell shock" diagnosis to describe the unexplainable psychiatric and physical symptoms seen in military soldiers. At this time, the military felt that panic, mutism, and night terrors were might be caused by lengthy deployments. Up to half of World War II, military discharges were for combat fatigue.[27] Treatment was immediate with rest and unit support.

During the Vietnam War, the military still used the term "combat fatigue." But after the war ended, the media began calling the psychological abnormalities seen in returning service members "post-Vietnam syndrome." One article describes post-Vietnam syndrome as a "growing apathy, cynicism, alienation, depression, mistrust, and expectation of betrayal, as well as an inability to concentrate, insomnia, nightmares, restlessness, uprootedness, and impatience with almost any job or course of study."[28]

In the late 1970s, the term "post-traumatic stress disorder" replaced the terms "combat fatigue" and "post-Vietnam syndrome," suggesting a higher understanding that the symptoms were due to a stress response rather than long deployments or exhaustion. In 1980, the American Psychiatric Association added post-traumatic stress disorder to the Diagnostic and Statistical Manual of Mental Disorders (DSM), applying the diagnosis to people who suffered a psychologically distressing effect "outside the range of usual human experience."[29]

Mental Health Effects of Military Service

Service members can experience more trauma in one day than most civilians experience in an entire lifetime. Understandably, this level of continuous adrenaline leads to mental health problems that can make it difficult for veterans to function after service. Several combat stressors have been shown to correlate with mental health issues. In a 2004 study, Army and Marine Corps combat soldiers who experienced more combat stressors

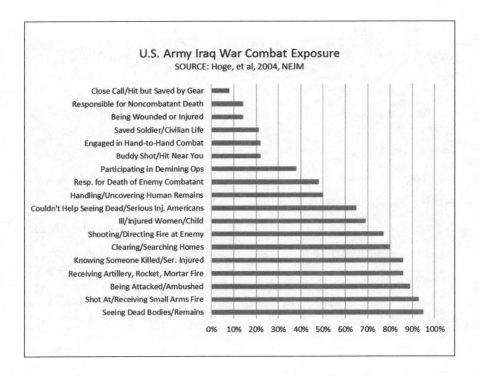

U.S. Army Iraq War Combat Exposure
SOURCE: Hoge, et al, 2004, NEJM

showed a higher incidence of generalized anxiety, major depression, and PTSD than those who experienced fewer stressful incidents.[30]

Research findings from Harvard University and the National Institute of Mental Health report that approximately 25 percent of all active-duty soldiers exhibit symptoms of a mental health condition.[31] Exposure to trauma during military service can cause several types of mental health issues—some immediate and some delayed.

Post-Traumatic Stress Disorder (PTSD)

As a survival mechanism, our brain chemistry changes with exposure to trauma. When we experience "fight-or-flight" situations, our bodies and minds have evolved to remember and replay them for future reference. While this would have been helpful during the more primitive phases of the human race, PTSD in today's world can be extremely debilitating.

PTSD is one of the most prevalent mental complications seen among service men and women. Military veterans are 15 times more likely to develop PTSD than civilians.[32] Service members may develop PTSD from either one-time or repeated exposure to military combat, abuse, sexual assault, life-threatening circumstances, or seeing the death of a comrade.

The DSM-V lists PTSD under "Trauma- and Stressor-Related Disorders." A wide range of criteria must be met to receive a PTSD diagnosis. In general, the patient must have been exposed to death or injury, or threats of death or injury by witnessing it, hearing about it, or experiencing it. The patient also re-experiences the traumatic event through thoughts, nightmares, or flashbacks. While re-experiencing the event, the patient may experience sudden emotional distress, tremors, rapid heart rate, or other physical reactions.

PTSD patients will often try to avoid any trauma-related stimuli that may trigger their memories. They may also experience negative thoughts and feelings that worsen over time, including memory loss around the traumatic event, negative thoughts about oneself, guilt, blame, decreased interest in activities, or feelings of isolation. PTSD patients also report aggression, hypervigilance, destructive behavior, heightened startle reactions, inattentiveness, and insomnia.

Finally, for a diagnosis of PTSD, the symptoms must be present for more than one month and create distress or functional impairment. The PTSD patient may also feel they are in a dream (derealization), detached from and observing their own lives (depersonalization). While symptoms of PTSD can start immediately after trauma, the full spectrum of PTSD symptoms may not be seen for six months or more.[33]

Many veterans with untreated PTSD are unable to hold gainful employment and have difficulty functioning socially. Some studies suggest that military veterans with PTSD may be at a twofold greater risk for developing dementia.[34] Over 20 percent of veterans with PTSD have a substance abuse problem, and nearly 33 percent of veterans who seek treatment for substance abuse also have PTSD. Researchers believe that veterans with PTSD turn to alcohol, tobacco, and prescription medications to alleviate problems with insomnia, depression, and traumatic memories.

Non-PTSD Psychiatric Conditions

Many war veterans who do not receive an official PTSD diagnosis may still develop severe depression, anxiety disorder, bipolar disorder, or schizophrenia. Data from the RAND Center for Military Health Policy Research suggests that 20 percent of Iraq or Afghanistan veterans suffer from PTSD or severe depression.[35] In 2010, researchers from the University of California in San Francisco and New York University School of Medicine found that depression seriously impaired normal functioning in 8.5 to 14 percent of Iraq war vets.[36] The rate of depression in military veterans is reported to be five times higher than that in civilians.[37] Depression is not just a pessimistic outlook or negative attitude. Similar to PTSD, depression is a function of brain chemistry and often requires medication.

Non-PTSD psychiatric issues can be equally or more debilitating than PTSD alone. Veterans with depression may suffer from constant fatigue, thoughts of hopelessness, life-threatening substance abuse problems, and suicidal tendencies. Anxiety disorder can cause constant muscle tremors, heart palpitations, jumpiness, anger, and incessant paranoia. Bipolar disorder creates waves of highs and lows in the veteran's life, with long periods of severe fatigue followed by manic episodes of hyperactivity, insomnia, and agitation. Schizophrenia may be the most debilitating of all, resulting in an altered sense of reality that may involve delusions, hallucinations, and extreme social isolation.

Traumatic Brain Injury (TBI)

One of the signature injuries of the wars in Iraq and Afghanistan is TBI, physical damage to the brain caused by the frequent use of roadside improvised explosive devices and the resulting shock waves from blasts. Keep in mind, however, that many TBIs do not come from improvised explosive devices. Other causes of TBI involve direct blows to the head. These may include in-service motor vehicle accidents or in-service falls where a veteran hits his head. They may also come from a personal assault or any other type of trauma where the head is injured.

According to the Defense and Veterans Brain Injury Center (DVBIC), 20 percent of veterans report some form of concussion during service.[38] Similarly, the RAND Center for Military Health Policy Research found that 19.5 percent of Iraq or Afghanistan veterans reported some form of TBI.[39] The consequences of traumatic brain injuries are far-reaching and affect many areas of a veteran's life. TBIs often produce not only physical problems but cognitive problems and behavioral problems. TBI symptoms may include difficulty communicating, headache, short attention spans, nausea, poor motivation levels, dizziness, anxiety, confusion, severe depression, irritability, and memory problems. These symptoms may appear immediately after blast exposure or years after.

A 2015 study found that Iraq and Afghanistan veterans who were near bomb blasts may experience faster aging of the brain.[40] Some studies suggest that TBI is associated with a higher rate of PTSD.[41] According to research published in the New England Journal of Medicine, military members who experience TBI are twice as likely to develop PTSD than service members without a TBI.[42] Research has also shown that veterans with a history of TBI may be 55 percent more likely to commit suicide, with concussion or skull fracture patients at the highest risk.[43] Repeated concussions may lead to chronic traumatic encephalopathy (CTE), often seen in football players who take their own lives.[44]

Mental health problems like chronic fatigue, depression, irritability, and substance abuse may also accompany chronic pain associated with TBI or musculoskeletal injuries. Nearly 50 percent of veterans—including an estimated 100,000 Gulf War veterans—report some form of chronic musculoskeletal pain (CMP), including back pain, knee pain, shoulder pain, or neck pain.[45]

Effective Treatments for Mental Health Disorders

Mental health disorders can make it very difficult for veterans to return home and successfully transition back into civilian society. Without proper and timely treatment, insomnia, depression, anxiety, and substance abuse can lead to isolation, divorce, unemployment, homelessness, and suicide. The risk for suicide is 22 percent higher among veterans when compared to U.S. non-Veteran adults.[46] While many veterans will adjust and settle into their new lives in a few short months, others may never adjust without significant treatment. The sooner treatment begins, the more effective it is.

There are currently two effective treatment avenues for mental health conditions: counseling and medication. These are often used in concert, though one or the other may work alone with certain conditions. Many veterans and others suffering from PTSD may question the effectiveness of counseling. How can simply speaking with someone correct the significant damage caused by trauma? Yet counseling sessions and group therapy sessions follow specific protocols that have been tested and proven to work.

For example, many PTSD patients respond well to prolonged exposure (PE) therapy. PE therapy involves up to 15 sessions of exposure to their traumatic memories with discussions and exposure to similar (but safe) situations. The technique effectively desensitizes the veteran to the traumatic experience that caused the PTSD.

Eye movement desensitization and reprocessing (EMDR) has also been shown to be effective in treating PTSD. This method involves eight phases of treatment designed to "refile" your traumatic memory in a functional way. The rapid eye movement (REM) we experience during sleep is connected with memory consolidation and brain stimulation. By having the patient follow motions with their eyes during therapy sessions around the traumatic event, the brain is theoretically shifted into memory processing mode. New information enters the brain around the traumatic event, replacing the old memory associations. Because the brain is finally able to process the memory, repeated recalls (in the form of nightmares and negative thoughts) slowly subside.[47]

Cognitive processing therapy (CPT) is another form of effective treatment for mental health conditions. This 12-session treatment asks patients to think about their traumatic experience by writing about it and then reading it to themselves, and aloud during therapy sessions, on a daily basis. CPT functions in a similar manner as PE therapy—by desensitizing the brain to the trauma of the past experience.

Drug treatments can be very effective for patients suffering from PTSD, depression, anxiety, bipolar disorder, and schizophrenia. For example, selective serotonin reuptake inhibitors (SSRIs) appear to be the safest and most effective pharmacological treatment for PTSD. Serotonin is a natural chemical in our brain that elevates the mood, reduces anxiety, and calms the mind. Normally, our brain keeps serotonin levels regulated by sequestering whatever serotonin is produced that it doesn't need. While the exact effect of SSRIs is unknown, scientists believe that SSRIs inhibit this serotonin reuptake, leaving more serotonin available to the brain. Paxil and Zoloft are the two SSRIs currently approved by the U.S. Food and Drug Administration (FDA) for the treatment of PTSD.

Obstacles to Obtaining VA Mental Health Benefits

Treatment for mental health conditions is critical for veterans, whether they suffer from PTSD symptoms, depression, social withdrawal, anxiety, irritability, suicidal thoughts, or alcohol, tobacco, or prescription drug addiction. Without proper treatment, these mental health issues can destroy a veteran's chance to lead a productive and fulfilling life.

The Department of Veterans Affairs offers significant benefits to cover the costs of inpatient and outpatient mental health treatment for both veterans and their immediate family members, including:

- Medical care
- Specialized PTSD treatment programs
- Family counseling
- Reintegration programs
- Substance abuse rehabilitation
- Suicide prevention programs

Depending on the severity of the disability, veterans may also qualify for monthly, tax-free monetary compensation and benefits to cover lost earning capacity. The VA also offers tax-free Dependency and Indemnity Compensation (DIC) to eligible family members who lose a loved one to suicide or a substance-abuse-associated death. PTSD benefits for veterans range from VA pension benefits (non-service-connected) and VA compensation benefits—to vocational rehabilitation and grants for adapted vehicles, housing, and equipment.

Yet, only around 50 percent of veterans who need mental health treatment will actually receive it.[48] One reason for this is the barrier created by stigma. Many veterans feel that seeking mental health care could mean fewer employment or promotional opportunities in both military and civilian life. Some worry that family and peers will judge them after discovering they are seeking mental health care.

However, this stigma is becoming less of an issue. The Department of Defense now acknowledges that those who do not seek treatment may be less fit to serve than those who deny a problem or opt out of treatment. As of 2014 military policy, speaking with a counselor or seeking treatment cannot determine your military career path or promotion opportunities. In addition, service members are not required to disclose mental health conditions to their chain of command and no longer risk losing security clearance for seeking mental health counseling. Treatment providers trained in military policy surrounding HIPAA (Health Insurance Portability and Accountability Act) privacy guidelines help you decide whether to report a mental health condition. If you need to report your condition, it cannot be factored into your military career or affect your promotion opportunities.

Some veterans are simply unaware of the benefits and treatment programs available to them or feel they cannot afford mental health care. Others think that VA services are just for combat veterans or those with severe physical disabilities. Some veterans think they are not eligible for service-connected benefits because they haven't been diagnosed with PTSD or TBI, or because they received an other-than-honorable (OTH) discharge. Remember, this is not the case. Even veterans with substance abuse problems, lethargy, depression, memory loss, cognition problems, and attention-deficit issues are eligible for VA benefits to cover treatment. And there are legal exceptions that may allow veterans to collect VA benefits with an OTH discharge.

Many veterans do not seek proper mental health treatment due to difficulty navigating the VA claims process. They may not understand how their sudden poor attention span or violent outbursts could be service connected. Other veterans simply give up once their initial claim for service connection gets denied.

It is important to understand that the VA itself admits its claims error rate is 38 percent. That means they make mistakes in almost four out of 10 benefits claims cases. One in three cases the VA is processing is for veterans appealing a denial. Approximately 11 to 12 percent of VBA decisions are appealed, with nearly 50 percent of those going to the Board of Veterans' Appeals. An appeal is almost necessary to succeed in getting VA benefits.

This brings us to another obstacle veterans face in getting prompt mental health care. Wait times. While the appeal rate has remained steady over the past twenty years, the volume has increased with the increase in claims decisions. In 2016, the average processing time for resolving appeals was three years. Those forwarded to the Board of Veterans' Appeals took an average of six years. Thousands of veterans had to wait even longer.[49]

The outrageous wait times don't offer much incentive for ailing veterans to seek VA benefits for mental health care. In 2017, the number of pending VA appeals on backlog hit 470,000. Data from the American Psychological Association suggests that 22 percent of veterans opt to fork over thousands of dollars for private mental health treatment over resorting to VA programs,[50] highlighting the unfortunate difficulty in obtaining prompt VA funding and treatment for mental health issues.

Winning VA Benefits for Mental Health or PTSD

With all of these obstacles to VA mental health benefits in the way, how are veterans able to file a successful claim? Most veterans who succeed at obtaining VA benefits for mental health conditions fit into one of these two categories: (A) they have an obvious record of trauma (military or medical documents recorded at the time), or (B) they have an experienced advocate who understands the claims process fully and has the legal expertise and investigative resources to prepare a bulletproof claim.

Scenario "A" is, of course, the most optimal. Having records of battle injuries or military documents reporting military mental trauma along with medical evidence supporting those claims can be extremely effective in getting VA benefits for mental health conditions. However, these supporting documents are incredibly rare. Many mental conditions are not the result of direct injury but rather the result of watching a comrade die or living in fear while at war. When abuse is concerned, rarely will a veteran report it—so no record exists at all.

This is where an experienced legal advocate comes in. You are up against a system that is doing everything in its power not to grant your benefits. If you have to appeal to the U.S. Court of Appeals for Veterans Claims, you are going up against highly skilled government lawyers who will argue that you don't deserve benefits for your PTSD. The U.S. government hires professional lawyers, many with 10 or 15 years of experience. These lawyers know the VA system backward and forward. They argue CAVC cases every day. What's more, they are excellent attorneys—and they're working as hard as they can to make sure you don't get VA benefits. With a veterans' benefits lawyer supporting you, you can fight fire with fire.

Your veterans disability lawyer helps you:

- Collect medical and military evidence to support your case
- Discover weaknesses and holes in the Board's decision
- Review the mountains of paperwork
- Prepare powerful, persuasive arguments for your claim

Over our many years of practice, the veterans disability lawyers at my firm have built relationships with many psychiatric professionals who can help build a case for veterans disability benefits. We help reduce the stress of dealing with benefits claims because we serve as a buffer between the veteran and the VA. We work together to build the strongest case possible, so when we come up against the government's lawyers, we're ready to shoot down whatever evidence and objections they raise. Denials and years upon years of appeals can be avoided when claims are properly developed by a skilled veterans disability lawyer.

Non-PTSD Psychiatric Claims

Mental health claims encompass all forms of psychiatric diagnoses, including PTSD, depression, anxiety, adjustment disorder, bipolar disorder, panic disorder, chronic pain disorder, schizophrenia, schizoaffective disorder, adjustment disorder, delusional disorders, and other psychotic disorders. With the exception of PTSD, the VA analyzes mental health claims under the basic principles for service connection. Veterans must establish the following three elements:

1) an in-service event or occurrence

2) a current disability, and

3) a nexus or a link between the in-service occurrence and the present disability.

You must be able to show a current diagnosis in accordance with the DSM criteria. Personality disorders are not considered for service connection because the VA believes that these are conditions that you are born with. Normally, to prove a service connection between mental illness and military service, you need to have a service treatment record documenting some psychiatric complaints. At the very least, you need to have a complaint of nervous trouble noted on your separation history.

When you can't point to combat with the enemy or witnessing the death of friends to prove service connection, how do you link a current psychiatric disability to military service? Most advocates working with veterans to qualify for benefits would consider it impossible to establish a service connection for a non-PTSD psychiatric disability without an obvious in-service mental health complaint. However, experienced veterans disability benefits lawyers know how to think creatively about how to approach the issue.

A mental disability does not have to be your primary disability type in order to get VA benefits. For instance, if you are service connected for a knee condition and a low back condition that produces such severe chronic pain as to cause depression, you can get service connection for the depression secondary to the service-connected chronic pain from your physical disabilities.

You should also know that if a veteran seeks benefits for one type of mental disorder and it turns out during the processing of his claim or appeal that he really suffers from a different type of mental disorder, the

VA cannot simply deny the claim on the grounds that the diagnosis doesn't match the psychiatric disability claim. Mental disability claims should be interpreted broadly. Therefore, if you are denied because you do not have a mental disability consistent with how you labeled the claim, but you have another type of mental disability, then you can re-characterize your claim to include that other mental disability, and the VA must consider it.

Perhaps the most prominent area right now concerns depression claims that are secondary to service-connected physical or other medical conditions. For example, a veteran can be service connected for a number of orthopedic problems involving his joints, which produce a devastating state of chronic pain that leads to debilitating depression. Usually, the more depressed a person feels, the more profound their experience of pain, and the more pain, the more depression. This can become a vicious cycle.

For example, if you are service connected for a chronic low back issue involving debilitating pain that produces depression, then you would be service connected for the depression secondary to the low back condition. Currently, secondary claims for depression constitute a large percentage of our depression claims in our office. If you suffer from depression and you are service-connected for other debilitating service-connected disabilities, then you may wish to consider pursuing the depression claim on a secondary basis. Regardless, to win a depression claim and obtain the appropriate rating requires aggressive representation. If the VA cannot deny the claim, then their next strategy will be to not assign a fair rating. If you have been denied an appropriate rating for depression or another mental health disability, then you need to aggressively respond to this with an appeal.

The VA is notorious for lowballing veterans on ratings or mental disabilities. In general, if you are unable to maintain a gainful occupation and have GAF scores of 50 and under, then you should be rated at the 100 percent rate, assuming that you are not otherwise functioning at a high level in other areas of your life.

In addition, sometimes the key to winning these claims involves establishing the onset of depression at a time close to discharge where there is an absence of intervening events that could otherwise explain the onset of depression. In other situations, a veteran may turn to drugs or alcohol during service as a way of self-medicating his feelings of depression. In these circumstances, it can be argued that the use of drugs or alcohol represents a symptom of underlying depression, which is masked by the illicit drugs or alcohol. Many times, a veteran's use of drugs and alcohol is a self-medicating attempt, and in our professional opinion, it represents the existence of psychiatric problems.

PTSD Claims

To get veterans' benefits for PTSD, you must establish a service connection between your PTSD disability and your time in service. PTSD is unique among veteran disability types because of the importance placed on stressors in diagnosing PTSD. In order to get VA disability benefits for PTSD, you will need to get a service connection by establishing a stressor or stressors that qualify you for a diagnosis of PTSD. There are essentially three different approaches to proving stressors:

- A combat veteran describes a stressor consistent with his or her combat exposure.
- A veteran describes a stressor that is not associated with his verified combat exposure.

- A veteran's PTSD stressor is related to fear of hostile military or terrorist activity while stationed in a combat theater of operations.

Credible supporting evidence is important in getting approved for PTSD VA benefits. But in practice, the "credible supporting evidence" requirement has been a major impediment to many veterans receiving compensation for their PTSD diagnosis. Many things that happen in service are never properly documented or recorded. As a result, it can be very difficult to prove that the stressor took place.

Fortunately, in July 2010, the VA issued a new rulemaking it somewhat easier to prove that a stressor event happened during service. Under the new regulation, if a veteran's claimed stressors are related to the veteran's fear of hostile military or terrorist activity, then he can qualify for PTSD based on this as a stressor.

Additionally, in order to get VA benefits for PTSD, you may need to get a private medical opinion to establish a connection between your service and your diagnosis. Once you have established the stressors that qualify you for a PTSD diagnosis and receive service connection, the VA will determine your level of disability and award benefits accordingly.

Sounds simple enough, right? However, the VA will search for every possible means to deny your claim. For example, the most common reasons why the VA denies benefits for PTSD are:

- The stressor is not verified. The veteran did not provide enough information to verify the stressor.
- The VA failed to submit the stressor information to the Joint Services Records Research Center (JSRRC), which is a government organization assigned to research veterans' claims (the VA cannot

simply do its own research and then deny the claim).

- The veteran doesn't have a PTSD diagnosis.

In many cases, if you are diagnosed with depression or generalized anxiety, the VA cannot simply reject your PTSD claim on the grounds that you have depression instead. The VA would have to investigate whether service connection is appropriate for depression or some other mental disability.

Another reason the VA denies PTSD benefits claims is because many veterans make the mistake of re-filing PTSD benefits claims without any new evidence—or they submit evidence that is not material to their PTSD. To ensure the highest degree of success in reopened disability claims, we recommend that you look very carefully at the reason why the VA denied your claim the last time.

For instance, if the VA denied your claim for PTSD disability benefits because there was no evidence linking your disability to service, then submitting more treatment records showing the severity of your PTSD disability is not going to help. In other words, if the issue is the lack of "linking" evidence, you should submit a medical report from a doctor stating that your disability is linked to service.

On the other hand, if the reason they denied you before was because there was no evidence of a present disability, then submitting a new medical record showing a diagnosed condition could potentially aid in getting your claim reopened. The new evidence you submit should address one of the reasons cited by the VA for denying your benefits the first time around.

In some cases, when the VA denies a claim for PTSD, it often neglects to consider whether the veteran was in a combat theater and in fear of a hostile military or terrorist attack. The Board may deny a veteran's claim for lack of a verifiable PTSD stressor. The Board may also claim that the fact that a VA exam had not previously been given demonstrates that there is no proof of a verifiable PTSD stressor.

Yet, under the PTSD regulation as amended in 2010, a veteran does not necessarily have to prove a verifiable stressor (38 § C.F.R. 3.304(f)(3)). If a veteran had a fear of hostile military or terrorist activity and a VA psychologist or psychiatrist confirms that this is sufficient to support a PTSD diagnosis, then his statements alone can establish the stressor. Given the evidence of the veteran's time, place, and circumstances of service, he was likely exposed to events that could make one fearful of hostile military or terrorist activity.

There are also numerous cases involving individuals who received OTH discharges and are seeking service connection for a mental health disability; approximately 250,000 Vietnam era veterans who received OTH discharges, barring them from receiving VA benefits. The Defense Department released new guidelines in 2014 to address discharge upgrade applications in situations where there were signs and symptoms of PTSD during service or at the time of discharge.

But what's a veteran to do if he can't get his discharge upgraded? Fortunately, there is an exception that veterans with OTH discharges can use. Veterans disability lawyers refer to this exception as the "insanity exception." This does not mean that a veteran has to be a stark raving lunatic. It simply means that he was suffering from a mental disease when he committed the offenses that led to his OTH discharge. If such a mental illness existed—such as PTSD or depression—a veteran can obtain his VA benefits even if he did not have an honorable discharge.

Traumatic Brain Injury (TBI) Claims

The old rating criteria for evaluating TBIs were clearly not sufficient to address the wide range of issues veterans face, so the VA revised the TBI rating criteria in 2008. Under the old rating system, no single subjective symptom could be given a service rating above 10 percent. A subjective symptom is one whose severity depends on self-reporting by the veteran and includes things like headaches, dizziness, or ability to concentrate.

Under the new VA disability rating system, symptoms are evaluated in three categories, and the overall rating is based on the combined total level of disability in all areas. The three main areas of dysfunction that need to be evaluated when considering veterans disability benefits for TBI are:

- Cognitive Symptoms of TBI—Decreased memory, concentration, attention, and executive functioning of the brain. Executive functioning includes goal setting, information processing, planning, organizing, prioritizing, problem solving, judgment, decision making, and mental flexibility.
- Emotional & Behavioral Symptoms of TBI—Emotional symptoms include PTSD, depression, anxiety, and other mental disabilities. Behavioral symptoms include irritability, aggression, withdrawal, and poor impulse control. Additionally, cognitive, emotional, and behavioral problems can lead to social problems, including immature behavior, over-dependency, excessive talking, inappropriate sexual behavior, and overspending.
- Physical Symptoms of TBI—Vision loss, hearing loss, and tinnitus, constant headaches, seizures, motor or sensory dysfunction, and pain in the face or other parts of the body. Some veterans also

report a loss of smell or taste and may be unable to communicate as they previously did. There are also endocrine dysfunctions and bladder or bowel impairments, and other autonomic nerve dysfunctions.

While the new VA disability rating system was expanded to acknowledge the complexity of TBI, it doesn't necessarily make TBI easier to diagnose. TBI is a complicated disability to properly diagnose for several reasons:

- TBI symptoms overlap with other disabilities. As noted earlier, a veteran with a TBI may also experience depression and PTSD.
- Each TBI is unique. The number and type of brain functions affected can vary widely from person to person. Additionally, some functions may be affected more severely than others. To further complicate the issue, symptoms may fluctuate in severity from day to day.
- Symptoms can change over time. The symptoms a veteran experiences in the days immediately after a TBI may be very different from the symptoms they experience months down the road.

The VA uses multiple diagnostic codes. The cognitive symptoms of TBI are evaluated using one set of diagnostic codes. Physical symptoms are evaluated under another. Emotional behavioral symptoms are evaluated using at least two different sets of diagnostic codes. The VA first assigns an evaluation for all the separately diagnosed conditions. Then they take the conditions that are not individually diagnosed and evaluated and classify them under one of 10 factors listed in the VA table.

VA evaluators then assign a scale to the different components of cognitive impairment. This scale goes from zero to four. They determine which symptoms are to be classified under each component and then assign the appropriate number. After each symptom has been classified and assigned a number, the VA takes the highest number assigned to any individual component. The highest number given to each component is the percentage evaluation that will be assigned. In practice, the VA should assign a 100 percent rating if any component is determined to be totally disabling.

The laws that govern the granting of service connection and the proper rating for these injuries can be complex. In our experience, one of the key issues involving TBI cases is cognitive impairment. For this reason, veterans with TBIs have an even harder time navigating the VA disability system. If you have suffered a traumatic brain injury, you are likely experiencing a wide range of difficulties, and you may need assistance with your claim. A qualified veterans' benefits attorney can connect you with the proper experts and help you make the strongest case possible.

Conclusion

Awareness and education around the mental health concerns of our soldiers have improved since the Vietnam, Korean, and Gulf wars. There are now numerous therapy protocols and FDA-approved medications that can treat symptoms of depression and PTSD. But we still have a long way to go to ensure that our honored veterans can return from service, recover from their mental health conditions, and lead productive, quality lives.

Stigma reduction programs that combine education and exposure to respected peers or veterans who have dealt with mental health problems could increase the use of mental health services.[51] Requiring mental health counseling for every service member before, during, and after deployment could lessen the issues of stigma and fears of career influence and reputation dramatically. Treatment throughout the various transition phases could also lessen the risk of potentially debilitating or life-threatening mental health conditions.

The VA must also intensify its efforts to decrease the disability benefits claims backlog and gain additional funding. The current appeals process is slow and confusing, and many VA locations still do not offer mental health treatment programs. Of the proposed 2018 total medical care budget of $75.2 billion, just $8.4 billion is set aside for mental health care. Veteran access to mental health professionals is alarmingly low.

Our veterans have come a long way. They deserve justice, honor, and vindication. They should be recognized for what they have done for our country. U.S. veterans deserve our respect and the VA disability benefits they earned. Although individuals cannot change the nature of the VA's dysfunctional claims and administrative appeals process, we can fight back.

MENTAL AND PHYSICAL HEALTH CONNECTION

Establishing Secondary Service Connection

Many of our nation's veterans suffer from mental or physical conditions that they feel couldn't possibly be connected to their time in service. How could heart disease, diabetes, dementia, schizophrenia, or other disorders that arise years after service be associated with events that happened years, even decades, in the past? Unfortunately, a vast number of veterans fail to seek the VA benefits they deserve because they fail to realize that their time in service did indeed lead to their current mental or physical condition.

A major problem lies in the fact that the Department of Veterans Affairs talks about disability only in isolation. You either have post-traumatic stress disorder (PTSD) or a knee injury from combat. You either have Gulf War Syndrome or a traumatic brain injury (TBI). What the VA often fails to consider is that the human body functions as one integrated machine, not a collection of separate physical and mental components. In evaluating a veteran's disabilities, the VA doesn't refer to the holistic component, the interrelationship between the different body systems and health in general. They don't acknowledge how impairing mental health will negatively impact physical health and vice versa.

A veteran's health is complex and multifaceted. One body system cannot be altered without affecting another. If a veteran begins gaining weight during service, the entire spectrum of obesity-related problems—including diabetes, heart disease, and orthopedic problems—is open for service connection. Likewise, if a veteran who suffers from service-connected PTSD develops obesity as a result of that PTSD, the entire spectrum of obesity-related problems is also open for service connection. Because the body and mind are fundamentally interconnected, mental disorders can often cause debilitating physical illness—and physical illnesses can lead to mental disability.

As a veterans disability attorney, I approach my clients from a holistic perspective, considering how the body and brain are interconnected. No matter what disabilities my clients have, I always research possible connections between their service-connected disabilities and other health problems. And the more research I do, the more evidence I find, establishing closer links between the mental state and the physical body. As long as scientific evidence exists suggesting a connection between the mental and physical issues, you can support your claim for secondary service connection and win VA benefits.

Mental Disorders Causing Physical Disease

"Disease results from an error in the mind." When I first heard that axiom, I was tempted to think it referred to psychosomatic illnesses. If you think your arm hurts, it eventually will. But decades of scientific research support that many physical diseases originate from error within a patient's state of mind. "There is no health without mental health," according to the World Health Organization. "Health is a state of complete physical, mental and social well-being—not merely the absence of disease or infirmity."[52] Most of us make distinctions between "mind" and "body." The mind handles consciousness, emotion, and thought processes, while the body handles movement, digestion, blood flow, sensation, and such. Of course, the distinction isn't quite so black and white.

Understanding the fundamental connection between mind and body is vital to establishing service connection or secondary service connection for VA benefits. Mental health has a major impact on physical health. Many veterans suffering from PTSD or other mental health difficulties not only deserve benefits to cover their PTSD, but also their sleep apnea, chronic obstructive pulmonary disorder (COPD), and liver disease. Why? Because these conditions go hand in hand. One actually causes or increases the risk of developing the other. As long as scientific evidence and expert medical opinion support your claim, you can gain secondary service connection for any health condition related to your service-connected PTSD or mental health condition.

PTSD Linked to Numerous Diseases

Our veterans disability law practice expands the scope of secondary claims that we make with respect to PTSD. VA examiners continue to view PTSD as a narrow, separate entity and fail to consider the integrated, symbiotic effects that psychiatric disease has on overall health. In PTSD cases, a traumatic event has made a significant, long-lasting impression on the mind, and therefore the body. For example, individuals who have experienced traumatic events show dysregulated neuroendocrine systems. This dysregulation can lead to impaired immune function and, when combined with genetic vulnerabilities and maladaptive psychological states, it can lead to behaviors that permanently impair a veteran's health.[53] PTSD can also lead to impaired fear inhibition,[54] eating disorders,[55] substance abuse,[56] and other risky behaviors that lead to life-threatening illnesses.

Several diseases associated with PTSD (though not all) relate to one of four common characteristics of PTSD patients, namely:

1. Tobacco and/or alcohol abuse
2. Physical inactivity upon return from service
3. Anxiety levels associated with PTSD
4. Medications taken to alleviate PTSD symptoms

An extensive span of scientific research shows that many physical disease states are associated with these four characteristics. Veterans who are service connected for PTSD and have developed cancer, diabetes, heart disease, or any other disease that can be linked to PTSD, are able to obtain secondary service connection for that disease. In some cases, the VA has granted our clients benefits for total disability ratings, based on individual unemployability (TDIU) related to secondary service connection, which is the 100 percent pay rate—even though their service-connected disability ratings did not add up to 100 percent.

Common PTSD-Associated Conditions

Soldiers returning home from service who suffer from PTSD tend to lead relatively inactive lifestyles, particularly when they are unable to work. Studies show that PTSD patients are at a higher risk for obesity (body mass index over 30) (32.6 percent) compared to non-PTSD civilians (24.1 percent).[57] Inactivity combined with unhealthy eating behaviors and a higher risk for binge eating disorder often leads to rapid weight gain. While the American Medical Association has categorized obesity as a disease, the VA does not recognize it as a disability for VA benefits purposes. But

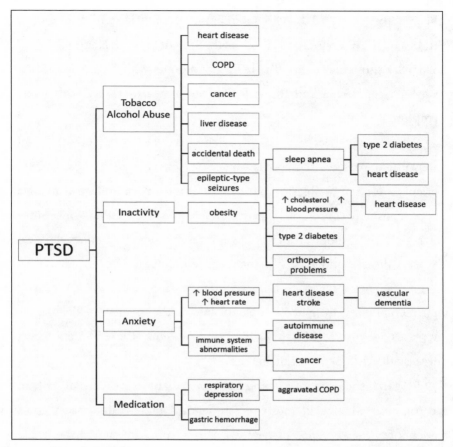

Inactivity Linked to Sleep Apnea, Heart Disease, Diabetes and Orthopedic Problems

obesity is a risk factor for numerous diseases, including sleep apnea, heart disease, type 2 diabetes, and orthopedic problems.

Since 2009, veterans' claims for sleep apnea have increased by 150 percent, with more than 94 percent of these coming from veterans of Gulf War I or the Iraq and Afghanistan wars.[58] According to the Department of Veterans Affairs Fiscal Year 2016 Annual Benefits Report, sleep apnea has become the most common service-connected respiratory disability, and it makes up more than 25.4 percent of all body system disabilities.[59] Studies by the VA San Diego Healthcare System and the National Center for PTSD show that over 69 percent of veterans with PTSD are at high risk for sleep apnea and the risk of sleep apnea increases with PTSD symptom severity.[60]

Patients with sleep apnea experience reduced sleep duration and intermittent periods of hypoxia—a lack of oxygen to the brain. These patients are often unable to hold gainful employment and need medical support (usually continuous positive airway pressure—CPAP—machines) during sleep. Without proper medical intervention, sleep apnea can lead to heart disease and type 2 diabetes. Sleep apnea can cause alterations in glucose metabolism. Both sleep deprivation and hypoxia exert a detrimental effect on glucose metabolism. As the severity of sleep apnea increases, glucose regulation in the body weakens. These alterations can increase the risk for type 2 diabetes.

Research shows that 83 percent of type 2 diabetes patients suffer from sleep apnea.[61] Medical literature recommends doctors evaluate sleep apnea patients for the presence of type 2 diabetes. While type 2 diabetes can go undiagnosed for several years, a sleep apnea diagnosis can lead to its early detection. If you have been diagnosed with sleep apnea and are also gaining weight, ask to be examined for the presence of type 2 diabetes. You may then file a claim for type 2 diabetes as secondary to the sleep apnea.

Similarly, if a veteran with PTSD is overweight and has been diagnosed with high cholesterol or high blood pressure, he is at serious risk for heart disease. In addition, I have had a number of cases involving veterans who are service connected for PTSD and suffer from obesity and knee disabilities. When the knee problem is not service related and is caused by joint stress associated with obesity, the VA will try to deny the claim. However, if the obesity stems from PTSD, one can conceivably argue secondary service connection for any resulting orthopedic problems.

Anxiety Linked to Heart Disease, Stroke, Dementia, Autoimmune Disorders, and Cancer

I have seen many cases where a veteran with service connection for PTSD had a heart attack or a stroke. When the veteran or a widow tries to get service connection for the heart attack or stroke, the VA denies the claim. The VA may argue that there was a total absence of heart disease symptoms during service or for years after. If you try to argue that your PTSD caused the heart attack, the VA may deny the claim based on the idea that psychiatric problems are separate from physical problems. However, my clients have often won service connection in this type of scenario, on an aggravation theory—a theory of service connection where an existing service-connected disability aggravates a non-service-connected disability and makes it worse.

PTSD is a stress-based illness. When you have a PTSD episode, there is a sudden release of catecholamines from the adrenal glands in response to a perceived threat—the fight or flight response. Catecholamine release results in a transient but significant increase in pulse, sweating, glucose, and blood pressure. Elevated blood pressure is an established risk factor for cardiovascular disease. Several studies have demonstrated the link between PTSD and heart disease. One study showed that PTSD patients were more than twice as likely to develop heart disease as those without PTSD.[62] A study from the VA Office of Public Health and Environmental Hazards states, "Cardiovascular alterations associated with autonomic arousal and cardiovascular health outcomes have long been reported to be associated with PTSD or wartime traumatic exposure. Persons suffering from PTSD and chronic PTSD have been shown to experience increases in basal heart rate and blood pressure, especially in response to stimuli such as loud sounds and visual slides that remind them of the trauma."[63]

In addition, depending on vascular health—the presence of a clot, an arterial aneurysm, an arteriovenous malformation—a spike in blood pressure can be enough to cause a stroke. PTSD events can incite inflammation and lipid changes that lead to arterial wall damage. Moreover, PTSD is associated with platelet dysfunction, which can contribute to clot formation. We know that PTSD contributes to physical problems, including heart disease and stroke. Therefore, if you are service connected for PTSD and develop heart disease or have a stroke, the scientific evidence supports a secondary relationship between your PTSD and the cardiovascular event. If you are a widow and the VA has denied your claim for DIC, you may also be able to link a terminal heart attack or stroke to your husband's service-connected PTSD.

PTSD can also lead to vascular dementia. I was recently contacted by a widow in her 90s (despite her age, she still plays golf on a daily basis at her Florida retirement community). Her husband of over 60 years served on active duty from 1943 to 1946. He returned from service with PTSD, which was later determined to be service connected. The veteran developed diabetes, hypertension, and vascular disease or vascular dementia. He eventually passed away. The cause of death was listed as vascular disease or dementia. An amended death certificate filed several years later listed PTSD as the cause of death.

The widow filed a claim for Dependency and Indemnity Compensation (DIC) benefits, only to have the VA deny her claim on the grounds that PTSD does not cause dementia. The VA supported their denial with several opinions by VA examiners, two out of three being Ph.D.-level psychologists who lacked the medical training necessary to properly address dementia or vascular disease. The issue in this case concerned whether or not PTSD can cause or aggravate diabetes and hypertension. If so, could this then contribute to vascular dementia or some other type of adult failure to thrive?

Fortunately, the widow hired our veterans disability benefits law firm to represent her DIC claim denial appeal. The U.S. Court of Appeals overturned the VA's denial and remanded the matter back to the VA Board. Our research uncovered a June 2010 article from the Archives of General Psychiatry reporting that adult male veterans with PTSD are at a nearly twofold higher risk of developing dementia than those without PTSD.[64] We also referred back to a highly cited PTSD Research Quarterly article showing an elevated prevalence of diabetes and cardiovascular disease among individuals with PTSD.[65] Numerous studies suggest that diabetes and cardiovascular disease can be relevant in the development of vascular dementia.

PTSD has also been linked to an increased risk of developing certain cancers. Research has shown that high anxiety levels and stress can lower the immune system's ability to fight abnormal cancer cell growth. Along with sleep apnea, emotional distress can inhibit deep sleep and melatonin production, a hormone responsible for regulating the immune system and cancer cell growth.[66] In addition, elevation in the stress hormones, norepinephrine and epinephrine, drives tumor cells to produce matrix metalloproteinases and vascular endothelial growth factor, enhancing cancer cell metastasis to other vital organs.[67] Stress also causes elevated cortisol levels and mineral depletion, which may suppress the immune system's ability to fight cancer.[68] Veteran's with service-connected PTSD who develop cancer should consider seeking secondary service connection for the cancer.

PTSD may also increase the risk of various autoimmune disorders. A recent study involving over 666,000 veterans of Iraq and Afghanistan reported that those diagnosed with PTSD were more likely to develop autoimmune disorders, including rheumatoid arthritis, multiple sclerosis (MS), lupus, thyroid inflammation, and inflammatory bowel disease (IBS).[69] The research team, led by Dr. Aoife O'Donovan at San Francisco Veterans Affairs Medical Center and the Northern California Institute for Research and Education, found a twofold increase in autoimmune disorders among veterans with PTSD compared to those who had no psychiatric diagnoses. In addition, veterans with PTSD showed a 51 percent higher risk of autoimmune disease than those with other psychiatric disorders. Studies have also demonstrated that veterans with PTSD are more likely to have hyperactive immune responses, higher immune cell counts, and higher antibody counts. These clinical markers are consistent with features of autoimmune disease.[70]

Scientists postulate that PTSD may cause immunological or hormonal changes that trigger the autoimmune disease. PTSD may also indirectly activate autoimmune disorders by fueling unhealthy behaviors like smoking, alcohol abuse, poor diet, or impaired sleep. Most likely, all of these factors come into play. It is important to note that studies have not shown that PTSD causes autoimmune disease; they have merely demonstrated a key relationship between the two. Proving causation from a scientific perspective is quite different from proving causation to establish VA service connection. Proving that PTSD causes autoimmune disease from a scientific perspective requires a high statistical significance. On the other hand, to prove a claim for VA compensation, we need only establish a 50 percent probability.

I remember one call I received, a veteran who had served onboard an aircraft carrier during the Vietnam War was concerned that trace amounts of Agent Orange present on the ship might have caused him to develop lupus and other autoimmune conditions. The caller was frustrated that his representative was not pursuing this aspect of his claim. As this call took place prior to the Blue Water Navy Vietnam Veterans Act of 2019, I explained that the VA almost never grants a Blue Water Navy veteran's claim for illness due to Agent Orange. In addition, the connection between Agent Orange and lupus is tenuous, so I suggested it might not be the best strategy. The caller then indicated he had a valid claim for PTSD that he expected the VA to grant. Here was a potential strategy for autoimmune disorder service connection. I encouraged him to first seek service connection for PTSD and then pursue a possible secondary service connection link between PTSD and autoimmune disease.

Secondary Service Connection—Alcohol and Tobacco-Related Illnesses

Individuals with PTSD show impaired reasoning and an increased tendency to engage in risky behavior that can cause serious health problems. For example, the National Comorbidity Survey reports that over 45 percent of American PTSD patients are smokers, compared to just 23 percent of the general adult population. Although half of all smokers eventually stop using tobacco, only 23 percent of smokers with PTSD quit smoking, placing PTSD sufferers third from the bottom in quit-rate rankings for 13 mental disorders.[71] Peer-reviewed studies show a 31.7 percent 10-year cumulative incidence of smoking among PTSD patients, compared to 19.9 percent in non-PTSD sufferers with a history of trauma and 10.5 percent in those with no history of trauma.[72] While the VA will not pay benefits for tobacco-related illnesses, if a veteran can establish a link between their service-connected PTSD and chronic obstructive pulmonary disease (COPD), heart disease, or cancer, they can establish secondary service connection and obtain VA benefits.

Several epidemiological studies also document a high prevalence of drug and alcohol abuse disorders among PTSD patients. The National Comorbidity Survey reports that 51.9 percent of lifetime PTSD patients have a lifetime alcohol abuse/dependence diagnosis and 34.5 percent have a lifetime drug abuse/dependence diagnosis.[73] Alcohol consumption can also lead to liver disease and cardiomyopathy, not to mention an increased risk for accidents associated with driving under the influence, pulmonary aspiration, and hypothermia. I recently had the privilege of working on an appeal for a veteran who developed a neurological seizure disorder secondary to alcoholism. The veteran's PTSD led to self-medication via heavy use of alcohol. This, in turn, led to a neurological impairment that resulted in the development of epileptic-type seizures.

A Vietnam veteran's widow recently contacted me concerning a claim stemming from her husband's death due to pancreatic cancer. Usually, if type 2 diabetes exists years prior to a pancreatic cancer diagnosis, we can establish a secondary relationship between the pancreatic cancer and the pre-existing diabetes. But in this case, her husband did not have type 2 diabetes at least six to seven years prior to the pancreatic cancer diagnosis. As the Vietnam veteran was service connected for PTSD, I sought to determine whether the pancreatic cancer was somehow linked to the PTSD. The widow confirmed that her husband suffered from a serious drinking problem. If the excessive drinking began after the traumatic event and scientific evidence shows a link between heavy alcohol use and pancreatic cancer, then the pancreatic cancer could be secondary to the service-connected PTSD—and the widow could win service connection for her husband's cause of death.

PTSD Medication May Aggravate COPD, Cause Gastrointestinal Complications

Although the VA will not pay benefits for tobacco-related illnesses, PTSD exhibits wide-ranging effects in other areas of pulmonary and gastrointestinal health. The stress and anxiety associated with PTSD may manifest in respiratory illnesses, like chronic obstructive pulmonary disease (COPD).[74] In addition, medications often prescribed to treat PTSD, like benzodiazepines, can lead to respiratory depression and aggravation of COPD.[75] Regarding gastrointestinal complications, I represented a widow whose husband, who was service connected for PTSD, suffered a gastric hemorrhage and died. She filed her DIC claim, trying to service-connect the cause of the veteran's death. The VA denied the claim repeatedly for almost 10 years. Once she retained our veterans benefits law firm to represent her, we successfully got her claim remanded from the U.S. Court of Appeals for Veterans Claims.

On remand, we obtained an expert medical opinion that conceded that there was no known linkage between the PTSD and the gastric incident. But we discovered that the veteran was taking non-steroidal anti-inflammatory medication (NSAID) along with a selective serotonin reuptake inhibitor (SSRI) medication that the VA had prescribed to treat the PTSD. We further learned that combining an SSRI with an NSAID increased gastric hemorrhage risks. Our medical expert explained this concept thoroughly, and, as a result, the Board granted service connection for the cause of death.

The VA's responsibility for our veterans is far-reaching and long-term. Beyond merely treating the acute injuries associated with combat, VA must consider the chronic illnesses—like heart disease—as part and parcel of PTSD residuals. Any disabled veteran with PTSD who also has other health problems should closely examine whether a link can be found between his PTSD and other physical problems. Admittedly, winning a claim for disability benefits secondary to PTSD often requires powerful evidence demonstrated through scientific findings and the opinions of top-notch medical experts. Such experts are hard to find if you are trying to handle your case on your own. So, if you are trying to win a secondary service connection claim, it is wise to hire a veterans disability lawyer who has built relationships with experts on the medical issues affecting veterans.

Non-PTSD Mental Disorders and Disease

Understandably, non-PTSD psychiatric diagnoses of depression, anxiety, adjustment disorder, bipolar disorder, panic disorder, chronic pain disorder, schizophrenia, schizoaffective disorder, adjustment disorder, delusional disorders, and other psychotic disorders can also lead to major adverse health conditions. With PTSD, we can point to combat with the enemy, assault, or witnessing the death of friends to prove service connection. But you can also link other psychiatric disabilities to military service, even when you have no record of an in-service event.

We recently won service connection for a veteran's myocardial infarction, secondary to a service-connected psychiatric disability. This veteran's psychiatric disability was different than the typical PTSD scenario. He had a psychiatric disability that produced a binge eating disorder and resulting obesity. His morbid obesity, in turn, caused metabolic syndrome and numerous cardiovascular problems. While the VA historically does not view obesity as a disability subject to service connection, no reasonable physician can dispute the fact that obesity is a medically significant physiological occurrence that carries numerous risk factors for a multitude of health problems.

In this particular case, the veteran developed a host of problems, including insulin resistance, high blood pressure, and cardiovascular problems. These problems eventually led to his myocardial infarction and a diminished workload capacity associated with his weakened heart. The VA denied service connection numerous times throughout the appeal process, starting at the Regional Office and going up to the Board of Veterans' Appeals and eventually to the U.S. Court of Appeals for Veterans' Claims. We were successful in getting the claim overturned on appeal at the U.S. Court of Appeals for Veterans' Claims, and then on remand we obtained an opinion from an outside consulting medical expert who determined that the psychiatric disability that drove the binge eating disorder was at the heart of the problem resulting in the myocardial infarction.

The VA supported its denial in this case based upon a VA medical examination report that continued to assert that binge eating does not cause heart problems. We, however, were able to locate significant scientific literature that did support a connection between binge eating disorder and heart problems. Based upon our research, the medical literature, and our articulate and well-reasoned medical expert, we were able to convince the Board of Veterans' Appeals that service connection for this disability was warranted. As a result, the veteran received retroactive pay for 22 years of past-due benefits. This is yet another example of how a medical scenario that is slightly different than usual can turn into a successful claim if an advocate understands the medical science and is willing to hire the right medical experts to prove the claim.

Physical Ailments Produce Mental Disorders

Just as mental disorders can affect physical health, physical disorders can lead to mental health problems. In evaluating patients, psychiatrists usually consider whether a physical condition is causing or contributing to the observed mental disturbances before drawing up a treatment plan. Research suggests that medical causes may account for between 10 and 46 percent of psychiatric symptoms exhibited by patients.[76,77] Head trauma and brain injuries can cause behavioral, emotional, and cognitive problems. Likewise, certain infections, gastrointestinal disorders, heart problems, and chronic pain can also cause a number of debilitating mental issues. Veterans with service-connected physical disorders may be able to establish secondary service connection for any resulting mental health problem.

TBI Causes Behavioral, Emotional and Cognitive Disorders

One of the signature injuries of the Iraq and Afghanistan wars is traumatic brain injury (TBI) due to the frequent use of improvised explosive devices and the resulting blasts. Other causes of TBI include in-service motor vehicle accidents, in-service falls, personal assault, or any other type of trauma where the head is injured. TBIs often produce not only physical problems but cognitive and behavioral problems. About 19 percent of troops surveyed report a probable TBI during deployment.[78] Traumatic brain injuries are difficult to identify and are often not easily distinguished from PTSD or depression. In fact, tens of thousands of troops suffer from PTSD and depression in addition to TBI.

As stated in the previous section, physical symptoms of traumatic brain injury include vision loss, hearing loss, constant headaches, seizures, motor or sensory dysfunction, loss of smell or taste, and various endocrine and autonomic nerve dysfunctions that cause bladder or bowel impairments.

Cognitive symptoms of TBI include decreased memory, concentration, attention, and executive functioning of the brain. Executive functioning skills include goal setting, information processing, planning, organizing, prioritizing, problem solving, judgment, decision making, and mental flexibility. Emotional symptoms of TBI include depression, anxiety, and other mental disabilities. Behavioral symptoms include irritability, aggression, withdrawal, and poor impulse control. Additionally, cognitive, emotional, and behavioral problems can lead to social problems, including immature behavior, over-dependency, excessive talking, inappropriate sexual behavior, and overspending.

Our veterans disability law practice recently received word of a victory for a veteran and an award of 100 percent disability compensation for delusional disorder. This case illustrates how superior advocacy can snatch victory in some of the most complex disability cases. Our client was in the Navy, working onboard a ship as a cook. He had no training as a Special Forces Operative, and his service personnel records indicate that he never set foot on the land of the Republic of Vietnam. Ship records indicate that his vessel did not get anywhere near the inland waterways or otherwise near shore.

Nevertheless, the veteran filed a claim for PTSD, recounting an elaborate story of Special Forces Operations in clandestine Vietnam missions. The claim for PTSD was obviously denied when the veteran could not corroborate the stressor. There was no proof that he had actually served in Vietnam and no proof that he had engaged in covert operations. His training and specialty were inconsistent with his description of his Special Forces operations. The case went up to the U.S. Court of Appeals for

Veterans Claims regarding the veteran's entitlement to service connection for PTSD or other psychiatric diagnosis. The Board denied the PTSD but remanded the psychiatric claim other than PTSD back to the Regional Office. After a thorough review of the case file at the U.S. Court of Appeals, we determined that there was no viable way to sustain an appeal for the PTSD denial.

But an interesting thing happened during our review. We began to notice uncanny parallels with the storyline and plot of the Vietnam-era movie *Apocalypse Now*, starring Robert Duvall. Our client's story read like a screenplay for the Francis Ford Coppola film. This veteran genuinely believed he had experienced these events in Vietnam as a Special Forces Operative, but there was virtually no way to prove his presence in Vietnam on a special mission to assassinate a rogue colonel. What could explain the sincere honesty with which this veteran recalled events and the directly contradictory official record?

After thoroughly reviewing the file, I determined that the veteran had at least two documented head traumas during active duty. We then had to ascertain whether or not head trauma can cause delusional disorder. We enlisted one of the top forensic psychiatrists available in veterans disability cases. This psychiatrist concluded that it was at least as likely as not that in-service head trauma had caused the veteran's delusional disorder. We presented these arguments directly to the Regional Office on the remanded claim. As a result, the Regional Office was forced to concede the validity of our theory of the case. They granted service connection and awarded a 100 percent disability rating for this veteran.

In-Service Infection Causing Mental Disorders

Several infections that veterans may acquire during service are likely to induce symptoms of mental disorder. Often, a veteran will not realize that prior infection is causing his mental difficulties since symptoms can take years to develop. Scientists have associated numerous pathogens with mental illnesses, including Borna disease virus, Epstein-Barr virus, and certain strains of the herpes virus. Other infections that can cause mental disorders include malaria, syphilis, legionella, typhoid, HIV, diphtheria, and rheumatic fever. Psychiatric symptoms have also been associated with parasites like ascaris, giardia, trichinae, and borrelia. A *Toxoplasmosis gondii* infection can cause delusions, emotional disturbances, and auditory hallucinations.

Infection with *Treponema pallidum*, the causative agent of syphilis, has had a deleterious impact on U.S. military personnel throughout history. World War II draftees from the southern Atlantic states had syphilis infection rates as high as 11.3 percent. During the Vietnam War, the average annual incidence of STDs was 26.2 percent, with 90 percent being cases of gonorrhea and just over 1 percent being cases of syphilis.[79] Many soldiers were treated for gonorrhea, but not syphilis. Unfortunately, modern-day cases of syphilis in the U.S. military are increasing. From January 2010 through August 2015, 2,976 members of the armed forces were diagnosed with syphilis, rising from 30.9 cases per 100,000 in 2010 to 47.4 cases per 100,000 in 2015. Male service members represented 88.7 percent of these recent cases.[80] Early symptoms of syphilis are not obvious. When left untreated, syphilis can remain latent for three to 15 years after the initial infection, eventually causing extensive organ damage, dementia, and even death.

Our firm recently represented a veteran who suffered from multiple psychiatric issues, including psychosis and depression. There were no verifiable stressors in his records; he did not have combat exposure, and there were zero psychiatric complaints noted in his service treatment records. His service medical records contained the usual litany of common ailments such as a cough, sore throat, sore muscles, dental problems, and the usual venereal diseases. To the casual observer, there was nothing of a psychiatric nature in the service treatment records. However, I knew the venereal disease diagnosis was the hook upon which could hang our proverbial service connection hat.

In this case, the veteran's records documented venereal disease symptoms such a penile discharge, skin rash, swollen lymph nodes, and pain on urination. The medical corps assumed a diagnosis of gonorrhea and prescribed the appropriate treatment. However, the problem persisted for some time. Buried in the service treatment records—in almost illegible handwriting—was a notation of "r/o syphilis," but there was no evidence that the medical corps did any work to actually rule out syphilis. Because I knew that the neuro-syphilis condition typical of the third phase of syphilis includes psychiatric problems like the ones my client was experiencing, I engaged a well-respected forensic psychiatrist who has had extensive experience treating venereal disease cases as a member of the medical corps in the Soviet military. We worked to establish expert testimony that our client had undiagnosed syphilis in service that progressed to the latent stage, resulting in a psychiatric pathology.

In cases like these, veterans must carefully analyze their service treatment records to determine if venereal disease was noted. If there is a diagnosis of gonorrhea, there is a one in five chance of concurrent syphilis. This can cause neurological and psychiatric problems in the subsequent years. Anyone with a VA appeal for the denial of VA benefits should take great care to fully research the possible underlying diseases of any symptoms noted in service treatment records.

Chronic Pain Linked to Mental Disorders

Claims of mental disorders may be secondary to service-connected medical conditions that involve chronic pain. For example, a veteran may be service connected for orthopedic problems involving his joints. This state of chronic pain can produce debilitating depression that gives way to a vicious cycle: the worse the pain, the worse the depression, and the more depressed a person feels, the more profound their experience of pain. Depression caused by chronic pain can render one incapable of maintaining a gainful occupation.

We have helped countless veterans obtain high ratings for depression involving secondary service connection. The key to winning these claims lies in establishing the onset of depression at a time and proximity to discharge where there is an absence of intervening events that could otherwise explain the onset of depression. In situations where a veteran has turned to drugs or alcohol during service as a way of self-medicating depression, it can be argued that the use of drugs or alcohol represents a symptom of the underlying depression.

Recently, we received a favorable Board of Veterans Appeals decision for a veteran who had been appealing the denial of his psychiatric claim since 1994. The veteran claimed that TBI during service had caused his psychiatric disorder. The VA denied his TBI claim in large part due to a delay in symptoms after the head injury, along with a post-service head injury that gave the VA reason to believe the veteran's problems came from the post-service accident. The case involved numerous medical opinions, most of which were unfavorable. Most of his VA doctors stated that post-concussion symptoms would normally resolve in a few months after the head trauma.

However, one VA medical examiner stated that the veteran's cognitive problems were due to chronic pain. The veteran happened to be service connected for a neck problem that he sustained in an in-service motor vehicle accident. The Board failed to consider whether there was a secondary service connection claim for the mental problems as a result of the chronic, service-connected pain. As a result, we were able to get the claim overturned on appeal at the U.S. Court of Appeals for Veterans Claims. We also obtained a notable neuropsychiatric expert and current research showing that there can indeed be a lengthy delay between head trauma and the onset of psychotic symptoms. The expert provided the much-needed testimony to establish the nexus between in-service head trauma and psychotic disorder. The Board granted service connection, and after more than 20 years on appeal, this veteran received his service-connected compensation.

In another case involving schizophrenia and major depression caused by chronic pain, we were able to get a veteran a 100 percent rating and $280,000 in back pay. This veteran filed a claim for increased ratings and schizophrenia in the mid-1990s. The Board denied his claims on the grounds that there was no evidence that the schizophrenia was related to service. The veteran hired us to appeal his case to the U.S. Court of Appeals for Veterans Claims.

Upon review of his file, we discovered that the Board had ignored evidence that the veteran suffered limitations due to the pain his service-connected disabilities caused him. The veteran's psychiatric records showed that he was preoccupied with physical pain and suggested that he suffered mental problems due to the constant pain. As a result, we successfully argued that the Board had failed to consider a claim for secondary service connection—that is, it failed to consider whether the veteran had a mental disability caused by the chronic pain from his service-connected physical disabilities.

We got his case remanded back to the Board. We then scheduled the veteran for an evaluation with a private forensic psychologist and a vocational expert. We obtained X-rays and MRIs. We had an expert radiologist review them and write a report. After an additional year of waiting, the regional office finally made a decision. They granted service connection for the veteran's mental disability as secondary to his service-connected physical disabilities. The result: 100 percent service connection for major depression with 13 years back pay, totaling more than $280,000.

Gastrointestinal Disorder Effects on Mental Status

There are numerous gastrointestinal problems for which service connection can be obtained, including ulcers, gastroesophageal reflux disease (GERD), cancer, and hemorrhoids. We frequently see cases of irritable bowel syndrome (IBS), functional dyspepsia, and functional abdominal pain syndrome, which fall under the category of Gulf War Syndrome for those who served in Southwest Asia during the Gulf War. Irritable bowel syndrome affects 11 percent of the global population,[81] and it is frequently associated with psychiatric disorders.[82,83] Therefore, an important consideration is the extent to which a service-connected gastrointestinal disability can affect your mental outlook and produce a state of depression. This depression, in turn, could be service connected on a secondary basis.

Heart Disease and Cognitive Decline

Cardiovascular disabilities like ischemic heart disease, hypertension, and other conditions affecting the cardiac system can produce secondary effects that can cause disabling stroke and heart attacks. Ischemic heart disease represents a large area of litigation given that the VA has only recently added it to the list of Agent Orange diseases. Also associated with Agent

Orange exposure is the resulting coronary artery bypass surgery that can come from this condition.

What a lot of veterans do not know, however, is that as many as 47 percent of coronary artery bypass surgery patients experience some form of cognitive decline.[84,85,86] This means that if you are service connected for ischemic heart disease and underwent a coronary artery bypass procedure, and you have suffered cognitive and mental decline, a secondary service connection claim should be made for the mental deficiencies. This is also crucial if you are making a claim for total disability. For instance, if you are rated 60 percent disabled for a heart condition, and the VA says you are merely disabled from sedentary work, but your mental alertness declined significantly following the heart surgery so that you cannot do sedentary work, then this must be considered when making a claim for total disability. If the VA grants you 60 percent for one disability under the heading of a heart disability, and you are not able to work, then you should make certain that the VA decides a claim for total disability at the same time.

Keep in mind: veterans can use the mental-physical health connection for any number of VA claim scenarios. For example, a veteran can use it to help verify a traumatic event that occurred during service, for which he has no medical record. While trying to prove the occurrence of an in-service personal assault, I retained a renowned psychiatric expert who explained how psychiatric problems can have dermatologic manifestations. In this particular case, the client broke out in hives when under stress. The presence of hives in his service medical records served as evidence to support the occurrence of the assault, and my expert used the stress-skin disorder connection to corroborate the in-service stressor. A creative-thinking, experienced advocate can help you determine how to establish connections that can help you win your claim for VA benefits.

The Value of Expert Opinions

I believe in developing a client's case to the maximum with experienced, private medical experts. The top practitioners in the veterans' bar understand this. Some firms could spend up to $500,000 per year or more on medical expert fees. I recently had a conversation with the CEO of a commercial lending institution that offered a financial product to contingency fee law firms to help them cover the cost of case expenses. This executive informed me that his company had an exhibition booth at one of the recent conventions of a veterans' lawyer organization. He was surprised that there was so little interest on the part of members of the veterans' bar in funding case expenses. His conclusion was that very few lawyers in the veterans' bar spend money on experts.

This is unfortunate. But his experience was consistent with my conversations with other veterans disability lawyers. I remember one seasoned practitioner who told me that she recalled hiring a medical expert on only one occasion in 20 plus years of practice. I was shocked and wondered how many cases were lost because of an unwillingness to aggressively develop the case with outside medical experts. I know of many cases I have won over the years that would have been lost but for my hiring top-notch medical experts.

What's revealing about this is that the majority of practitioners are not willing to hire outside experts. It's costly, yes. Most disabled veteran clients do not have the money, and most veterans disability lawyers don't want to pay out of their own pockets. But this is what often separates the average lawyer from the top-tier practitioner who wins big awards in complex cases. If you are considering which law firm to represent you, consider carefully the firm's track record and case histories. Look to determine if they have won complex cases with high-powered experts. Ask them directly if they are willing to hire outside experts to win a case. A good veterans' benefits attorney who believes in your case should be willing to advance the cost of retaining medical experts.

Our nation's veterans have the right to VA benefits, benefits that can help them heal and lead productive, successful lives after service. If you are a veteran suffering from a mental or physical disorder and feel that your condition could not possibly be connected to your service, I ask that you think again. Seek the VA benefits and care that you deserve, and don't give up until you have considered every possible option.

THE DEADLY WAIT

'Dangerous Flaws in Medical Care Access

In Indianapolis, disabled veteran Ralph Patterson was made to wait nearly seven hours to get results from an X-ray for severe knee pain. Patterson left the Army in 1984 with an honorable discharge after injuring his left leg. Years of relying on his right leg to get around had taken their toll. He ended up falling and injuring his right knee, which caused constant pain and limited his mobility.

Two days after the fall, Patterson ended up at the ER. He was promptly scheduled for an MRI, which revealed severe trauma to his knee. He needed to see an orthopedic specialist. The VA Orthopedic Services division told him they had an opening in 29 days. Since his appointment was one day before the established 30-day deadline, he wasn't able to seek out an orthopedic specialist outside of the VA under the Veterans Choice Program.

During his wait, he returned to the VA emergency room in severe pain. After an X-ray, doctors told him to wait in the emergency room for the results. He spent a total of nearly seven hours before the emergency doctor told him, "They're not going to come down. They're just going to discharge you." He was handed a prescription for painkillers and dismissed.[87]

In another disturbing example of our nation's unacceptable medical care access for veterans, on September 28, 2013, a doctor examined 71-year-old Navy veteran Thomas Breen who was seeing blood in his urine. Breen's physician decided the situation was urgent and asked that a urologist evaluate Breen within one week. Breen and his wife called the VA daily for two months trying to get an appointment, but Breen lost his life to bladder cancer on November 30. Six days later, the VA called to schedule his "urgent" appointment.[88]

With today's medical advances and technology, there is no excuse for making any patient in need wait for medical care, especially when that patient has spent time serving our country. While our nation vows to take care of its veterans, VA hospitals continue to delay patient care appointments, in some cases long enough to result in death. Medical care access for veterans is in an appalling state, and it's been this way for decades. Veterans can't get good health care; they must wait dangerously long for appointments. The VA's medical systems are lying to cover up these long wait times, staff are overwhelmed, and the system is outdated.

Many cases of veteran death due to medical causes or suicide could have been averted if it weren't for the VA's medical access failures, yet despite numerous legislative efforts to fix the problem, the VA continues to ignore recommendations, failing our veteran men and women. Following numerous scandals and with the help of new leadership, our country may finally be on track to take control of the problem. But veterans are asking, will new legislation transform the Veteran's Health Administration (VHA) for better or for worse?

A History of Medical Access Problems

Have veterans always struggled with access to medical care? Reports claim veterans have faced difficulties trying to get timely medical assistance since at least John F. Kennedy's presidency,[89] but it is hard to get a definitive answer. Investigation results suggest VA clinics have hidden away or falsified records to conceal the problem for decades. Historically, issues with access to medical care tend to increase with waves of demand. Yet, these demand increases should be relatively predictable.

One would think data on how many veterans enter service, how many are discharged, and when, should be easily accessible. We also know approximately how many veterans are likely to suffer from physical or mental health disabilities. So, why hasn't the VA been able to ensure that adequate clinic numbers and hospital staff are available to care for every single veteran in need?

In the 1990s, medical access got particularly rough. With thousands already receiving care and surges of veterans set to return home from the Gulf War, legislators decided to expand veteran eligibility for medical care at VA clinics to include all veterans—no income restraints or service connection requirements. Unfortunately, VA hospitals weren't prepared. The move resulted in a bottleneck of patients and severe delays in medical care. By October 1993, the U.S. General Accounting Office (GAO) reported that many veterans were waiting eight to nine weeks to obtain appointments in specialty clinics.[90]

In 1996, to help alleviate the problem, Congress started requiring all nonurgent primary and specialty care VA clinics to schedule appointments within 30 days of request. Patients had to be seen within 20 minutes of their scheduled appointment time. The timeliness standard also required that veterans have access to urgent care 24 hours per day.[91] But by 2001, the GAO was still reporting excessive VA clinic wait times.[92] An inspection of 54 specialty care clinics revealed that just 33 percent met the VA's 30-day standard, while 66 percent had wait times ranging from 33 to 282 days.

The GAO emphasized that many of the delays in both primary and specialty care clinics were "the result of poor scheduling procedures and inefficient use of staff," and that on account of the inefficiencies they found, "it was difficult to determine the extent to which clinics would have benefited from additional staff." Some clinics would automatically reschedule missed appointments without determining why the original appointment had been missed and without notifying patients of their new appointment. Some clinics would schedule appointments for patients who didn't need to be seen by a doctor.

Over the years, as medical technology and access to battlefield care improved, many more veterans were able to return home alive—but with permanent disabilities that require years of consistent medical care. Even though the U.S. veteran population dropped by 5.8 million between 1986 and 2012, the number of service-connected disabled veterans increased by about 1.3 million.[93] Veterans struggling with PTSD and Agent Orange exposure continued to fight for their right to VA benefits. And as eligibility expanded, VA health care clinics struggled to meet demand.

The VA health care system has long blamed scheduling failures and unsafe wait times on staff shortages. However, the problem appears to be more one of incompetence and indolence. In 2012, the GAO reported that poor training, inconsistent scheduling systems, deficient staff guidelines, and faulty staff utilization were leading to extended wait times—not low staff numbers, stating, "Outpatient medical appointment wait times reported by the Veterans Health Administration, within the Department of Veterans Affairs, are unreliable."

"Some schedulers at Veterans Affairs medical centers that GAO visited did not record the desired date correctly," said the 2012 GAO report. "For example, three schedulers changed the desired date based on appointment availability; this would have resulted in a reported wait time that was shorter than the patient actually experienced." In addition, the GAO stated,

"Officials at all VAMCs GAO visited reported that high call volumes and a lack of staff dedicated to answering the telephones impede scheduling of timely medical appointments."[94]

The Phoenix Scandal

At this point, even VA employees were starting to be concerned about veteran safety. In early 2012, VA emergency room physician Dr. Katherine Mitchell took incoming Phoenix VA Health Care System Director Sharon Helman aside to tell her the Phoenix emergency room was "overwhelmed and dangerous." In response, Mitchell says the administration transferred her out of the ER for "deficient communication skills."[95]

By mid-2013, Phoenix VA Medical Center administrators claim their wait time reduction programs have been successful, and patients are getting in to see doctors within a reasonable time. Yet, employees complain that this is not the case. "I think it's unfair to call any of this a success when veterans are waiting six weeks on an electronic waiting list before they are called to schedule their first PCP [primary care provider] appointment," Carl T. Hayden VA Medical Center program analyst Damian Reese said in an email in July 2013. "Sure, when their appointment was created, it can be 14 days out, but we're making them wait 6-20 weeks to create that appointment. That is unethical and a disservice to our veterans."[96]

In September 2013, Dr. Mitchell was placed on administrative leave after her confidential complaint filed with the VA Office of Inspector General (OIG) was directed back to the VA. The following month, Phoenix VA internal medicine physician Sam Foote filed a complaint alleging that the only improvements in wait times were coming from falsified scheduling data and that the excessive wait times were costing veterans their lives.

Investigators visited Phoenix VA Medical Center in December 2013 to examine the employees' multiple allegations of wrongdoing. The investigation revealed that dozens of veterans may have died waiting for appointments with Phoenix VA hospitals and that the Phoenix VA Health Care System kept separate records to hide the dangerous appointment wait times.

An interim report from the OIG said Phoenix was reporting 24-day wait times, but the actual wait times averaged nearly four months, and at least 1,700 veterans who had made appointments weren't even listed on the schedule. In May 2014, President Obama announced VA Secretary Eric K. Shinseki's resignation.

In June of 2014, the interim head of the department, VA Deputy Secretary Sloan Gibson, visited the Phoenix VA hospital and found that 18 of those 1,700 veterans who weren't scheduled for appointments had died.[97] Soon after, the VA reported that a total of over 57,000 veterans had been unable to see a doctor due to misrepresented or sidetracked patient scheduling, and around 64,000 other veterans had never been scheduled after requesting an appointment.

Other Phoenix VA Health Care System employees started to come forward, including scheduling clerk Pauline DeWenter. DeWenter publicly stated that she was responsible for maintaining and hiding the lists showing the actual patient wait times. She said staff altered records to hide the deaths of at least seven veterans. "Deceased notes on files were removed to make statistics look better, so veterans would not be counted as having died while waiting for care," DeWenter told CNN. She explained that new requests by veterans wanting treatment "went into a desk drawer. . . That would be the secret list."[98]

At a September 2014 hearing before the House Veterans Affairs

Committee, the assistant inspector general for health care inspections admitted that delays had contributed to deaths, revealing that, in addition to the six veterans who died after experiencing delays, 293 veterans died out of 3,409 cases it reviewed in Phoenix.[99] A July 2015 OIG investigation reported that:

- 87 patients died waiting for appointments with 116 open consults
- Non-providers canceled consults for vascular patients (potentially to hide a patient's death while they waited for an appointment)
- Waitlists for consults contained over 35,000 patients
- Patients waited over 300 days for vascular care
- 1,100 veterans waited over 30 days for a doctor's appointment

The OIG stated that one veteran died while waiting for a cardiology appointment that could have saved his life. Regarding canceled chiropractic consults, the report stated, "We analyzed 30 consults canceled from January through March 2015 and found that the staff responsible for scheduling inappropriately canceled all 30 consults."[100]

In at least one case, staff members sent a letter to the patient informing them they should schedule the consult, and then sent a consult cancellation on the same day. According to regulations, staff should make three attempts to contact patients before canceling a consult. The OIG also found that "Nearly 4,800 patients had open consults for PVAHCS care for more than 30 days, and 10,000 Patients had open consults for community care exceeding 30 days."

In March 2016, the Chief of Specialty Care Clinics and Scheduling Operations at the Phoenix VA Health Care System, former Army Infantry officer Kuauhtemoc Rodriguez, filed a whistleblower complaint claiming that physicians were blocking off valuable appointment times and making themselves unavailable to patients for between three and five hours per day. Rodriguez also alleged physicians were canceling veteran appointments at rates of up to 35 percent—causing veteran wait times to exceed 400 days.

In a tragic display of the low level of concern for veteran wait times, on May 23, 2016, Department of Veterans Affairs Secretary Robert McDonald made a very inappropriate remark about VA wait times. At "The Monitor Breakfast," a public forum hosted by the Christian Science Monitor, Secretary McDonald said, "When you go to Disney, do they measure the number of hours you wait in line? Or what's important? What's important is, what's your satisfaction with the experience? And what I would like to move to, eventually, is that kind of measure."[101]

Failed Efforts to Improve

In the light of the Phoenix scandal, the White House and Congress launched an investigation and a temporary solution, the "Veterans Choice Program," which aimed to expand community care to increase veterans' access to medical care and diminish scheduling delays. The government also asked the Commission on Care, a board of specialists formed under the Veterans Access, Choice and Accountability Act of 2014 (Choice Act), to investigate the VHA in more detail and identify chronic problems in its organizational culture. The Commission released the results of its investigation on June 30, 2016.

The report said the Choice Program hadn't solved the wait times issue. It also shed light on many problems that required urgent attention—problems that may have been the most important consequence of the past VA scandal. Concerning the Choice Program, the 300-page report informed that it only "aggravated wait times and frustrated veterans."

Among the issues identified by the Commission, "chronic management and system failures, along with a troubled organizational culture" were some of the most critical.

The report also noted that the VHA "has not effectively empowered its staff to identify problems and make changes to improve the overall quality of care." The document not only brought to light the VHA's inability to adapt and learn from its mistakes but also the difficulties it faces when it comes to integrating behavioral health and primary care, a critical aspect for "many who have suffered from the effects of battle and for whom VHA is a safety net."

To ensure that there is no doubt about the VHA's critical situation, the report's authors did not shy before calling its organizational structure "chaotic" and pointing to "staffing shortages and vacancies at every level of the organization and across numerous critical positions." Finally, the 2016 Commission on Care's Final Report[102] proposed a dramatic restructuring of the VHA, providing 18 recommendations on how to fix the problems:

- Create area-specific networks of VA health care providers (VHA Care System)
- Improve VHA support staff to free up physicians
- Adopt clinical appeals process to help resolve patient care disputes
- Utilize the Veterans Engineering Resource Center to share ideas on best-practices
- Fund Office of Health Equity to eliminate health care disparity among veterans
- Give Board of VHA Care System full control over assets and facilities
- Streamline VA computer systems for all-inclusive information sharing

- Reorganize supply chain management to cut costs by removing administrative involvement in purchasing
- Create a board of directors to govern VHA
- Create VHA culture that aligns staff and leadership in a single mission
- Model VHA leadership pipeline after more successful models seen in private sector
- Reorganize management to empower local leadership and eliminate redundancy
- Create a private sector-type model to measure personnel performance
- Ensure that leadership, staff, and employees understand veteran-specific needs
- Rewrite laws governing employment system to match private sector
- Employ Chief Talent Leader to ensure HR changes are implemented and monitored
- Extend health care eligibility to those with OTH discharges with extenuating circumstances (PTSD, TBI).
- Establish a group of experts to re-evaluate and reformat benefits eligibility design.

These recommendations would essentially restructure the VHA to function as an independent entity, and their implementation would help resolve many of the system's most pressing issues. By this point, the VHA had received numerous recommendations on how to fix medical care access problems, most of which were never executed.

In November 2016, the VA inspector general confirmed that managers at the VA hospital in Tucson told nurses to record appointment dates as "desired dates." In addition, the Inspector General found that VA hospital executives pressured employees to alter patient wait times exceeding seven days 92 percent of the time.[103]

On March 22, 2017, the Department of Veterans Affairs supplied data on two Iowa medical centers showing zero patient wait times of over 90 days—a claim that appeared suspect right off the bat. Committee staff immediately questioned the data, and in June 2017, Iowa Republican Senator Chuck Grassley said the VA was still trying to hide just how bad the wait times were.

A whistleblower produced data revealing that more than 1,500 veterans had indeed waited longer than 90 days to receive care—with hundreds waiting as long as two years. The former employee of an Iowa City VA hospital supplied documents showing that:[104]

- 537 veterans waited 91-180 days for appointments
- 539 veterans waited 181-365 days for appointments
- 232 veterans waited one-two years for appointments

In addition, data from a VA hospital in Des Moines showed hundreds of Iowa veterans had waited more than 90 days for appointments. But, according to Grassley, the VA reaffirmed that there were no wait times over 90 days. "The appearance of an attempt to mislead the committee about the extent of the wait times in these facilities is extremely disturbing," Senator Grassley said in a press release.[105] "As of March 2017, hundreds of veterans were waiting for an appointment between one and two years. This is completely unacceptable."

In response to Senator Grassley's probe into the contradiction between the Iowa VA hospital's reported wait times and the whistleblower's data on actual wait times, VA Secretary David Shulkin said, "I assure you that was not our intent and believe this was a case of misunderstanding between VA and Committee staff."

Grassley replied to Shulkin, stating that the VA's information was inaccurate and "hid the true extent of lengthy wait times at two Iowa facilities." The legislator emphasized that he had brought up the issue twice. "The last time I did so," he argued, "I specifically said, 'Are you sure, are you absolutely positive, that there are no wait times over 90 days?' The VA representatives responded yes and further noted that they had double-checked the over-90-day numbers that morning and could confirm that the numbers were correct."

Grassley reported that VA officials eventually confirmed the accuracy of the data supplied by the whistleblower. "How can veterans, Congress and the public have confidence that the VA is turning itself around when it apparently misrepresents basic facts?" Grassley said. "The VA has to come clean about wait times in Iowa and the rest of the country. We need to get past the point of burying bad news or the VA will never reliably deliver what veterans deserve—good health care in a timely manner."

In August 2017, Kuauhtemoc Rodriguez filed a second whistleblower complaint against the Phoenix VA system claiming VA doctors were refusing to see patients during available work hours—contributing to the dangerous appointment wait times. Rodriguez also filed an anti-retaliation suit against executives who were allegedly threatening termination in response to his complaint. He alleged that veterans were still waiting over 150 days for mental health care and that executives were continuing to permit VA psychiatrists to schedule large blocks of time off or cancel appointments.[106]

The Current State of Affairs

To help address the challenges associated with lack of access to VA health care, President Trump signed the MISSION Act (Maintaining Internal Systems and Strengthening Integrated Outside Networks) into law in June 2018, allowing veterans to choose their health care providers outside of the VA system when:

- Services are unavailable
- State residence lacks full-service VA medical facility
- Veteran has 40-mile legacy/grandfathered from Veterans Choice Program
- Best medical interest
- VA medical service line doesn't comply with VA quality standards

That same month, four years after the initiation of the Veterans Choice Program, GAO inspectors evaluated the program for improvements in veteran medical access. Their findings showed little progress. Veteran wait times through the Veterans Choice Program were still longer than legally required. Veterans were now waiting an average of 64 days for appointments, though the VA claimed it was 51 days. Mistakes in scheduling had caused veterans to be booked for appointments with the wrong type of doctor or in the wrong state. A veteran who needed to see a urologist was scheduled to see a neurologist. A Florida veteran was scheduled with a physician in California, and an Idaho veteran was scheduled with a doctor in New York.

The GAO also found scheduling procedures were masking veterans' real wait times, whether by mistake during manual data entry or on purpose. The report claimed that efforts to expand community care to increase veterans' access to medical care and diminish scheduling delays wouldn't work until the VHA can fix its appointment scheduling problems.[107]

On January 30, 2019, the VA announced that it would be basing medical care access standards under the MISSION Act on the average time it takes to drive to a doctor and the average time it takes to get an appointment.[108] For primary care and mental health services, the VA proposed a 30-minute drive time standard, and a 60-minute rule for specialty care. The VA proposed an appointment wait time standard of 20 days for primary and mental health care and 28 days for specialty care. Veterans who can't access care within those time limits are free to choose an eligible provider outside of the VA system.

"Most Americans can already choose the health care providers that they trust, and President Trump promised that veterans would be able to do the same," VA Secretary Robert Wilkie said in a statement. "With VA's new access standards, the future of the VA health care system will lie in the hands of veterans, exactly where it should be." The new access standards have been enforced since June 2019.

Results of a highly publicized study published in the *Journal of the American Medical Association* (*JAMA*) in January 2019 touted improvements in wait times for appointments at VA hospitals, saying they are now, on average, shorter than wait times in private hospitals. Researchers calculated and compared mean 2017 wait times for primary care, dermatology, cardiology, and orthopedics appointments in VA and private sector facilities, reporting that, overall, VA hospital wait times averaged 17.7 days, while patients waited an average of 29.8 days for appointments with private practitioners. Among the individual practice areas, the study reported that orthopedics was the only specialty with higher wait times in VA hospitals (20.9 days) compared to the private sector (12.4 days).[109]

But appointment data was gathered from VA hospitals for 2017, around the time when the VA was being criticized for manipulating and fabricating wait times to appear shorter than they actually were. Thus, the accuracy of these study results is questionable. And we can't ignore the fact that the senior author of the publication was David Shulkin, former Secretary of the Department of Veterans Affairs. Carolyn Clancy, Executive in Charge of the VHA, was also an author. "There's an impression that VA hospitals are not as efficient as the private sector," Shulkin said. "This study shows that we've made significant progress, and now wait times in many cases are actually shorter than in the private sector."[110] Critics can't help but question a conflict of interest.

In February 2019, the Office of Special Counsel disclosed whistleblower allegations that veterans seeking medical care at Orlando VA Medical Center were experiencing long wait times. An investigation revealed that 453 veterans had waited longer than 30 days for endoscopy procedures, including colonoscopy—a critical tool in detecting cancer and treating it early. In addition, the investigation found that the Acting Chief of Medicine of the Orlando VAMC instructed staff to not refer patients to community care, a violation of the Choice Act. The report concluded that a "substantial and specific danger to public health and safety exists at Orlando."

In response, U.S. Senator Marco Rubio wrote a letter to VA Secretary Robert Wilkie saying, "It is my understanding that your department has not taken any disciplinary action to hold the responsible personnel accountable for these violations. The delays and failure to refer Veterans to the Veterans Choice Program are unacceptable and must be prevented from happening in the future. I would appreciate an explanation on disciplinary actions that have been executed, and if there are none, the reason."[111]

Meanwhile, emergency room wait times in VA hospitals are also getting dangerous. A 2019 investigation found that veteran patients in around 70 percent of VA hospitals must wait hours to be seen. The median emergency room wait time at the VA hospital in Loma Linda, California, was reported to be seven and a half hours. The report found that VA hospital patients were experiencing longer ER wait times than non-VA patients.[112]

Recently, the media has been directing its attention toward the multiple veteran suicides at VA clinics and hospital campuses, many involving complaints of denied emergency mental health visits. Despite widespread knowledge that nearly 75 percent of veterans suffer from PTSD and insomnia and 70 percent report depression, reports say 34.8 percent of veterans had a hard time accessing mental health care at the VA, 36 percent had difficulty scheduling appointments, and 26 percent had trouble finding a clinic in their area.[113]

The lack of mental health care facilities is proving deadly. On April 9, 2019, a veteran shot himself to death in the waiting room of the Austin Veterans Affairs clinic after being transferred there from a local VA hospital in Temple. "When he found out he couldn't get the help he needed there, he chose to take his own life," said McLennan County Veteran's Service Officer, Steve Hernandez. "There is no facility in the state or in the country dedicated to serving veterans with mental health issues," Hernandez told reporters. "What's going on is concerning and the actions undertaken so far speak for themselves."[114]

One week after this veteran took his own life, the VA sent out a press release reminding veterans that it offers all veterans same-day 24/7 access to emergency mental health care at any VA health care facility across the country.[115] But transferring veterans from one clinic to another—which is what happened to this patient—doesn't count as "emergency mental health care." Offering 24/7 same-day access in facilities that can't handle the patient load doesn't solve anything. A lack of mental health care facilities in rural areas means thousands of veterans will still go without access to emergency mental health care.

Challenges Moving Forward

While our nation's government has been commended for opening up private health care options in an attempt to solve the veteran medical access problem, some veterans and legislators worry that expanded access to private medical care will shift VHA funds into the private sector and erode the quality of VA hospital care programs.

President Trump's 2020 budget request included $80.2 billion for the VA medical system, including payments to private medical care (up 9.6 percent from the amount approved for 2019). Proposed community care funding, including funds to implement the MISSION Act, accounted for 19.2 percent of the VA's medical budget (up from 18.8 percent in 2019).

Disabled American Veterans, Paralyzed Veterans of America, and Veterans of Foreign Wars have commented that the budget for veteran health care is $4 billion less than the amount needed to meet demand. Senator Jon Tester of the Senate Veterans' Affairs Committee told AARP, "Now is the time to make sure the VA has the funding it needs to maintain the continuity of quality care and timely benefits that veterans have earned."[116]

Some are also concerned about the proposal to decrease funding for VA infrastructure improvement and construction by 44 percent, further eroding the VA health care system and leading to privatization. Senate Veterans' Affairs Committee members say the cut in infrastructure funding is just cutting into building new facilities and that focusing all funding on the improvement of existing facilities will help prevent any shift to complete privatization.

Aside from budget concerns, the GAO released a report on April 10, 2019, suggesting that VA systems may be insufficient to handle the new community care program as the VA hasn't yet implemented any of the recommendations to improve these systems. According to the report, problems still exist with appointment scheduling systems, referral systems, communication within the VA, and timely care access monitoring.

In addition, the VA has yet to implement GAO recommendations regarding community care customer service records. The GAO also detected insufficient provider numbers in community care networks and questioned the VA's ability to make timely payments to community care providers. Several claims for payment have already been denied due to inadequate provider credentials and faulty reimbursement requirements.[117]

A report released by the U.S. Digital Service in March 2019 suggested that the VA was using a flawed software tool that increased appointments by five to 10 minutes per day, potentially resulting in enough time lost to exclude three veteran visits per day per clinic—a nationwide decrease of around 75,000 veteran appointments per day.

The flawed software is also designed to analyze veteran drive times and wait times. "Calculating drive time depends on an information system that uses mapping data of roadways, speed limits and other metadata to compute an optimal route and estimate the time required," said the USDS. "Differences in specific technical implementations for gathering this type of data will likely result in different estimates. . . These nuanced details can affect whether or not the veteran is eligible for community care and may lead to the public perception that the criteria are arbitrary, inconsistent or unfair."[118]

Conclusion

It is extremely frustrating to observe that so little has changed after years of reform efforts. The Phoenix scandal and later reports furnished proof that too many veterans have died because of the VA's inefficiency and lack of ethics across its bureaucratic system. Time and again, we've learned of managers who advised staff to alter records in order to make things "look better," while very little has been done to truly address veterans' complex health problems. A timely doctor's appointment can save lives, and in too many cases, VA health services have failed to provide it.

Naturally, learning about the VA medical program's systemic failures will help no one unless action is taken urgently and efficiently. If the administration fails to do it, we will be left with a ghastly picture of everything our government is not doing for its valued service men and women.

So far, the billions of dollars pumped into the VA following the wait times scandal have done little to improve things, and we are faced with a picture of an organization that seems to be all talk, no action. One can only hope that the MISSION Act and expanded community care will truly change our outlook regarding medical access for veterans, rather than proving mere legislative changes solely aimed at appeasing veterans and keeping important and justified system critiques at bay.

Dangerous Doctors

VA Medical Negligence

U.S. veterans seeking medical care are faced with deadly wait times and poor access to health care resources. Once they are finally admitted for therapy, treatment, or surgery, they are also at risk for receiving low quality, potentially dangerous medical care—many times leading to further complications or even death.

Over the past two decades, the VA has paid out millions of dollars in medical malpractice claims. Between 2006 and 2016, American taxpayers paid $871 million in VA medical malpractice settlements (4,353 malpractice settlements averaging $200,000 per payout). Today, these settlement payments are on the rise, totaling $230 million between 2014 and 2016 alone. Over that period, there were eight settlements surpassing $1 million.[119]

Veterans routinely have to fight for compensation for devastating, often permanent harm caused by misdiagnosis, treatment delays, unsafe conditions, and surgical neglect. Staffing shortages, medical equipment issues, and unsanitary supply storage are just a few of the problems putting patients at risk. Overworked physicians with less-than-optimal medical supplies end up providing negligent care, or worse, creating life-threatening mistakes. And despite numerous recommendations on how to improve the quality of care, these egregious problems persist.

Poor Quality of Care Ratings

It doesn't take much effort to find cases of VA malpractice across the nation, though the VA itself tries to downplay the issues. In early September 2017, after an unofficial investigation led to the release of shocking data, the Department of Veterans Affairs finally released updated quality of care ratings for all of its 168 VA medical centers. Numerous VA facilities scored lower than three out of a possible five stars.[120]

The Memphis VA Medical Center scored an unacceptable one star, based on 1,000 reports of threats to patient safety in 2016, up from 700 the previous year. In one case, a diabetic veteran who checked into the Memphis VA Medical Center seeking an examination of a blood vessel in his leg went back home with a 10-inch piece of plastic tubing dangerously lodged in a critical artery. The veteran ended up having his leg amputated a few weeks later. During the amputation, neither the veteran nor his doctors were aware of the presence of the foreign object inside his leg. The surgeons only discovered it after they started cutting and split the tube in two.

In other cases of alleged negligence at the Memphis VA Medical Center, one veteran had to undergo a repeat biopsy after staff mishandled the sample, while another had their colon perforated during a colonoscopy. One patient in critical condition had to leave for another hospital after waiting two hours in the Memphis VA's emergency room without being seen. On account of their poor performance, the facility is one of four hospitals the VA chose to scrutinize through weekly briefings—the others are in Marion, Illinois; Washington D.C.; and Manchester, New Hampshire.

Even facilities with slightly higher ratings than Memphis showed shocking conditions and malpractice, with investigators citing cases of death connected with poor patient safety, fly-infested operating rooms, and surgical materials accidentally left inside the bodies of veterans.[121] Investigative reports revealed that nearly 50 VA hospitals have higher rates on at least three out of four avoidable bacterial infections than private sector hospitals, including potentially life-threatening sepsis and intestinal infections.[122]

In a separate report on the VA Medical Center in Washington D.C., the VA Office of the Inspector General (OIG) described "a number of serious and troubling deficiencies at the Medical Center that place patients at unnecessary risk,"[123] including:

- No effective system to ensure staff didn't use recalled equipment or supplies on patients
- Critical staffing shortages (no Associate Medical Center Director, Associate Director for Patient Care Services, Chief of Human Resources, Chief of the Business Office, Chief of Mental Health, Chief of Integrated Health and Wellness, or Chief of Radiology)
- Lack of critical medical supplies (equipment used to prevent burns on laparoscopy/endoscopy patients, dialysis bloodlines and needles, nasal cannulas used to deliver oxygen, bone cements used in knee replacement surgeries, alcohol pads, wound dressings, clip appliers used to close off blood vessels during surgery, vascular patches, Doppler probes, compression devices used to prevent blood clots during surgery)
- Surgeon used expired surgical equipment on a patient during a surgical procedure
- Expired sterility indicator strips found in sterile processing
- Storage areas used to store sterile equipment and supplies mixed clean and dirty supplies, lacked environmental detectors,

were shared as office space and lacked systems to reduce cross-contamination

Rarely does the OIG release its findings before completing an investigation. However, VA Inspector General Michael Missal stated, "we believed it appropriate to publish this Interim Summary Report given the exigent nature of the issues we have preliminarily identified and the lack of confidence in [Veterans Health Administration] VHA adequately and timely fixing the root causes of these issues."

In its report, the OIG listed recommendations for immediate implementation, "to ensure all veterans receive appropriate care, and that financial losses to the Federal Government are minimized." The recommendations included that the Washington D.C. VA Medical Center take immediate action to:

- Ensure that necessary supplies and equipment are available in patient care areas
- Implement an effective inventory management system
- Ensure that current stock does not include recalled equipment or supplies
- Ensure the environmental integrity of sterile storage areas
- Create an inventory and ensure orderly movement of goods and supplies from the warehouse to minimize loss to the Government
- Expedite hiring of certain permanent positions

Whether these issues have been addressed has yet to be reported.

Doctor Shortages

One major contributor to the substandard quality of medical care we provide our veterans is the insufficient number of health care providers available. When there aren't enough nurses, technicians, or physicians, patients are rushed through the system, misdiagnosed, given the wrong medications, or subjected to the wrong medical procedures. Medical histories are skimmed over carelessly—if at all—and rarely does a patient have a single medical provider they see regularly.

Physician recruitment and retention are challenging for VA hospitals. As of March 2018, there were 1,673 vacant physician positions. In total, the personnel shortage was 33,642, around 90 percent of that representing health services.[124] Much of the problem is due to poor personnel management. A GAO report released in June 2018 outlined several issues. For one, the VHA doesn't even know how many contract doctors or physician trainees it employs. The GAO described the data on how many doctors work at VA medical centers as "incomplete." Because of this incomplete data, the VHA also "lacks sufficient guidance" on how to determine the number of physicians and support staff it needs for medical and surgical specialties. The GAO also said the VHA hasn't evaluated or assessed the effectiveness of the strategies it uses to recruit and retain its physician workforce.[125]

The hazardous shortage of health care providers is also due in part to funding. If a surgeon can earn twice as much working for a private hospital in the same area, why work for the VA? Regarding this problem, an OIG report stated that outdated Office of Personnel Management classifications affected the VHA's ability to offer competitive salaries and advancement opportunities within the organization. "This resulted in facilities being less competitive in attracting new staff and retaining highly skilled staff."[126]

Unqualified Medical Staff

In numerous cases, VA hospitals will attempt to fill their vacancies with nurses or doctors who are ill-equipped to handle the job. Doctors who have been disciplined for risky behaviors or reported for malpractice are hired and maintained on the VA's payroll. Because VA health care facilities don't require doctors to carry their own medical malpractice insurance, an automatic "filtering out" of bad doctors that takes place in other hospitals doesn't happen at VA hospitals. Risky doctors who can't secure insurance due to a bad record can't get jobs in hospitals that require that insurance. So, they end up at VA facilities, where they are apparently welcome.

Yet legally, they aren't welcome. By law, the VA is expected to evaluate job applicants critically and select only qualified health care providers. But despite strict regulations on hiring, the Department of Veterans Affairs continues to hire nurses, dentists, and doctors who have revoked licenses, previous medical malpractice claims, or a track record of disciplinary actions for providing substandard care.

For example, in 2011, Russell Monaco, a healthy father of two, scheduled a surgery with a Wyoming neurosurgeon, Dr. John Schneider, to relieve pressure on the nerves in his lower back. Despite having low blood oxygen levels, Mr. Monaco was discharged after surgery and sent home with a deadly mix of pain relievers—Demerol, fentanyl, Oxycodone, and Valium. He took the medications as prescribed, went to bed, and never woke up. In 2014, the Wyoming Board of Medicine revoked Dr. Schneider's medical license after Mr. Monaco's family filed a wrongful death suit against him. But the neurosurgeon still held a Montana medical license and continued to practice medicine.

A 1999 federal law prohibits the VA from hiring health care providers who have had their medical license revoked by any state board. However, in 2002, the VA issued new guidelines giving hospitals the right to hire surgeons whose licenses have been revoked, at their discretion and as long as they have active licensure in another state. Tragically, in April 2017, an Iowa City VA hospital hired Dr. Schneider as a neurosurgeon.

By that time, Dr. Schneider had racked up a reported 15 malpractice claims against him—including claims of surgical malpractice that left patients paralyzed, with severe brain damage, or dead. After starting work at the Iowa City VA hospital, Dr. Schneider conducted four brain surgeries in one month on a single patient. That veteran died. Another veteran had to undergo three invasive spinal surgeries to treat an infection that arose after a surgery performed by Dr. Schneider. Those surgeries reportedly left him permanently unable to control bladder and bowel movements. Dr. Schneider denies any wrongdoing.

Initially, the VA stated that, before hiring Dr. Schneider, a group of medical peers had thoroughly reviewed his application and deemed him competent, and that the neurosurgeon had disclosed all of his past issues. However, after the 2017 investigation into the matter, VA officials found that hiring Dr. Schneider was indeed illegal. The neurosurgeon resigned soon after.[127]

Other disturbing cases unearthed by investigators include an Oklahoma VA hospital hiring a psychiatrist who had been disciplined by the state board several times, once for sexual misconduct. Not surprisingly, the psychiatrist went on to have sexual relations with one of his VA patients. A Mississippi VA hospital hired an ophthalmologist after the Georgia Board of Medicine had cited him for several problems. The eye doctor went on to perform surgery on veterans, allegedly implanting the wrong lens in one patient's eye and leaving another veteran permanently blind. A Louisiana

VA clinic even hired a psychologist with several felony convictions under his belt. He was fired years later after an internal investigation found him to be a "direct threat to others."

Unfortunately, the publication of the 2017 investigation results didn't solve the problem. On February 28, 2019, the Government Accountability Office (GAO) reported that the VHA had hired and retained several unqualified health care providers, allowing them to deliver patient care. According to the report, the VHA hired providers who "had administrative or other non-disqualifying adverse actions reported in the [National Practitioner Data Bank] NPDB."

In some cases, the VHA claimed it overlooked or was "unaware of the disqualifying adverse-action information in NPDB," like when it hired a nurse who had had her license revoked for patient neglect. In other cases, the VHA claimed the adverse actions weren't serious in nature. For example, a doctor surrendered his license after failing to complete continuing education requirements. The VHA explained to the GAO that hiring staff overlooked or missed disqualifying information in the national database. VHA officials said they "didn't know that providers with valid licenses were ineligible if they had surrendered a license or had one revoked in another state."[128]

Failing to Review Medical Histories

Failing to review a patient's medical history can also lead to dangerous misdiagnoses or inappropriate treatments. For example, our legal team represented a veteran who served during the Korean War era. While stationed in Okinawa, he developed prostatitis. Doctors put him on high doses of antibiotics over the course of many years. As a side effect of the long-term antibiotics, he developed significant gastrointestinal problems, variously diagnosed as either ulcerative colitis or inflammatory bowel disease. None of the VA doctors could definitively diagnose the gastrointestinal problem, and successful treatment remained elusive.

On one occasion, the veteran visited a non-VA emergency room with severe gastrointestinal symptoms. Laboratory tests revealed the presence of *Clostridium difficile* colitis, a bacterial infection of the large intestine that causes fever, diarrhea, and severe abdominal cramping. The veteran left the private hospital and continued his treatment at the VA facility. Yet, the VA facility never requested his medical records from the private hospital and never learned of the *C. difficile* colitis diagnosis.

The veteran's *C. difficile* colitis went untreated for years. By some accounts, it took up to 13 years for the VA to finally discover the veteran's condition. During infection, these bacteria generate toxins that attack the intestinal wall, causing intestinal ulcers. Long-term infection can cause weakness, dehydration, fever, nausea, vomiting, and blood in the stool. In fact, a 2011 study by the Centers for Disease Control and Prevention (CDC) linked *C. difficile* colitis to 29,300 American deaths per year.[129]

After years of suffering from the infection, the veteran attempted to get VA benefits. He argued that his *C. difficile* colitis was a direct result of long-term antibiotic usage to treat the service-connected chronic prostatitis, and appropriately so. The CDC reports, "Patients who take antibiotics are most at risk for developing *C. difficile* infections."[130] But the VA denied the veteran's argument for almost two decades, claiming he did not have the type of colitis that was associated with long-term antibiotic usage.

Luckily, in 2007, the veteran retained our veterans' benefits team to represent him in an appeal. We succeeded in getting the case overturned at the U.S. Court of Appeals, and the matter was remanded back to the Board.

We continued to litigate the case, hiring a forensic medical examiner to determine the exact type of colitis this veteran had. The forensic medical examiner found a striking concern. He noticed that the veteran had tested positive for *C. difficile* colitis and determined that the VA never followed up on the diagnosis made by the private hospital and never offered any treatment.

The forensic medical examiner concluded that the veteran's *C. difficile* colitis had reached a high level of severity because of negligence on the part of the VA medical facility. The VA attempted to defend itself by saying it had no knowledge of the private hospital's *C. difficile* colitis diagnosis. But further research conducted by our legal team discovered that several Federal District Court cases found the presence of medical negligence when doctors fail to inquire as to prior medical history, obtain prior medical records, and review them. In March 2016, after 19 years on appeal and a total 27-year battle with the VA, the veteran finally won his claim for gastrointestinal disability. This veteran suffered for years and developed a severe disease because a VA facility never requested his prior medical records.

Giving the Wrong Medications

Another scary problem seen in VA medical facilities involves veterans either being prescribed the wrong medication or having the wrong medication administered. For example, in February 2017, 64-year old Ralph Keogh, an Air Force veteran and former BlueCross BlueShield computer programmer, died after medical staff at William Jennings Bryan Dorn VA Medical Center in South Carolina "negligently and erroneously" gave him the wrong medication. Keogh, a leukemia patient, was prescribed a medication called filgrastim to stimulate white blood cell growth. Instead, he was given pegfilgrastim, a similar drug but with a longer half-life.

According to the medical malpractice suit, the error resulted in acute lung injury. Mr. Keogh died soon after receiving the treatment. After filing a medical malpractice claim, his family reached an $800,000 settlement with the federal government. The VA admitted no liability.[131]

VA Nursing Home Abuse and Neglect

Problems with negligent care are also a very real threat for veterans who reside in VA nursing homes. The stories are frightening. One that ended tragically involves U.S. Navy Vietnam War Era veteran Earl "Jim" Zook. In January 2017, he walked out of a "secured" unit in an Alabama VA nursing home and was never found. After Jim was declared dead in 2018, his wife of 38 years, Leslie Roe, asked to see the last three years of inspection reports on the nursing home—not too much to ask as inspection reports for private-sector nursing homes are posted publicly and easily accessible online. But the VA hasn't posted inspection reports for years.

VA nursing home residents were found to be nearly three times as likely to develop bedsores than private nursing home residents. Investigators found that nurses and aides failed to empty bedside urinals or provide clean drinking water at night. Inspectors found nurses sleeping in locked rooms during their shifts. In one case, inspectors found a resident's oxygen tank empty, after the patient was left unmonitored for hours. When some nurses complained to superiors about the poor care, they were ignored. Good nurses often quit their jobs soon after discovering the dangerous environment and lack of concern for patients.[132]

An investigation into 99 VA nursing homes across the U.S. found that, between April and December 2018, nearly 53 percent of the facilities were cited for deficiencies that caused "actual harm" to veterans. Facilities in 25 states, the District of Columbia, and Puerto Rico were cited for deficiencies causing harm to veterans. Three facilities put veteran health and safety in "immediate jeopardy," while inspectors found cases of both "harm" and "jeopardy" in eight facilities. Many VA nursing homes failed to meet standards of care in as many as 10 key categories, including treating residents with dignity. One facility failed in 12 key categories.

In over 50 percent of the VA nursing homes investigated, residents were exposed to hazardous environments or were not properly monitored. Over 65 percent of the VA nursing homes investigated had staff who failed to follow routine safety protocols like changing into sterile gowns and using sterile gloves when treating residents. More than two dozen VA nursing homes were cited for neglecting to prevent and treat bedsores.[133]

Inspectors cited three facilities for allowing residents to bathe and wash hands in water as hot as 128°F. The U.S. Consumer Product Safety Commission recommends facilities set water heaters no higher than 120°F to help prevent the approximately 3,800 injuries and 34 deaths that occur each year, mostly in children and elderly, due to scalding from excessively hot tap water.[134]

Veterans' Rights

While financial recovery can never replace a veteran's health, mobility, or life, the law does provide veterans who are victims of VA medical negligence with the right to collect monetary damages for medical bills, lost wages, pain and suffering, disfigurement, disability, emotional distress, and other issues. In the case of wrongful death, the late veteran's spouse or dependents may also seek compensation. Compensation can be obtained for any type of medical negligence, including mental health malpractice, substance abuse clinic malpractice, and even family support clinic malpractice.

The Federal Torts Claims Act

Several options exist for veterans to recover financially from medical malpractice. One of them is the Federal Torts Claims Act (FTCA). Typically, a veteran who feels they have been injured by medical negligence will file a complaint with the VA known as Standard Form 95. The agency reviews the complaint and may offer a settlement. If the VA doesn't settle the claim, offers an unacceptable amount, or doesn't respond to the claim for six months, a veteran may then take the case to federal court.

Under the FTCA, VA medical negligence victims may receive three types of damages:

- Economic damages—Medical bills, lost wages
- Non-economic damages—Pain and suffering, disability, disfigurement, emotional distress, quality of life issues
- Future damages—Future lost income, home care costs, estimated future medical expenses

The FTCA doesn't allow for punitive damages,[135] i.e., amounts awarded to punish the wrongdoer and discourage future similar acts. In addition, although these are federal cases, the court will follow state laws regarding certain rules, including caps on damages.[136] Unfortunately, this means many injured veterans come away with very little compensation for their injuries.

For example, those in California are limited by the Medical Injury

Compensation Reform Act of 1975, which caps damages for pain and suffering at a mere $250,000. Veterans who must pay for a lifetime of home care due to a brain injury, or families who lose the breadwinner to VA malpractice, get $250,000 max—that's it. So even though these cases are filed in federal court, several state laws still apply.

Strict statutes of limitations apply to claims filed under the FTCA. You must file a medical malpractice claim against the VA within two years of the date of the injury or when you first became aware of the injury.[137] Once that date has passed, a veteran victim of VA medical malpractice can no longer file a claim. In cases involving health care providers who are private contractors, the statute of limitations may be just one year. VA centers may employ 100 or more private contractors, and currently, VA medical centers aren't required to notify veterans when they receive medical care from a private contractor.

There are exceptions to the several statutes of limitations. For example, in the Fall of 2013, Glenford Turner, a healthy, 57-year-old veteran who served 20-plus years in the Army, went in for prostate surgery at the VA Connecticut Healthcare System, West Haven. Mr. Turner experienced minor pelvic pain after his robot-assisted prostate surgery, but nothing serious. Nearly four years later, Mr. Turner went in for an MRI to examine a dizzy spell. While lying on the table, he suddenly experienced piercing abdominal pain. Technicians did a CT scan of his abdomen and saw a clear image of a 5-inch scalpel handle lying in Mr. Turner's pelvic region. Three weeks later, Mr. Turner went in to have the surgical instrument removed.[138]

Though the surgeon left the scalpel in his abdomen in 2013, Mr. Turner filed a medical malpractice lawsuit against the VA in 2018—four years later and way over the two-year statute of limitations. Fortunately, most courts recognize that these time limits may need to be extended, as long as the effects of the negligent act are constant and ongoing. Scientific evidence backing up the case for an extension is usually necessary.

In Mr. Turner's case, he didn't realize his surgeon made a mistake until nearly four years later, experiencing only minor, continuous, abdominal pain post-op. Some patients may never discover that a foreign object has been left behind after surgery unless they have an X-ray, CT scan, or MRI. Studies suggest that the time between surgery and detection of a surgical tool left behind ranges from seven days to 21 years,[139] with the average time between surgery and the removal of a surgical gauze left behind being five years.[140] Studies like these can be helpful in convincing the court that it was reasonable not to have detected a foreign object for several years after surgery.

Surgeons leaving something behind in a patient constitutes negligent behavior that can cause severe pain and disability, and often requires more surgeries, months of rehabilitation, increased medical expenses, and other damages. In severe cases, objects left inside after surgery can be fatal. Surgical clips, needles, surgical sponges, gauze, or scalpels left inside the patient, all of these may be considered medical malpractice.

Section 1151 Claims

Veterans can also collect compensation for injury caused by a VA health care provider by filing a section 1151 claim.[141] If "carelessness, negligence, lack of proper skill, error in judgment, or similar instance of fault" or "an event not reasonably foreseeable" in examination, care, or treatment provided at a VA hospital causes a patient's injury or death, veterans and their families can seek Section 1151 benefits, as discussed in chapter one.

Section 1151 claims differ from claims of medical malpractice under the Federal Tort Claims Act in several ways. First, Section 1151 claims are administrative claims with the VA Benefits Administration instead of lawsuits against the federal government. Second, there is no statute of limitations on Section 1151 claims. Section 1151 claims also have a lower burden of proof than FTCA claims. Instead of having to prove that the health care provider didn't act reasonably under the circumstances by a "preponderance of the evidence" as in an FTCA case, a Section 1151 claim only requires an "as likely as not" standard of proof, or a mere fifty percent probability.

Instead of a settlement or verdict amount, veterans who successfully file Section 1151 claims receive service connection for any additional disability that results from the medical negligence, just as if they had received the injury during service. However, several VA benefits aren't awarded in successful Section 1151 claims, including:

- 10-point civil service preference
- 38 U.S.C. 1312(a) special allowance
- 38 U.S.C. 31/38 U.S.C. 35 education benefits
- Civilian Health and Medical Program of VA (CHAMPVA)
- Loan guaranty funding fee waiver
- Public Law (PL) 87-377, §156 REPS special allowance
- Service-Disabled Veteran's (RH) Insurance
- Surviving spouse loan guaranty benefits
- VA burial allowance

In some cases, a veteran may file a claim under both the FTCA and Section 1151 for the same injury. But, again, a veteran can't receive an award from both claims. Instead, the VA will typically offset the Section 1151 benefits by the amount received from the successful FTCA claim.

Conclusion

Military men and women enter service and risk their lives with the guarantee that they will receive quality medical care as needed when they return home. Yet, the system continues to fail our valued veterans. Not only is it incredibly difficult to access medical care, but veterans have to see doctors and nurses who are overworked, underqualified, and often alarmingly negligent.

The VA must work diligently to fix these issues. As the GAO recommends, VHA officials responsible for hiring must receive regular, mandatory training. The VHA must thoroughly and critically examine each applicant for proper references, education, licensing, and credentials. Staffing shortages are not an excuse to hire dangerous health care providers. Medical professionals with any history of adverse actions involving risky behavior should not be accepted into the VA system, and VHA officials should conduct regular reviews of providers who have any adverse actions listed in the National Practitioner Data Bank.

Staffing shortages are a critical issue that needs correcting. The VA must rework personnel management to create a more effective approach that will accurately quantify the staff on hand, detect areas of need, and offer accessible avenues to fill vacancies with highly-qualified professionals. Without serious restructuring, many veterans and talented medical professionals will seek out medical care and employment in the private sector, further eroding the VA health care system and confidence in the VA overall.

AGENT ORANGE AND VIETNAM VETERANS

A Generation of Health Problems

It has been more than 40 years since the Vietnam War ended. But its legacy lives on in the lives of thousands of U.S. veterans who served in the Republic of Vietnam. The signature feature of this legacy for most of these veterans is the lingering effect of Agent Orange exposure.

Veterans exposed to Agent Orange in Vietnam have put up a long hard fight trying to get the VA disability benefits they deserve. An estimated 2.4 million U.S. service members were exposed to some level of Agent Orange in Vietnam between 1962 and 1971. According to recent estimates, the VA's backlog of Agent Orange disability cases amounts to 500,000 pending cases.[142]

With the number of VA claims increasing every year for diseases associated with Agent Orange exposure, competition is tough. It is important that American veterans understand how to win these disability compensation claims for Agent Orange exposure.

Even if a certain condition is not on the VA's list of presumptive diseases caused by Agent Orange exposure, a veteran can still win his VA claim for benefits.

How Does Agent Orange Cause Disease?

Most veterans who served during the Vietnam War are familiar with the toxic herbicide Agent Orange. Between 1962 and 1971, the U.S. Military sprayed 12,000 square miles of Vietnam forests with over 20 million U.S. gallons of defoliant in an herbicidal warfare effort, resulting in major—often deadly—consequences for over one million Vietnam vets.

Because the VA bases most of its decisions around claims on medical and scientific evidence of Agent Orange causality, a brief understanding of how Agent Orange affects the human body is important.

Agent Orange contains a toxic contaminant known as TCDD, classified by the U.S. Environmental Protection Agency (EPA) as a human carcinogen (causes cancer). TCDD is a dioxin that easily enters the body through touch or ingestion. In the body, TCDD travels to the nucleus of cells, where it damages genetic material.

This genetic damage leads to a variety of cancers and other illnesses, symptoms of which may not show up for 50 years or more. Researchers also suggest TCDD causes birth defects in the children of those exposed to Agent Orange.

Was a Veteran Exposed to Agent Orange During Vietnam Service?

Reviewing a brief history of the use of Agent Orange can help determine whether veterans were at high risk of exposure during service. Agent Orange development started during World War II. In 1943, the U.S. Department of the Army hired Arthur Galston, a graduate student in the University of Illinois at Champaign-Urbana's botany department, to study the effects of Agent Orange chemicals on grain crops. The idea was to eventually find an herbicide that could be used to destroy enemy food supplies and remove vegetative cover.

Britain was the first to use Agent Orange in herbicidal warfare during the Malayan Emergency of the 1950s. Using Britain's actions as precedent, the U.S. decided that the process of spraying large enemy areas with defoliant should be a legal strategy in war. In November 1961, President John F. Kennedy authorized a U.S. Air Force herbicide program in Vietnam—codename: Operation Ranch Hand.

The U.S. military produced millions of gallons of the herbicide, labeling the barrels with a large orange stripe—hence the defoliant's popular name.

Beginning in January 1962, U.S. helicopters, boats, trucks, and C-123 transport planes sprayed nearly 18 percent of South Vietnam's forests, plus parts of Cambodia and Laos, with various herbicides, with peak sprays between 1967 and 1969.[143] And the military didn't tread lightly.

Spray mixtures held over 13 times the concentration of defoliant recommended by the USDA for domestic use.[144] In some areas, TCDD soil concentrations were 180 million times higher than levels considered safe by the EPA.[145] Concerned about its serious health and environmental effects, Arthur Galston himself and other dioxin toxicity experts opposed Operation Ranch Hand.

In 1966, United Nations resolutions suggested the U.S. was violating the 1925 Geneva Protocol by carelessly spraying the toxin over wide areas of land. The U.S. argued that, since Agent Orange was merely an herbicide and defoliant, it should not be considered a chemical or a biological weapon. The argument worked, and the U.S. continued spraying Agent Orange. It was not until 1971, after scientists began protesting the use of the herbicide using evidence of cancers and birth defects in laboratory animals, that the spraying stopped.

Blood tests done in the 1970s confirmed toxic levels of TCDD in U.S. military members who served in Vietnam. Studies found the highest levels of TCDD exposure in those living and working around the Vietnam—Cambodia border and the Long Mountains near Truong Son.[146]

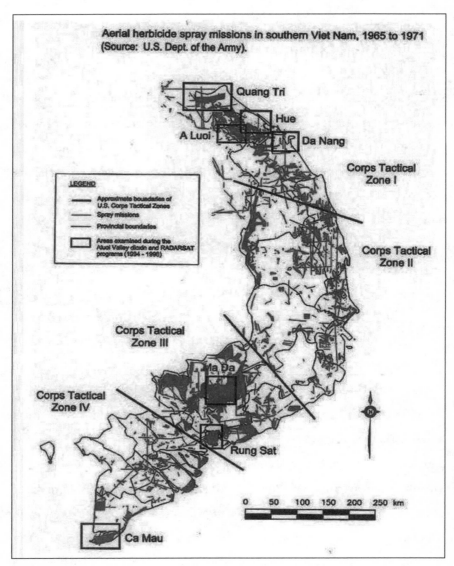

Map of Aerial Herbicide Spray Missions in Southern Vietnam

The VA presumes that veterans who served in Vietnam between January 9, 1962 and May 7, 1975 were exposed to Agent Orange. But

Vietnam veterans aren't the only ones who can file a claim for disability benefits due to Agent Orange exposure.

When Operation Ranch Hand ended in 1971, and the spraying of Agent Orange stopped, the military reassigned C-123 planes used for spraying to East Coast USAF Reserve squadrons for use in routine airlift missions. These planes were still heavily contaminated with Agent Orange. For this reason, non-Vietnam veterans working in and around these planes in the U.S. between 1972 and 1982 are also eligible for compensation due to Agent Orange exposure. Veterans who were stationed at the Navy's Camp Garcia bioweapons site in Vieques, Puerto Rico, during the 1970s may also have been exposed to Agent Orange.

My experience with Agent Orange claims includes helping my client and friend, Marine Sergeant Hermogenes Marrero, win his appeal for benefits due to Agent Orange exposure after working in this location in hazardous airborne chemicals testing between 1970 and 1972. His case took us 14 years to win, and we had to hire numerous experts, which cost us thousands of dollars. Marrero's case was featured in a documentary film produced for German public television.[147]

The likelihood of exposure to Agent Orange is highest for veterans who were:

- Stationed at bases that stored Agent Orange
- Stationed at bases that tested or prepared Agent Orange
- Serving as flight crew of C-123 transport planes
- Serving as aircraft mechanics for C-123 transport planes
- Working on helicopters, trucks, or boats that sprayed Agent Orange
- Working as medical evacuation crews on C-123 transport planes

- Non-Vietnam veterans working on C-123 aircraft in the U.S. between 1972 and 1982
- Non-Vietnam veterans stationed at the Navy's Camp Garcia in Vieques, Puerto Rico

VA Starts Granting Benefits for Diseases Caused by Agent Orange Exposure

In 1980, the New Jersey Agent Orange Commission and Rutgers University organized The Pointman Project, a research project to study the health effects of Agent Orange. Scientists found that blood and adipose TCDD levels were higher in Vietnam veterans,[148] including Marines, Army, and Navy members, than in individuals not exposed to Agent Orange.

As early as 1977, veterans began to file claims for VA disability payments with the belief that Agent Orange exposure had caused their health problems. If the veterans couldn't prove their problems had begun during service or within one year of discharge, the VA denied their claims.

In 1991, after scientific evidence showed that symptoms of Agent Orange toxicity can take decades to appear, Congress enacted the Agent Orange Act. Under the Act, the VA declared a specified list of health conditions as 'presumptive' to Agent Orange exposure, stating that it could grant treatment and compensation to Vietnam veterans with these health conditions.

But the list of presumptive conditions was small. By 1993, the VA had received over 39,400 claims from soldiers exposed to Agent Orange and granted compensation to only 486.[149]

Diseases and Health Problems Associated with Agent Orange Exposure

During the Vietnam War, the government ignored warnings from researchers and told our soldiers that the herbicide being sprayed all around them was harmless. Now, our veterans are experiencing the tragic, disabling effects of the toxin. Ongoing research by the National Academy of Sciences and further scientific evidence keeps associating more and more diseases with Agent Orange exposure.

Currently, the VA lists the following presumptive diseases and conditions as eligible for compensation and disability benefits due to Agent Orange exposure.[150]

- AL amyloidosis
- Chronic B cell leukemias (including hairy-cell leukemia and chronic lymphocytic leukemia)
- Chloracne (and skin disorders like chloracne)
- Hodgkin's disease
- Ischemic heart disease
- Multiple myeloma
- Non-Hodgkin's lymphoma
- Parkinson's disease
- Peripheral neuropathy (acute and subacute)
- Porphyria cutanea tarda
- Prostate cancer
- Respiratory cancers (throat and lung)
- Soft tissue sarcoma (excluding chondrosarcoma, Kaposi's sarcoma, mesothelioma, and osteosarcoma)

- Type 2 diabetes mellitus

And if these conditions are service connected and produce total disability, then a veteran can file for TDIU or individual unemployability if his service-connected conditions prevent him from working.

Diseases like these may be more aggressive in individuals exposed to Agent Orange than in unexposed patients. Recent research suggests that prostate cancer is twice as aggressive in veterans exposed to Agent Orange.[151]

Birth Defects in Children of Veterans Exposed to Agent Orange

Because of the genetic impact of Agent Orange exposure, many children of Vietnam veterans are inheriting its toxic effects. Research carried out by Vietnam's Huế College of Medicine suggests that children of military personnel who served in Agent Orange affected areas are at higher risk of being born with mental disabilities, cleft palates, hernias, and polydactyly, among other health issues.[152] The VA already grants benefits for children born with spina bifida if a parent was exposed to Agent Orange during service.[153]

Diseases Associated with Agent Orange Not Included on VA Presumptive List

Many other cancers and illnesses that the VA doesn't include on its list of presumptive conditions may still be linked to Agent Orange exposure.

With solid scientific evidence and expert medical opinion, any veteran with these conditions may be eligible for VA benefits due to exposure to Agent Orange during service.

These health conditions include (but are not limited to):

- Myeloproliferative neoplasms (myelofibrosis, essential thrombocytopenia, polycythemia vera)
- Hypertension
- COPD and other respiratory disorders
- Parkinsonism (Parkinson's-like symptoms)
- Bladder cancer
- Hypothyroidism
- Pancreatic cancer (especially if secondary to type 2 diabetes)
- Organic Brain Syndrome
- Neurological Disorders
- Glioblastoma and other brain cancers
- Myeloproliferative Neoplasms

Currently, myeloproliferative neoplasms (MPNs) like myelofibrosis, essential thrombocytopenia, and polycythemia vera are not on the VA's presumptive list. Yet more and more veterans are developing MPNs[154] according to MPN Advocacy and Education International. Hematologic oncologists working at the Memorial Sloan Kettering Cancer Center are currently studying the association between MPNs and Agent Orange.

Hypertension

According to the VA, over 300,000 Vietnam veterans suffer from hypertension.[155] In 2006, a study published by VA researchers in the Journal of Occupational and Environmental Medicine found that U.S. Army Chemical Corps veterans exposed to Agent Orange were at higher risk for developing hypertension.[156]

The addition of hypertension as a disease associated with Agent Orange exposure could mean secondary service connection for kidney failure, stroke, and other problems linked to hypertension. While the VA has not yet added hypertension to the list of diseases associated with Agent Orange exposure, the existing scientific evidence may be strong enough to win a claim for benefits for this health condition.

COPD and other Respiratory Disorders

The CDC and VA are now examining whether an association exists between Agent Orange and chronic pulmonary obstruction disorder (COPD), along with other respiratory disorders. I recently helped a widow win retroactive pay of nearly $100,000 after the death of her ex-husband, a veteran who died of lung cancer from Agent Orange exposure during service.[157]

Parkinsonism, Bladder Cancer, and Hypothyroidism

In March 2016, the National Academy of Sciences' Institute of Medicine (IOM) released a review of health problems linked to herbicide exposure. Of one million Vietnam veterans, doctors diagnosed 1,833 with Parkinsonism, 5,484 with bladder cancer, and 15,983 with hypothyroidism.[158]

Parkinsonism, not to be confused with Parkinson's disease, shows symptoms similar to Parkinson's—including rigidity, tremors, postural instability, and bradykinesia. Currently, a diagnosis of Parkinson's disease creates eligibility for presumptive service connection.

Not so with Parkinsonism. The IOM review concluded that there is no rational basis for excluding Parkinsonism from the presumptive list. With this evidence, veterans with Parkinson's-like symptoms should be able to collect VA benefits associated with Agent Orange exposure.

Pancreatic Cancer

I am a strong advocate for adding pancreatic cancer to the presumptive list after seeing many Vietnam veterans lose their lives to pancreatic cancer— veterans who had no risk factors for developing pancreatic cancer other than Agent Orange exposure.

While pancreatic cancer is not on the VA's list, our Veterans Benefits law firm has been able to win service connections for veterans diagnosed with pancreatic cancer associated with Agent Orange exposure using strong medical and scientific evidence.

The most reliable method to prove service connection for pancreatic cancer is based on a secondary relationship with service-connected type 2 diabetes. Usually, a long-standing type 2 diabetic condition that pre-dates the pancreatic cancer diagnosis is the strongest basis for a claim.

In the case referenced above, the veteran died within 26 days of diagnosis. His widow filed a claim for service connection for the pancreatic cancer, arguing that diabetes from Agent Orange exposure had caused the cancer.

The VA denied her claim. She appealed for 14 years, until she decided to call us. With the help of our medical experts and an extensive review of scientific research, we helped her win her claim for service connection and VA compensation.

Neurological Disorders, Organic Brain Syndrome, and Brain Damage

We have come across many Vietnam veterans who suffer from a variety of neurological conditions, organic brain syndrome, and brain damage because of exposure to toxins. Research has shown that serious neurological issues can result from exposure to Agent Orange.

Even though these conditions are not on the list of Agent-Orange-related diseases, we have helped countless veterans obtain service connection for conditions involving neurological and brain disorders.

Glioblastoma and other Brain Cancers

Doctors are diagnosing more and more Vietnam veterans exposed to Agent Orange with glioblastoma multiforme and other brain cancers. Data from the VA shows that more than 500 Vietnam veterans have been diagnosed with glioblastoma at VA hospitals since 2000[159] (this number doesn't include the unknown number of Vietnam veterans diagnosed at private hospitals).

From 2000 to 2007, VA doctors diagnosed between 22 and 31 Vietnam veterans with glioblastoma each year. From 2008 to 2013, the numbers doubled to 45 to 61 veterans diagnosed annually (while non-Vietnam veterans diagnoses showed no alteration). This jump could be due to the incubation time needed for glioblastoma to develop or to the increase in Agent Orange sprays seen between 1967 and 1969.

With strong medical and scientific evidence on their side, Vietnam veterans and their widows who can show that brain cancer has been caused by Agent Orange exposure during service could be eligible for tens

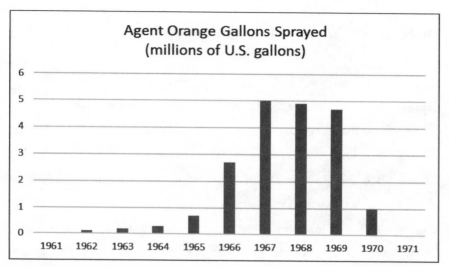

SOURCE: *U.S. Department of Veterans Affairs, Herbicide Exposure Assessment—Vietnam*

of thousands of dollars in retroactive compensation. Since 2009, wives of deceased husbands have won around 24 brain cancer VA cases out of 100, even though brain cancer isn't on the presumptive conditions list. Veterans must remember two things:

1. Never assume that you can't win service connection for Agent Orange exposure because your illness is not on the presumptive list, and

2. Never give up on your claims or appeals. Scientists release new evidence frequently regarding the association between Agent Orange and diseases not included on the list. And you can use that evidence to support your claim.

How to Win VA Benefits for Agent Orange Exposure

Between 2002 and 2015, the VA awarded benefits for Agent Orange exposure to over 650,000 veterans. Not surprisingly, this number is growing fast. An estimated 2.4 million U.S. military members were exposed to some level of Agent Orange in Vietnam.

In 2015, the VA released data showing the projected increase in demand for VA benefits,[160] noting that 40 years after the end of the Vietnam War, the number of veterans receiving disability compensation has not yet peaked. For decades, the percentage of veterans receiving benefits held at a consistent 8.5 percent, but over the past 15 years, it rose to 19 percent.

Many Vietnam veterans are now reaching the age where Agent Orange exposure is causing ischemic heart disease, prostate cancer, and type 2 diabetes. Because of this expectation, the VA is anticipating an increasing volume of claims.

For Veterans Whose Disability Is on The Agent Orange List

To prove service connection and get disability benefits for any of the diseases on the VA's presumptive list, you need to show:

1. Medical diagnosis of a disease the VA lists as resulting from Agent Orange exposure,
2. Proof of service in Vietnam or Agent Orange exposure from another area, and
3. Medical evidence that the disease started within the specified time frame, if applicable.

While the items listed above make getting your claim approved sound easy, the VA continues to deny these types of Agent Orange claims for several reasons, including:

- Deadline has elapsed since discharge, and the first documentation of a claimed disability that must manifest within a certain time period.
- Veteran is not a doctor and therefore not competent to offer opinions of medical causation or diagnosis.
- Medical condition did not appear during service or for many years thereafter.
- Veterans' separation physical exam showed normal findings on clinical examination.
- Doctor did not review the claims file, and thus, his report is less probative.

For Veterans Whose Disability Is Not on the Agent Orange List

For many disabled veterans exposed to Agent Orange, winning service connection for a disease not included on the VA's list can seem impossible. Yet, many of these cases can be won.

The key to a successful claim for VA benefits covering a disability associated with Agent Orange exposure is to carefully craft the legal and medical strategy using top-notch experts. Strong medical and scientific evidence is indispensable for a successful outcome.

You must show that the unique features of your disease and how it manifests compel the conclusion that it could only have resulted from exposure to a toxin like Agent Orange.

Typically, scientific research requires a higher degree of proof than the level of certainty needed to prove service connection. For example, medical science may not recognize causation unless researchers find a high degree of certainty. But for VA purposes, we just have to show that the service-related cause is 50 percent probable. Understanding the difference—and educating the medical experts on this distinction—is vital to success in these cases.

How to Find Medical and Scientific Research Experts to Support Your Claim

Most of us aren't medical experts or research scientists, but it is our job as advocates for veterans to find someone who is. That is one of the reasons why our law firm employs an in-house physician. It takes strong and indefatigable advocacy to win Agent Orange cases that are not on the presumptive list. But our aging and disabled Vietnam veterans deserve our best efforts. This is why, as attorneys, we must strive to develop these claims to the maximum, search out the best experts, and build a solid case.

Military Toxin Exposure

Military service members, family members, and civilians working and living around military bases have been plagued with debilitating toxin exposure for over a century. From jet fuel leaks and hazardous waste disposal to chemical experiments and toxic warfare methods, the effects of chemical toxins can be everlasting. The children of exposed pregnant mothers are sometimes born with life-long congenital disorders. Those who come away healthy often find themselves developing life-threatening conditions decades down the line.

Millions of veterans exposed to toxins during service have put up a long fight trying to get the VA disability benefits they've been promised. Recent scientific evidence of negative health effects associated with toxin exposure has prompted new legislation to expand the benefits available for certain cancers, respiratory diseases, and immune disorders. However, the available benefits still fall disturbingly short.

With the number of VA claims expected to increase yearly for diseases associated with Agent Orange exposure, airborne burn pit toxins, and hazardous Camp Lejeune water, competition for these promised benefits is intense. According to a 2019 Wounded Warrior Project Survey, 70 percent of respondents said they were exposed to "toxic substances or hazardous chemicals" during service, including chemical warfare agents, ionizing radiation, burn pits, and other potentially toxic substances. Only 9 percent said they received VA treatment for their exposure.[161]

History of Military Toxin Exposure

Soldiers have been exposed to toxins during service for over 100 years. For example, with the start of World War I, the Germans, the French, the British, and the U.S. military began actively developing chemical weapons. In April 1915, the Germans used 150 tons of lethal chlorine gas against French soldiers. The Germans first introduced mustard gas into warfare in 1917. Future president Harry S. Truman served as captain of a U.S. artillery unit that used poison gas against the Germans in 1918.

As opposed to World War I, World War II was not fought using chemical weapons. The prevalence of gas masks and protective clothing had rendered them ineffective. Instead, the opposing forces resorted to the development of nuclear weapons. About 200 atmospheric nuclear tests were performed between 1946 and 1962. American troops were sent to Japan to clean up the cities following the atomic attacks. In programs like Operation Buster-Jangle, Operation Ivy, and Operation Bravo, the U.S. placed servicemen just miles from nuclear test detonation sites to study the effects of exposure on humans.

Since the establishment of the Edgewood Arsenal in 1948 and until 1975, the U.S. Army Chemical Corps conducted classified research on human subjects to assess the impact of chemical agents on military personnel. More than 7,000 military service members participated in these Maryland-based experiments. They were exposed to over 250 chemicals to test the effectiveness of vaccines, protective clothing, and medications. Chemicals tested on the service members included the anticholinesterase nerve agents sarin and VX, mustard gases, carbamate pesticides, organophosphorus, nerve agent antidotes like scopolamine and atropine, LSD, PCP, irritants, and alcohol. The toxins' health effects were measured soon after exposure. Long-term follow-up tests were never scheduled, and much of the data remains classified.

Similarly, between 1954 and 1973, the U.S. army carried out a biodefense research program that involved infecting U.S. Army personnel with pathogens that were likely to be used in a biological attack. Based at Fort Detrick, Maryland, these "Operation Whitecoat" experiments infected over 2,300 army service members with various pathogens like tularemia and Q fever and experimental vaccines for hepatitis and yellow fever. Minimal long-term follow-ups were performed on around 500 of the 2,300 participants. Follow-up reports stated that there was no conclusive evidence of adverse health outcomes.[162]

Vietnam War Exposures

The signature issue of the Vietnam War was Agent Orange exposure. Although this is not to diminish the emergence of higher rates of PTSD in Vietnam War veterans, Agent Orange is the thing that makes Vietnam unique. A wide array of severe health problems have been shown to be associated with Agent Orange exposure. To name just a few:

- AL amyloidosis
- Chronic B-cell leukemia
- Chloracne
- Diabetes mellitus type 2
- Hodgkin's disease
- Ischemic heart disease
- Multiple myeloma
- Non-Hodgkin's lymphoma

- Parkinson's disease
- Early-onset peripheral neuropathy
- Porphyria cutanea tarda
- Prostate cancer
- Respiratory cancer
- Soft tissue sarcoma
- Bladder cancer
- Hypothyroidism
- Parkinsonism
- Hypertension
- Monoclonal gammopathy

Veterans fought for decades to obtain VA benefits for Agent Orange exposure. Service members were exposed to the toxic herbicide between 1962 and 1975. Not until 1991 was the Agent Orange Act passed, granting presumptive benefits for exposed veterans. Today, it still takes a monumental fight and decades of lost time for veterans to prove to the U.S. government that service-related toxin exposure is causing a disease. Events reported as problematic as far back as the 1980s and early 1990s are just now being officially acknowledged.

Major Sources of Toxin Exposure Since Vietnam

The most controversial topics surrounding recent military toxin exposure include subjection to hazardous fumes and airborne particulates released from burn pits and exposure to toxic water supplied to residents and service members at Camp Lejeune. Thousands of veterans have battled the VA for decades to obtain benefits to cover the numerous debilitating health problems caused by contaminated water at Camp Lejeune and exposure to burn pit toxins. Only recently is the legislature starting to recognize the startling medical fallout of these exposures and compensate veterans.

What Are Burn Pits?

Most veterans who served after 1990 are familiar with burn pits. Outdoor trash incineration was a daily practice in the military during Desert Shield/ Desert Storm and Operations Iraqi Freedom, New Dawn, and Enduring Freedom. The military used burn pits to dispose of aluminum cans, metal, munitions, unexploded ordnance, human waste, discarded food, lubricants, electronics, medical waste, paint, petroleum (mostly JP-8 jet fuel), plastics, rubber, Styrofoam, wood, and dangerous chemicals.

Many military bases burned around 30 to 200 tons of waste daily. And these burn pits were huge. Veterans have described them as spanning the size of a football field.[163] Thousands of service members living and working near these burn pits unavoidably inhaled the emitted toxic smoke and airborne particulate matter.

The U.S. military used burn pits long before the 1990s. To help prevent illness and infection among military personnel, it has historically used landfills, spot burials, incinerators, and burn pits to reduce waste. While breathing fumes from burning metal, human waste, munitions, wood, and rubber was certainly dangerous, modern plastics, electronics, insulators, and shipping foams made burn pits significantly more threatening.

Burn pits are still in use today. According to a report to Congress, there were still nine burn pits in operation in Afghanistan, Egypt, and Syria as late as 2019. The Department of Defense (DoD) stated, "Generally, the use of open burning is limited to short-term contingency operations outside of the United States where no feasible alternative exists."[164]

Health Effects of Burn Pit Toxins

Concerns over burn pits causing health problems started during the Persian Gulf War in the early 1990s. Military officials didn't act on these concerns for decades. Complaints from Gulf War veterans prompted studies on waste burning. A 2005 report linked lung cancer to burn pit toxin exposure but found inconclusive evidence of other health problems, concluding "this report cannot answer the question of whether service in the Gulf was associated with such exposures and whether specific health outcomes are due to the exposures."[165]

"While we would like to have more definitive answers to questions about the specific diseases that may be associated with these substances, in most cases, the evidence simply is not strong enough or does not exist," Dr. Lynn Goldman said in a statement, adding, "It should be emphasized that smoking is the major culprit for lung cancer, accounting for 80 percent of all cases, according to the American Cancer Society."[166]

During the early 2000s, no burn pit regulations were in place for overseas combat operations. In 2006, military guidelines for field waste management stated, "the preferred method of [solid waste] disposal in the field is incineration (unless smoke and flames would compromise the tactical situation)." The guidelines warned that "all burn operations should be conducted as far downwind as possible (at least 450 feet) from troop locations and living areas."[167]

Many veterans returning from Iraq and Afghanistan reported serious health problems that they felt were directly related to breathing smoke from burn pits on bases, particularly from a massive open burn pit at Joint Base Balad (JBB) in Iraq. Air samples taken from JBB contained dangerous levels of both cancerous and non-cancerous toxins, including dioxins like

2,3,7,8-tetrachlorodibenzo-p-dioxin (TCDD) (a highly toxic chemical also found in Agent Orange), furans, PAHs, VOCs, arsenic, particulate matter, and carbon monoxide. However, a 2008 health risk assessment for JBB concluded, "there is inadequate/insufficient evidence of an association between exposure to combustion products and cancer, respiratory disease, circulatory disease, neurologic disease, and adverse reproductive and developmental outcomes in the populations studied."[168]

In 2009, veterans testified before Congress on what it was like to live and work around the thick smoke at JBB. Environmental and medical experts testified that inhaling fumes from JBB burn pits could lead to cancer, asthma, arthritis, vomiting, lung damage, and Parkinson's disease.[169] Outrage around the public hearing testimony and media coverage accelerated military burn pit regulation and legislation. In October 2009, the National Defense Authorization Act was passed, requiring the DoD to tighten regulations around the use of open-air burn pits. In April 2010, the VA released a training letter on processing disability claims related to burn pits.

A 2011 study published in the New England Journal of Medicine looked at cases of constrictive bronchiolitis, an irreversible disease of the lungs that causes shortness of breath and fatigue and is rare among the general population, in soldiers returning from Iraq and Afghanistan. The study found that "In 49 previously healthy soldiers with unexplained exertional dyspnea and diminished exercise tolerance after deployment, an analysis of biopsy samples showed diffuse constrictive bronchiolitis, which was possibly associated with inhalational exposure, in 38 soldiers." [170]

That same year, at the VA's request, the National Academies of Sciences, Engineering, and Medicine published the results of a study on the long-term health consequences of burn pit exposure in Afghanistan and Iraq.

The study states, "Particular controversy surrounds the burn pit used to dispose of solid waste at Joint Base Balad (JBB) in Iraq, which burned up to 200 tons of waste per day in 2007." [171] Researchers stated that "insufficient evidence prevented the Institute of Medicine (IOM) committee from developing firm conclusions about what long-term health effects might be seen in service members exposed to burn pits. Along with more efficient data-gathering methods, the report recommends that a study be conducted that would evaluate the health status of service members from their time of deployment to JBB over many years to determine their incidence of chronic diseases, including cancers, that tend to not show up for decades."

In 2013, President Obama signed the National Burn Pit Registry into law. In June 2014, the Department of Veterans Affairs (VA) created the Airborne Hazards and Open Burn Pit Registry, allowing veterans and service members to "document their exposures and report health concerns through an online questionnaire," specifically those who served in Operation Enduring Freedom/Operation Iraqi Freedom/Operation New Dawn; Djibouti, Africa, on or after September 11, 2001; Operation Desert Shield/Operation Desert Storm; or Southwest Asia on or after August 2, 1990. A reported 179,553 veterans and service members signed the registry between June 2014 and September 2019. Participation in the burn pit registry exam did not impact a veteran's chances for VA benefits covering burn pit exposure. The Airborne Hazards and Open Burn Pit Registry and burn pit registry exam was merely a resource to help officials study the effects of burn pit exposure.

In September 2018, President Trump signed the Helping Vets Exposed to Burn Pits Act to provide $5 million in additional funding and resources for identifying and treating the negative health impacts of exposure to burn pits. Veterans stationed in Djibouti or Afghanistan after September

11, 2001, and those stationed in Southwest Asia after August 2, 1990, were considered at high risk of burn pit toxin exposure–particularly those stationed in the following regions:

- Afghanistan
- Arabian Sea waters
- Bahrain
- Djibouti
- Gulf of Aden
- Gulf of Oman
- Iraq
- Kuwait
- Oman
- Persian Gulf waters
- Qatar
- Saudi Arabia
- United Arab Emirates
- Red Sea waters

For example, burn pit locations in Afghanistan and Iraq included, but were not limited to:

Warhorse	Camp Delta	FOB Marez
Tallil Air Base	Camp Cropper	FOB Gabe
Scania	Camp Courage	FOB Freedom
Saddam Air Base	Camp Chesty	FOB Fenty
Q-West	Camp Cedar	FOB Endurance
Camp Echo	Camp Bucca	FOB Caldwell

Navistar	Camp Bastion	Diwaynia Camp Fallujah
Mosul	Camp Arifjan	Camp Victory
LSA Anaconda	Camp Al Ramadi	Camp Stryker
Kirkuk	Camp Anderson	Camp Speicher
Kandahar	Camp Taji	Camp Shield
Kalsu	Camp Adder	Camp Scania
Kabul	Camden Yards	Camp Rustamiyah
Jalalabad	Baqubah	Camp Ridgeway
Green Zone	Balad Air Base	Camp Pennsylvania
FOB Warrior	Bagram Air Base	Camp Loyalty
FOB Sykes	Abu-Ghraib Prison	Camp Liberty
FOB Summerall	Al-Sahra	Camp Geiger
FOB Sharana	Ali Air Base	Qayyarah Airfield West
FOB Salerno	Al Taqaddum	Baghdad International Airport
FOB Orgun-E	Al Quo	Kut Al Hayy Air Base
FOB McHenry	Al Asad Air Base	

In April 2019, the Department of Defense submitted an Open Burn Pit Report to Congress, stating, "The disposal of hazardous waste, medical waste, tires, or plastics in open burn pits during contingency operations can emit harmful smoke or fumes and is therefore strictly prohibited by DoD Instruction. . . unless the Combatant Commander determines that no feasible alternative exists."[172]

On July 26, 2019, VA Secretary Robert Wilkie announced the VA's new program, Airborne Hazards and Burn Pits Center of Excellence (AHBPCE), stating it would "specialize in clinical and transitional research related to airborne hazards and burn pit exposure."[173] Regardless, the VA still held its

position that there was no evidence that exposure to burn pits causes long-term health issues, and burn pit exposure did not serve as evidence of a condition caused by service. The VA stated, "At this time, research does not show evidence of long-term health problems from exposure to burn pits. VA continues to study the health of deployed Veterans."[174]
Interestingly, a 2019 McClatchy report on VA health care data from 2000 to 2018 showed a significant increase in cancer among veterans being treated in the VA health care system.[175]

- Up 96 percent: Liver and pancreatic cancer
- Up 61 percent: Bladder, kidney, and ureter cancer
- Up 23 percent: Prostate cancer
- Up 18 percent: Lymphoma, myeloma, and leukemia

The VA disagreed with these findings but did admit that the rate of cancer among veterans receiving treatment at the VA had increased significantly since 2001. Among U.S. civilians, pancreatic cancer was fairly rare–accounting for around 3 percent of all cancers.[176] It was increasing among U.S. veterans, and it was also increasing among civilians, but only at a rate of 0.5 percent annually over the past decade. Researchers claimed the increase was due to improvements in diagnostics and increases in obesity and diabetes. More than 75 percent of pancreatic cancer diagnoses among U.S. civilians occur between ages 55 and 84. Meanwhile, Iraq and Afghanistan veterans were dying from pancreatic cancer as young as 40.[177]

Major headway was made in April 2021 when Congress introduced the Veterans Burn Pits Exposure Recognition Act. The bill proposed to eliminate the veterans' burden to prove they had been exposed to burn pits while serving where burn pits were in use; presume that veterans who served near burn pits were exposed to airborne hazards, toxins, and particulate matters, eliminating the requirement to prove exposure; and require full VA medical examinations on veterans to determine service connection for diseases caused by burn pit exposure.[178]

In August 2021, the VA reported scientific evidence associating the development of respiratory conditions with the inhalation of burn pit airborne particulates. burn pit exposure finally received its own presumptive disease list; the VA determined there was enough evidence to associate three respiratory conditions with the inhalation of airborne particulate matter from burn pits: rhinitis, sinusitis, and asthma. But many veterans had also started developing rare respiratory cancers, suggesting burn pit exposure as a possible cause.

On November 11, 2021, President Biden issued an order requiring the VA to review the research and determine whether burn pit exposure was associated with the development of these rare cancers. Biden gave the VA 90 days to report the results. Finally, in April 2022, the VA officially stated that veterans could have been exposed to disease-causing airborne toxins via "particulate matter or large burn pits in Iraq, Afghanistan, and Djibouti in the Horn of Africa, a large sulfur fire at Mishraq State Sulfur Mine near Mosul, Iraq, hexavalent chromium at the Qarmat Ali water treatment plant in Basra, Iraq, or pollutants from a waste incinerator near the Naval Air Facility at Atsugi, Japan."[179] VA officials admitted a "biological plausibility between airborne hazards and carcinogenesis of the respiratory tract," adding that "the unique circumstances of these rare cancers warrant a presumption of service connection."[180]

The VA announced it would automatically presume service connection for Gulf War, Iraq War, and Afghanistan War veterans diagnosed with nine rare cancers after the VA found evidence associating these cancers with burn pit smoke and fume exposure. The nine cancers added to the VA presumptive list included:

- Typical and atypical carcinoid of the lung
- Adenosquamous carcinoma of the lung
- Adenocarcinoma of the trachea
- Sarcomatoid carcinoma of the lung
- Squamous cell carcinoma of the trachea
- Squamous cell carcinoma of the larynx
- Salivary-gland-type tumors of the trachea
- Salivary-gland-type tumors of the lung
- Large cell carcinoma of the lung

Still, thousands of veterans exposed to burn pits were developing illnesses not included on the list. To obtain VA benefits for these illnesses, they had to either try and associate them with some other verifiable service event or obtain legal counsel and medical experts to help them prepare a case proving to the VA that the toxins emitted from the burn pits were likely to have caused their condition.

VA Benefits for Burn Pit Toxins

On August 10, 2022, President Biden signed the *Sergeant First Class Heath Robinson Honoring Our Promise to Address Comprehensive Toxics Act* (PACT Act) into law to help veterans exposed to toxins get the funds and treatment they deserve.[181] The PACT Act is named after Ohio National Guard Sergeant First Class Heath Robinson, who died in 2020 at age 39 from an extremely rare form of lung cancer caused by prolonged exposure to toxins emitted from burn pits. Through the PACT Act, veterans and others who meet certain criteria will automatically qualify for VA benefits and health care to help compensate and treat toxin exposure.

The PACT Act introduced several changes to the VA claims process, expanded eligible veteran service dates and locations, and enhanced coverage for diseases caused by burn pits, Camp Lejeune drinking water, radiation exposure, and Agent Orange exposure. Those eligible to collect financial compensation and VA health care benefits include former military members, family members, and caregivers who developed health conditions listed on the burn pit presumptive list.

To receive PACT Act benefits, claimants must meet date and location requirements. Under the PACT Act, veterans who served during the following dates in the listed locations are presumed to have been exposed to burn pit toxins:

Active military, Air Force, or Navy on or after September 11, 2001, in (or in the airspace above):

- Yemen
- Uzbekistan
- Syria
- Lebanon
- Jordan
- Egypt
- Djibouti
- Afghanistan

Active military, Air Force, or Navy on or after August 2, 1990, in (or in the airspace above):

- United Arab Emirates
- Somalia
- Saudi Arabia
- Qatar
- Oman
- Kuwait
- Iraq
- Bahrain

With the advent of the PACT Act, the VA now presumptively connects 23 health conditions with burn pit exposure. There is no longer a 10-year limit on the manifestation of symptoms. The VA burn pit presumptive list includes:

- Asthma
- Brain cancer
- Chronic bronchitis
- Chronic obstructive pulmonary disease (COPD)
- Chronic rhinitis
- Chronic sinusitis
- Constrictive/obliterative bronchiolitis
- Emphysema
- Gastrointestinal cancer
- Glioblastoma
- Granulomatous disease
- Head cancer
- Interstitial lung disease (ILD)

- Kidney cancer
- Laryngeal cancer
- Lung cancer
- Lung sarcomatoid carcinoma
- Lymphatic cancer
- Lymphoma
- Melanoma
- Neck cancer
- Pancreatic cancer
- Pleuritis
- Pulmonary fibrosis
- Reproductive cancer
- Respiratory cancer
- Salivary gland carcinomas
- Sarcoidosis
- Tracheal cancer

The long-term effects of burn pit exposure include serious, potentially deadly health consequences for over three million service members. Most veterans don't exhibit symptoms of burn pit exposure until decades later when cellular and genetic damage starts to manifest in cancer, organ failure, and other disorders. Many post-9/11 veterans are just now starting to show the devastating signs of burn pit exposure.

Despite the PACT Act, the VA continues to deny perfectly valid claims for burn pit benefits, for example, when a veteran has developed an illness that is not yet included on the burn pit presumptive disease list or when the VA mistakes a burn pit VA benefits claim for another claim type from a similar service period.

The VA erroneously interprets many burn pit claims as Gulf War Illness claims, which involve disease caused by exposure to environmental toxins–but not toxins released by burn pits. Often, the VA argues that the veterans' separation physical exam did not report health problems or that too much time has elapsed between service and disease symptoms. We know that the toxins emitted from military burn pits can take decades to produce disease. But in processing millions of claims for VA benefits, the VA often misses this important distinction.

What Happened at Camp Lejeune?

U.S. Marine Corps Base Camp Lejeune was established in North Carolina in 1942. ABC Cleaners Inc. began operations in the early 1950s. The dry-cleaning facility was located just 500 ft north of Camp Lejeune, and discarded waste near the underground storage tanks and wells supplying water to Hadnot Point and Tarawa Terrace housing units. Between 1953 and 1987, up to one million Army, Navy, National Guard, and Reserves members and their families living at Camp Lejeune in Jacksonville, North Carolina, drank, cooked with, and bathed in water contaminated with highly toxic organic compounds from the nearby dry-cleaning company and runoff from military equipment cleaning stations.

In 1982, the Marine Corps found volatile organic compounds (VOCs) in the water from two of the eight water treatment plants on base. Water sample tests revealed over 70 toxins in the water supplied to Tarawa Terrace and Hadnot Point, the most concerning being the degreaser tetrachloroethylene (TCE), the TCE byproduct vinyl chloride, and the solvents benzene and perchloroethylene (PCE). Water from the Hadnot Point treatment plant contained TCE (trichloroethylene). The contamination came from multiple sources: industrial spills, damaged underground storage tanks, and waste disposal. Water from the Tarawa Terrace treatment plant contained PCE (perchloroethylene or tetrachloroethylene), the source of this chemical was determined to be waste disposal from ABC Cleaners.

Levels of all four chemicals exceeded U.S. Environmental Protection Agency (EPA) maximums. For example, the EPA maximum for PCE and TCE in drinking water is 5 parts per billion (ppb). In 1982, tests measured TCE in Hadnot Point water at up to 1,400 ppb and Tarawa Terrace water at up to 215 ppb. The Agency for Toxic Substances and Disease Registry (ATSDR) found PCE concentrations exceeding the EPA maximum level of 5 ppb in tap water from the Tarawa Terrace treatment plant for 346 months, from November 1957 to February 1987. [182]

Contaminated Hadnot Point wells were shut down in early 1985. The Tarawa Terrace water treatment plant continued operations until 1987. Since the toxic water was the only supply of water military personnel and their families had for everyday use, the VA presumes that any veteran who served at USMC Base Camp Lejeune or Marine Corps Air Station (MCAS) New River for at least 30 days from August 1953 to December 1987 was exposed to toxic levels of contaminated water.

Health Effects of Camp Lejeune Water Toxins

The EPA classifies TCE, benzene, and vinyl chloride as known human carcinogens. PCE is a likely human carcinogen. The major route of exposure to these volatile chemicals is through inhalation of vapors coming from the water, though some will also enter the bloodstream through ingestion and touch. The toxins in the water at Camp Lejeune were colorless and odorless. Someone who used the water regularly would not notice a problem–experiencing only mild symptoms (headache, fatigue, dizziness, skin irritation) if any. Most people do not notice any symptoms of disease from these toxins until decades later.

After exposure, the body metabolizes the toxins into dangerous byproducts. TCE and PCE byproducts go on to invade the central nervous system, immune system, kidney, liver, and male reproductive system. Studies suggest these metabolic byproducts have DNA-binding capacity, leading to DNA and chromosomal abnormalities that cause a variety of cancers and other diseases.

Vinyl chloride byproducts can bind protein, RNA, and DNA. It is mutagenic in humans, causing spontaneous DNA synthesis and chromosomal mutations that result in cancers of the liver, brain, lung, blood, and lymphatic system. Byproducts of benzene metabolism can disrupt cell structures, create cancer-causing free radicals, induce DNA strand breaks, and alter gene expression control mechanisms. Exposure is known to cause bone marrow depression, aplastic anemia, and chromosomal damage leading to various diseases and cancers.

A 2014 study by the Agency for Toxic Substances & Disease Registry (ATSDR) found that Marines and Navy members stationed at Camp Lejeune had higher mortality rates for certain cancers than a similar veteran population stationed at a non-contaminated location.[183] These cancers included esophageal cancer, leukemia, Hodgkin lymphoma, cervical cancer, rectal cancer, pancreatic cancer, soft tissue cancer, lung cancer, and prostate cancer. Both the American Chemical Society and U.S. Environmental Protection Agency have reported links between vinyl chloride exposure and brain cancer, soft tissue cancer, and nervous system cancer.[184,185] A 2017 ATSDR review found positive associations between Camp Lejeune toxins and brain cancer, breast cancer, cervical cancer, leukemias, esophageal cancer, lung cancer, ovarian cancer, prostate cancer, rectal cancer, and soft tissue cancer.[186]

A 2014 ATSDR evaluation of Camp Lejeune veteran mortality found evidence of association with Hodgkin's disease.[187] Other studies, particularly human epidemiological studies, have also reported a potential link between exposure to benzene and Hodgkin's disease.[188] Research has attributed various autoimmune diseases to TCE and PCE exposure, including scleroderma and systemic lupus erythematosus.[189] Exposure to organic solvents is known to cause lymphopenia, and benzene is known to induce immunodeficiency diseases like pancytopenia and leukocytopenia.[190]

Reports have associated cases of chronic liver disease, liver cirrhosis, portal hypertension, and fibrosis with vinyl chloride exposure.[191] Organic solvents like TCE have been associated with hepatic necrosis and hepatitis.[192] Some studies suggest vinyl chloride could be associated with steatohepatitis or fatty liver disease.[193] Studies have associated atopic dermatitis with benzene exposure[194] and severe generalized skin disorders with exposure to TCE[195] and other Camp Lejeune water toxins. Multiple Camp Lejeune veterans also report cases of diabetes mellitus, sleep apnea, depression, fibroid sarcoma, colon cancer, mesothelioma, prolactemia, gynecomastia, Crohn's disease, hidradenitis suppurativa, amyloidosis, endocrine disorders, skin conditions, urinary tract conditions, and cardiovascular disorders.

Scientific data also shows that the toxins in the water at Camp Lejeune can cause reproductive issues, pregnancy complications, and birth defects in the children of those exposed. Numerous studies support an association between the toxins discovered in Camp Lejeune water and birth defects. To mention a few, prenatal exposure to volatile organic compounds has been associated with congenital male genital abnormalities, neural tube defects, and asthma in infants.[196] Parents who lived or worked near vinyl chloride facilities have also reported high rates of birth defects, including fetal death, central nervous system defects, genitalia defects, and clubfoot.[197] Other studies have associated TCE and PCE with cardiac defects, low birth weight, and fetal growth restriction.[198]

Reproductive issues associated with Camp Lejeune water toxins also include:

- Female infertility
- Miscarriage
- Small gestational size
- Oral cleft defects
- Neural tube defects
- Choanal atresia
- Major malformations
- Low birth weight
- Cardiac defects

VA Benefits for Camp Lejeune Toxin Exposure

The VA approved a meager 25 percent of the 5,792 Camp Lejeune water toxicity claims filed between January 2011 and June 2019.[199] In January 2017, based on the strength of the scientific evidence associating Camp Lejeune toxins with various diseases, the VA established a Final Rule offering disability benefits to Camp Lejeune veterans diagnosed with any of the following eight conditions:

- Parkinson's disease
- Non-Hodgkin's lymphoma
- Multiple myeloma
- Liver cancer
- Kidney cancer
- Bladder cancer
- Aplastic anemia/myelodysplastic syndromes
- Adult leukemia

Under this Rule, the VA automatically granted service connection for disability compensation to veterans who served at USMC Base Camp Lejeune or MCAS New River for at least 30 days between August 1953 and December 1987, did not receive a dishonorable discharge and had one of the eight diseases on the presumptive list. Veterans who met all three of these criteria did not have to prove a link between their disease and their service at Camp Lejeune to get disability benefits.

But at the time of the Final Rule, many Camp Lejeune veterans were still developing the debilitating health problems caused by toxin exposure that had occurred decades ago. And many conditions that are scientifically linked to Camp LeJeune toxins were not listed among the VA's eight presumptive conditions. For example, it did not include neurobehavioral problems like poor coordination, learning difficulties, chronic headaches, visual perception issues, confusion, poor concentration, delayed reaction times, depression, anxiety, or mood disorders. But a significant pool of scientific literature points toward a positive association between volatile organic compound exposure and neurobehavioral problems, including reports from the National Research Council, the Institute of Medicine, Oregon Health and Science University,[200,201,202] and others.

On June 16, 2022, the U.S. Senate agreed to pass the Camp Lejeune Justice Act 2022, a federal mandate providing financial recovery to military personnel, civilians, and families who lived and worked at Marine Corps Base Camp Lejeune and developed health problems. As part of the PACT Act, the Camp LeJeune Justice Act introduced several changes to the VA claims process, presumptive disease lists, and eligible service dates and locations for Camp LeJeune veterans.

Importantly, the Camp LeJeune Justice Act increased the VA's presumptive disease list, adding numerous toxin-associated health conditions. The Camp Lejeune Justice Act's presumptive disease list includes:

- Adult leukemia
- Aplastic anemia
- Bladder cancer
- Breast cancer
- Esophageal cancer
- Female infertility
- Hepatic steatosis
- Kidney cancer
- Leukemia
- Liver cancer
- Lung cancer
- Miscarriage
- Multiple myeloma
- Myelodysplastic syndromes
- Neurobehavioral disorders
- Non-Hodgkin's lymphoma

- Parkinson's disease
- Renal toxicity
- Scleroderma

As scientific and medical evidence of causation expands, the VA's Camp LeJeune presumptive list will likely incorporate numerous other conditions. For example, listed below are other health effects that have been linked to TCE, PCE, benzene, and/or vinyl chloride in populations other than Camp Lejeune who worked with and/or drank water contaminated with these chemicals. These causal links are based on studies demonstrating positive associations between exposures to these chemicals and the development of health issues.

Other conditions with scientifically proven links to Camp Lejeune toxin exposures may include:

- Brain cancer
- Cervical cancer
- Choanal atresia
- Esophageal cancer
- Eye defects
- Hodgkin's disease
- Impaired immune function
- Liver cirrhosis
- Low birth weight
- Major congenital malformations
- Neural tube defects
- Neurological effects (delayed reaction times; problems with short-term memory, visual perception, attention, and color vision)

- Oral cleft defects (including cleft lip)
- Ovarian cancer
- Prostate cancer
- Rectal cancer
- Severe, generalized hypersensitivity skin disorder
- Soft tissue cancer

Camp Lejeune Lawsuits

Another important and precedent-setting development is the new right granted to Camp LeJeune victims to file a lawsuit against the U.S. government for financial compensation. Anyone who lived or worked at Marine Corps Base Camp Lejeune or North Carolina's Marine Corps Air Station New River between August 1, 1953, and December 31, 1987–for at least 30 consecutive days—and is diagnosed with a health condition associated with Camp Lejeune water toxins is eligible to file a Camp Lejeune lawsuit.

Under the Camp Lejeune Justice Act, victims of water contamination can file lawsuits to recover economic and non-economic damages, with no cap on compensatory damages. Available damages include compensation for lost income, medical expenses, lost earning capacity, future medical costs, and pain and suffering. Those who can file lawsuits include military members, civilians, family members, and anyone who developed health conditions or congenital disabilities from in-utero exposure.

Veterans who receive VA disability benefits for Camp Lejeune-associated disabilities can still file a Camp Lejeune lawsuit. Winning a Camp Lejeune lawsuit does not affect monthly VA disability payments. However, a veteran's VA benefits may affect their Camp Lejeune lawsuit payout. For example, the lawsuit settlement amount may be offset by any VA payments you have already received from the VA (or Medicare or Medicaid) for the same Camp Lejeune disability(s).

There are time limits on filing Camp Lejeune lawsuits. For claims that accrued before August 3, 2022, victims must file a claim by August 3, 2024, or 180 days after the government denies a claim—whichever is later. Victims must first file a claim with the Navy Tort Claims Unit in the Office of the Judge Advocate General (JAG). If the JAG approves the claim, the case is concluded. If the JAG denies the claim, the victim must file a Camp Lejeune lawsuit in federal court. Camp Lejeune lawsuits must be filed in the U.S. District Court for the Eastern District of North Carolina. If the plaintiff does not reside within the district, they must file their claim in the Southern Division of that court.

Did the PACT Act Fall Short?

The passing of the PACT Act was a momentous victory for veterans across the U.S., but it wasn't immediate, and a number of amendments were made along the way. Once the PACT Act passed the House, the Senate proposed several amendments.

Amendments from Senator Jon Tester and Senator Mike Lee proposed substantive changes to the PACT Act compared to previous proposals. For example, a pair of amendments by Lee (SA 5048 and SA 5049) made it appear that Lee was looking to pump the brakes on some conditions proposed to be presumptively service connected by requiring a mandatory removal of presumption (versus permissive authorization).

One of Tester's amendments is in the nature of a substitute (SA 5051) included the following changes:

- Removing references to certain benefits related to mammograms.
- Keeping a requirement that DIC claims involving presumptions be re-evaluated.
- Would still require a report on jet fuels, except there wouldn't be a requirement that it be done on a biennial basis (like the House version does)
- Adds some provisions related to claims processing
- Adds a requirement for an epi study re: Ft. McLellan veterans
- Omitting references to PFAS/PFOS. (the House version would otherwise require a registry)
- Removing a requirement that the DOD introduce guidelines for active-duty personnel related to potential risks and prevention of toxic exposures.
- Keeping in place that medical opinions should take into account total potential exposure through all applicable deployments and synergistic, combined effect of all toxic exposure risk activities.

Another notable difference is that the final version of the PACT Act appears to have eliminated the "as likely as not" standard for the Camp Lejeune Federal Tort Claims, presumably shifting the standard to "by a preponderance of the evidence," as with most civil tort cases. And, in the version that passed the Senate, it appears that a new effective date rule only applies to DIC:

> *Under the Honoring our PACT Act, the Secretary must perform*
> *outreach to veterans who previously filed claims and were denied for*
> *a condition that falls under the new presumptions. VA is not required*

to automatically readjudicate previously denied claims. However, if a veteran reapplies (i.e., files a Supplemental Claim) for a previously denied claim based on a newly established presumption, VA must assign an effective date as though the presumption was in effect on the date of the previously denied claim. This applies equally to claims for Dependency and Indemnity Compensation (DIC).[203]

Perhaps the Senate quietly eliminated the broader earlier effective date rule as a cost-saving measure. Either way, any veteran who previously claimed service connection for a condition that is presumed to be linked to Camp LeJeune, but got denied, can file a Supplemental Claim and get many years' worth of retroactive benefits.

Compensation and health care benefits for veterans exposed to toxins during service have come a long way across the past two decades. Still, numerous health conditions caused by toxin exposure are not listed on VA presumptive lists. Further research and legislation are needed. Until then, veterans diagnosed with health conditions that are not listed on the VA presumptive lists can still collect compensation and health care benefits with the aid of experienced legal counsel and an informed, compelling medical opinion citing scientific evidence to support their case.

Other Emerging Areas of Toxin Exposure

Various other cases of toxin exposure that resulted in severe health conditions are also just now being acknowledged, including some events dating back over seven decades. For example, the PACT Act has expanded eligible veteran service dates and locations to include enhanced coverage for diseases caused by radiation exposures in the Marshall Islands; Palomares,

Spain; and the Thule Air Force Base in Greenland. Meanwhile, the VA has yet to create presumptive disease lists for the hazardous exposures at Red Hill in Hawaii, Fort McClellan in Alabama, and Camp Garcia on Vieques Island, Puerto Rico.

Radiation Exposures

During World War II, the U.S. gained control of the Marshall islands via the Gilbert and Marshall Islands campaign. Between 1948 and 1958, the United States performed 43 nuclear tests on the Enewetak Atoll. In the 1970s, the U.S. decided to give the atoll back to the Marshall Island Republic and brought in around 6,000 service members to participate in a cleanup project from May 1977 to May 1980, resulting in radiation exposure that is only now beginning to manifest disease. Those who served on the cleanup teams or nuclear response teams at the Enewetak Atoll from January 1, 1977, to December 31, 1980, are now eligible for veterans benefits under the PACT Act.

On January 17, 1966, a United States B-52 bomber collided with a KC-135 tanker over the Mediterranean Sea during in-flight refueling. The B-52 was carrying four thermonuclear bombs, which were later found near a fishing village in Palomares, Spain. Two had detonated, contaminating 0.77 square miles with radioactive plutonium. Those who served on the cleanup teams or nuclear response teams at the Palomares, Spain, B-52 plane crash site from January 17, 1966, to March 31, 1967, are now eligible for veterans benefits under the PACT Act.

A similar incident occurred on January 21, 1968, when the cabin of a U.S. B-52 bomber carrying four thermonuclear bombs caught fire over Baffin Bay. The crew tried to land at Thule Air Base but had to bail out.

The plane crashed in North Star Bay, Greenland. The explosives detonated, resulting in radioactive contamination. Those who served on the cleanup teams or nuclear response teams at the B-52 plane crash site at Thule Air Base from January 21, 1968, to September 25, 1968, are now eligible for veterans benefits under the PACT Act.

Radiation exposure-associated diseases listed among the PACT Act's presumptive diseases include:

- Myalgic encephalomyelitis
- Chronic fatigue syndrome
- Gastrointestinal disorders (functional)
- Fibromyalgia
- Cancers of the bile ducts, bone, breast, colon, esophagus, gall bladder, liver (primary site, but not if cirrhosis or hepatitis B is indicated), lung (including bronchoalveolar cancer), pancreas, pharynx, ovary, salivary gland, small intestine, stomach, thyroid, urinary tract (kidney/renal, pelvis, urinary bladder, and urethra)
- Leukemia (except chronic lymphocytic leukemia)
- Lymphomas (except Hodgkin's disease)
- Multiple myeloma (plasma cell cancer)

Camp Garcia - Vieques, Puerto Rico

There are numerous other incidents of toxin exposure, responsible for causing debilitating disease in thousands of veterans, that the VA still does not compensate without a complex legal battle. For example, only recently are U.S. Navy and Marine veterans collecting compensation for health problems caused by exposure to toxins at Camp Garcia on the island of Vieques, Puerto Rico. In this location, chemical weapons were tested, burned in open-air pits, and dumped into the sea resulting in dangerous exposure to lead, arsenic, napalm, uranium, and cadmium.

Physical ailments associated with these toxins include Lou Gehrig's disease, heart failure, diabetes, cancer, and partial blindness. The VA continues to deny claims without sufficient proof of exposure and causation. In 2007, over 7,000 Vieques residents filed a class action suit against the U.S. Navy for the health problems they experienced as a result of their exposure to the dangerous toxins, yet the Federal Appeals Court denied their claims, ruling that the U.S. government had sovereign immunity.

Red Hill Fuel Storage Facility - Joint Base Pearl Harbor-Hickam, Hawaii

In November 2021, the Navy reported a 14,000-gallon fuel leak from a fire suppression drain line near its Red Hill Underground Fuel Storage Facility in Honolulu. The spill entered a tunnel system about 100 feet above an aquifer that supplies drinking water to around 400,000 Hawaii residents and military base occupants. Beginning on November 28, thousands of military families in and around Joint Base Pearl Harbor-Hickam started smelling fuel in tap water and reported symptoms of rashes, headaches, nosebleeds, cramps, and nausea. Reports included pets getting sick or dying.

On December 10, 2021, health officials confirmed contamination with jet propulsion fuel-5 (JP-5) and petroleum at 350 times over the safe drinking level. The Navy confirmed the contamination, closed the facility, and relocated 3,500 military families from Joint Base Pearl Harbor-Hickam to a safe location.

According to the CDC's Agency for Toxic Substances and Disease Registry (ATSDR), JP-5 jet fuel can enter through the skin, ingestion, or inhalation of fumes from contaminated water or soil. Common sources of exposure are drinking, cooking, bathing, swimming, doing laundry, and breathing fumes from tap water.

Studies suggest that long-term exposure to jet fuel can damage the heart, lungs, liver, nervous system, and immune system and impair hearing.[204] The International Agency for Research on Cancer classifies jet fuel as a Group 3 carcinogen-meaning it is known to cause cancer in animals, but there is not enough evidence to claim that it causes cancer in humans.

Thousands of military service members and families stationed on the island of Oahu could have been exposed to contaminated water. Once officials can establish the health problems associated with fuel exposure at Joint Base Pearl Harbor-Hickam, they may offer presumptive service connection. Until we get a presumptive list, military families stationed at Joint Base Pearl Harbor-Hickam can file a claim for disability compensation based on service-connected toxin exposure.

Fort McClellan - Alabama

From 1945 to 1999, Fort McClellan housed the Army Chemical Corps, where service members conducted tests on nerve agents and sulfur mustard. Stores of these toxins leaked into the soil, water, and supply wells. In addition, the nearby Monsanto Plant was releasing airborne polychlorinated biphenyls (PCBs) into the environment. A 1998 study by the U.S. Army Environmental Center found dangerous chemicals at Fort McClellan, requiring further investigation and extensive cleanup before they could transfer the land to public use. Meanwhile, more than half a million soldiers stationed at Fort McClellan were exposed to the hazardous chemicals.

In 2005, a report from the National Academy of Medicine found that Fort McClellan was among the most severely contaminated Army sites. Researchers found volatile organic compounds (VOCs), TCE and PCE, semi-volatile organic compounds (SVOCs), pesticides, lead, radioactive material, and chemical warfare material in the soil and groundwater.[205] But the VA is holding back on benefits for Fort McClellan veterans based on two reports, from 2008[206] and 2015,[207] by the Agency for Toxic Substances and Disease Registry (ATSDR), which concluded that exposure levels were too low to pose a health threat.

Extensive scientific and clinical data show that the toxins found at Fort McClellan can cause numerous health effects, many with symptoms that don't appear until years after service, including:

- Adult leukemia
- Aplastic anemia and myelodysplastic syndromes
- Bladder cancer
- Brain cancer
- Cervical cancer
- Esophageal cancer
- Eye defects
- Hodgkin's disease
- Impaired immune system
- Kidney cancer
- Kidney disease
- Liver cancer
- Liver cirrhosis
- Lung cancer
- Memory problems

- Multiple myeloma
- Neurobehavioral effects
- Non-Hodgkin's lymphoma
- Ovarian cancer
- Parkinson's disease
- Prostate cancer
- Rectal cancer
- Reproductive problems
- Scleroderma
- Skin disorders
- Soft tissue cancer
- Thyroid problems
- Vision problems

With the clear evidence of groundwater and soil contamination at Fort McClellan, there is no justification for failing to implement a health registry to determine its long-term health effects on veterans. Until the government moves forward in its obligation to care for veterans exposed to hazardous substances, veterans can still win compensation using a strong medical nexus opinion supporting their claim for benefits.

THE MILITARY SEXUAL TRAUMA
EPIDEMIC

The current state of affairs for United States veterans is dreadful—from a physical and mental health perspective to the continued rejections and life-threatening delays our veterans face in getting VA benefits. In particular, military sexual trauma (MST) illustrates the do-nothing policy of military institutions, the tragic repercussions of that attitude, and the VA's failure to address and treat the damage.

Rates of sexual abuse and repeated sexual harassment in the military are increasing at an alarming rate. A 2015 Pentagon-commissioned study reports that 10,400 men and 8,500 women on active duty experienced some form of unwanted sexual contact in 2014—numbers that are actually much higher since 81 percent of men and 67 percent of women who suffer military sexual trauma (MST) do not dare report it.[208] Threats of retaliation, irreparable career damage, ostracization, and further abuse dissuade service members from even anonymously bringing forward MST allegations.

While both men and women are potential targets for sexual abuse in the military, male-on-male sexual assaults are the most common. Tragically, males in the military are ten times more likely to be sexually assaulted than male civilians,[209] and men exposed to MST show significantly higher rates of suicide and PTSD than females exposed to MST.

The MST situation is a sad commentary on how our nation treats its veterans and how inappropriate the skepticism about the prevalence of military sexual trauma is. Military sexual trauma can cause debilitating, persistent mental and physical complications, destroying careers, families, and lives. In many cases, the most severe circumstances could be alleviated if veterans experiencing MST received proper benefits from the start. Proper benefits that adequately compensate these veterans for their impairments could prevent many of the financial disasters that result in homelessness, addiction, suicide, and other problems associated with MST.

Obtaining VA benefits for MST-induced complications isn't easy. Even those who do report MST during service may have to go through several appeals to win their claim. For veterans who wait many years to file a claim or who have no record of their MST incidents during service (the majority), getting VA benefits can seem futile.

As a veterans disability attorney who represents victims of military sexual trauma, I am routinely challenged to build solid claims with no official documentation that any stressful event took place. It can be done. Even with negligible evidence, my clients continue to win these claims. The secret to winning a claim for VA benefits to cover complications resulting from MST is to (1) know the "markers" of MST, (2) identify these markers in your own life, and (3) compile evidence of those markers—supported by medical expert opinion.

The Veterans' MST Benefits Dilemma

VA benefits are critical for veterans who experience MST. Because sexual abuse during service often leads to severe PTSD, chronic depression, anxiety, and social deterioration, the VA offers benefits to compensate veterans who experienced sexual abuse or repeated sexual harassment during military service. Disability benefits for physical and mental issues associated with MST can include monthly non-taxable compensation,

VA health care, a 10-point hiring preference for federal employment, and other valuable benefits.

But many veterans never see these important benefits. The number of pending VA appeals increased by almost 100,000 cases between 2015 and 2017, reaching 470,000 in 2017. The average wait time for an appeal on a veterans disability claim is over five years. In addition, some veterans never file a claim. They feel too much time has passed to seek MST benefits or believe they can't get them because they never reported the incident. Many simply stop seeking benefits after their first or second VA claim denial.

Veterans exposed to MST who feel VA benefits are beyond their grasp may suffer further trauma. Studies show that MST survivors who perceive great logistical barriers to obtaining mental health care exhibit higher levels of depression and PTSD.[210] A major factor that prevents veterans exposed to MST from getting prompt VA benefits is the lack of documentary evidence to corroborate an incident of sexual assault during service. In military sexual assault cases, the VA will not grant a claim for PTSD resulting from MST unless there is independent corroborating evidence that the stressor took place. Yet, a large majority of veterans do not report MST incidents right away, if ever. Therefore, official reports are often nonexistent, making these cases difficult to prove.

Roger's Case

From November 1967 to December 1969, our client, Roger, served in the United States Marine Corps. Roger encountered some traumatic experiences shortly after entering boot camp. Because his physical exam revealed some vision trouble, he had to schedule an additional exam at a local medical center. This exam made him miss a day of training—training on how to enter the duty hut.

To make up for the missed session, Roger's drill instructor ordered him to present to the duty hut. But since he missed the training, he reported to his drill instructor in the "wrong way." As punishment, sergeants, privates, and the drill instructor forced Roger to stand prone against a wall until he fell to the ground. They then screamed at him, ordered him to perform push-ups, kicked him, and shouted offensive sexual comments.

This initial assault caused Roger to become anxious and fearful, leading to severe disciplinary problems in service, including going AWOL. Roger's 1967 records reflected injuries resulting from the initial attack and listed several punishments for multiple unauthorized absences, fainting, feigning homosexuality to avoid service as a recruit, and attempting to maim another recruit by jumping on his knee.

A year later, Roger's drill instructor raped him in a personal confinement facility. Out of fear, Roger did not report the rape during service. But what his records did show were a 1969 diagnosis of rectal discomfort and rectal venereal warts, plus records of many years of psychological treatment after the in-service sexual assault and documented changes in behavior that began almost immediately following the attack—ranging from multiple AWOL's, resisting civilian authority while AWOL, traffic violations, and physical outbursts.

After service, Roger filed a claim for VA benefits for service-connected psychiatric disabilities secondary to the military sexual trauma, but because he never reported being raped, the VA denied his claim. Although the VA acknowledged the treatment records for the physical injuries, they did not give them much weight because the injuries did not relate to psychiatric problems and did not indicate treatment of anything consistent with sexual assault. The VA refused to acknowledge the rectal venereal warts in any way.

We took Roger's case to the U.S. Court of Appeals for Veterans' Claims, where we successfully had the claim remanded back to the Board of Veterans' Appeals. We reasoned that one does not acquire rectal venereal warts absent some type of sodomy. The fact that Roger was not a homosexual in his post-service life further supported his claim that he was sexually assaulted and raped during service. Additionally, we sent Roger from his home in Dayton, Ohio, to see a specialist in Cleveland who had extensive experience treating veterans in MST cases. The former Army psychologist concluded that Roger definitely exhibited MST symptoms and that his records corroborated a traumatic event during service.

After submitting this expert opinion to the Board of Veterans' Appeals, the Board promptly returned a fully favorable decision. With the powerful evidence we presented, the Board had no choice but to grant this claim. Legal aid, investigative resources, and perseverance can pave the most straightforward path to your benefits check.

Prevalence of Military Sexual Assault

Specifically, the VA defines Military Sexual Trauma as "psychological trauma, which in the judgment of a VA mental health professional, resulted from a physical assault of a sexual nature, battery of a sexual nature, or sexual harassment which occurred while the veteran was serving on active duty, active duty for training, or inactive duty training."[211] This means MST can occur even when you are off base or off duty. The VA's definition of MST also includes sexual harassment, defined as "repeated, unsolicited verbal or physical contact of a sexual nature which is threatening in character."

Any unwanted sexual activity may be considered MST, including being physically forced into a sex act, participating in sexual activity because of a threat of negative consequences or promise of beneficial treatment, or any situation where the service member is unable to consent—i.e., if they are intoxicated. MST can include offensive sexual remarks, unwelcome touching, and unwanted sexual advances.

For those unfamiliar with what goes on in service, the rate of military sexual trauma in the United States armed forces is astounding. According to data from the VA's MST screening program, one in four women and one in 100 men say they experienced MST during service.[212] More than 95,000 military service members were sexually assaulted between 2006 and 2011.[213] In 2015, the VA reported 1,307,781 VA outpatient visits for MST-related care.[214]

A significant amount of rape in the military is male-on-male. In 2012, there were over 14,200 reports of male rape.[215] In 2014, reports suggested 38 military males were sexually assaulted each day.[216] In 2016, 8,600 women and 6,300 men reported sexual assault, but these numbers represent only the 19 percent of men and 33 percent of women who chose to report it.[217] Because most sexual assaults occurred more than once, estimates suggest over 70,000 assaults in 2016, with over 25 percent of women and 33 percent men assaulted by someone in their chain of command.[218]

Victims of MST Remain Silent

While these numbers are shocking, they are very low compared to the actual number of sexual assaults occurring in the U.S. military. Most data on MST comes from VA reports, meaning it only reflects those individuals who seek VA health care, and an estimated 81 percent of males and 67 percent of females chose not to report MST at all. When you compare this number to civilian data, where only 60 percent of sexual assaults go unreported,[219] it becomes clear that an obvious incentive not to report sexual assault exists in the military.

One in four service members say they choose not to report MST for fear of retaliation, including peer exclusion, harassment, reprisal, or damage to their military career. Victims who report MST say they have been ostracized and receive more disciplinary actions, undesirable work shifts, threats by peers, and further assaults by other offenders.[220]

In 2015, 58 percent of women and 60 percent of men who reported sexual assault experienced retaliation, in 77 percent of these cases, from someone in their chain of command.[221] Retaliation in the military appears to be a team effort. Overall, 73 percent of retaliators are people other than the offender, including those in the MST survivor's chain of command, coworkers, friends, family members, or other superiors. In 2015, the retaliator was the offender in only 7 percent of reported cases.[222]

While more military men than women experience sexual assault, females are more likely to report sexual assault.[223] This discrepancy among genders may be due to the genuine fear men face of being labeled a homosexual or bisexual by family, friends, coworkers, or superiors. The potential label of homosexual can alone be enough reason for a service member to never consider reporting an incident of male-on-male sexual assault, as many men hope to protect their masculine image.[224]

Fear regarding career repercussions is also a decisive factor for service members considering reporting sexual assault. Reports of MST often lead to a diagnosis of a mental or personality disorder. Many are afraid of the potential consequences associated with this mental health stigma. Worse, service members who report MST but refuse a mental health evaluation may be accused of making false allegations and given an other-than-honorable discharge.[225] Of those who reported sexual assault in 2015, 33 percent were discharged within an average of seven months,[226] and 24 percent of MST survivor discharges were less than honorable (compared to 15 percent of all military discharges).[227] Many service members also fear that permanent records of a personality disorder diagnosis will reduce their credibility, negatively impacting their military career and any potential civilian career.

Many service members don't report MST because they feel nothing will be done about it. A significant 33 percent of those who did not report MST in 2016 said they feared an unfair process or that nothing would be done. And they may be right. In 2014, the military justice system convicted only 7 percent of all MSP cases that went to trial.[228] In 2016, just 13 percent of MST cases were prosecuted, and only four percent of the perpetrators were convicted of a sex offense.[229]

To help alleviate the fears behind reporting MST incidents and improve the accuracy of MST frequency data, victims have the option to make either restricted or unrestricted reports. Restricted reports allow the MST survivor to receive counseling and treatment under anonymity, without having to report the assault to the authorities. Unrestricted reports require the service member to name names, give details, and pursue criminal charges against the offender. In 2016, the Department of Defense reported 4,591 unrestricted MST reports and 1,581 restricted reports.[230]

Yet, many MST survivors say that filing unrestricted reports caused them to experience rejection and feelings of incompetence.[231] Shame and self-blame can lead to even further trauma for an MST survivor. Some fear no one will believe their claims of sexual abuse, especially when the abuser is of high rank. Others fear they will be blamed for the sexual activity, or officials will minimize the situation.[232] Most MST survivors feel that ignoring the problem is their best option.

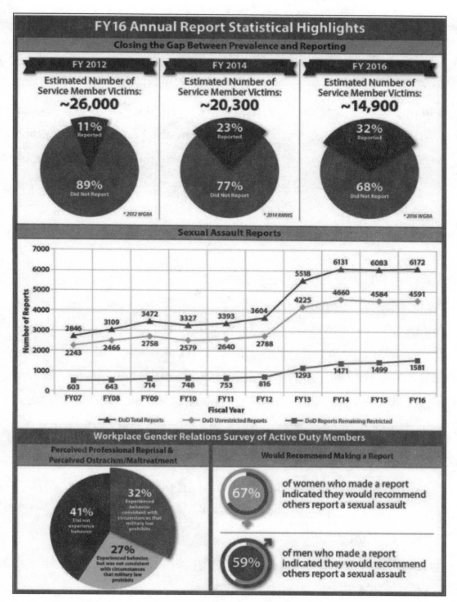

Department of Defense Annual Report on Sexual Assault in the Military Fiscal Year 2015 (2016)

Physical and Mental Aftermath

As most MST survivors soon realize, ignoring the problem does not make it disappear. While the veteran tries to cope with the trauma and stress of MST on his own, an arsenal of mental and physical health issues inevitably begins to crop up. In most cases, MST veterans' lives take an irreparable turn for the worse. I've spoken with many veteran clients who were raped 30 and 40 years ago and still experience the trauma as if it had happened yesterday. Anger and resentment consume them, forever rendering them psychiatric basket cases.

Veterans exposed to MST are often unable to hold a job, have failed relationships, and must live on what little money they can get from Social Security. Many are homeless, suffering from severe drug or alcohol addiction, and the physical health problems that follow, including cirrhosis, hepatitis C, and other diseases associated with intravenous drug usage. Although we achieved an excellent result for our client Roger—and a substantial back paycheck—the veteran's life will never be the same. MST is associated with the development of:

- PTSD (flashbacks, nightmares, social isolation, paranoia, anxiety, insomnia, mood swings, depression)
- Chronic pain/headaches
- Sexual dysfunction, problems with intimacy
- Eating disorders (obesity, anorexia)
- Gastrointestinal problems
- Sexually transmitted diseases (genital herpes, genital warts, HIV)
- Loss of emotion
- Thoughts of suicide

- Inability to stay focused
- Memory problems
- Drug and alcohol abuse
- Trust issues
- Problems with authority

In my practice, I have noticed drastic differences in the way male rape victims relate to the trauma when compared to the way females do it. Both male and female MST victims show significant increases in depression, feelings of shame and betrayal, difficulties with intimacy, social isolation, digestive issues, and self-harm.[233,234] Yet, male veterans who experience MST develop more severe PTSD, mood disorders, and depression symptoms. Male MST victims also develop PTSD nearly twice as fast as PTSD resulting from combat.[235] Studies have also shown that MST victims who experience feelings of institutional betrayal are more likely to develop PTSD.[236] The ongoing belief that the military has created an environment that allows MST to occur, and is taking no action to prevent it, is traumatic in itself.

Men victims also exhibit a higher rate of suicide than females who experience MST.[237] In a recent study, researchers examined the records of nearly six million male and 361,000 female veterans who experienced MST and received VA health care from 2007 to 2011. While both men and women were at higher risk for suicide overall, male veterans who experienced MST were 70 percent more likely to commit suicide than male veterans without MST exposure. In comparison, female MST victims were 50 percent more likely to commit suicide than female veterans without MST exposure.[238]

In both genders, MST is associated with a higher risk for homelessness.[239] An analysis of the records of 601,892 Iraq and Afghanistan veterans found that nearly 12 percent of men and 9 percent of women who experienced MST were homeless within five years of seeking VA care, more than double the rate of those who did not experience MST. Researchers found that 1.6 percent of MST victims were homeless within 30 days of being discharged, and 4.4 percent were homeless within 12 months.

MST Markers Win VA Benefits Claims

Without prompt treatment and rehabilitation, veterans who suffer from MST face a frightening future of mental, physical, and social challenges. Learning to compile powerful evidence for your VA benefits claim for psychiatric disabilities secondary to the military sexual trauma can ensure that you receive the compensation and treatment you deserve. In general, direct evidence is the best evidence. Direct evidence might include official U.S. Department of Defense reports of the MST incident, service medical records, police reports, and related investigative reports completed at the time of the incident. But, as we discussed, most veterans do not report MST, so these forms of direct evidence rarely exist in MST cases.

In addition to expert legal aid, I find that winning MST claims requires knowing and taking advantage of regulations and laws that provide some remedy for proving these in-service assaults. Because of the overwhelming lack of direct evidence available in MST cases, the VA relaxed evidentiary standards for MST claims in 2002. VA regulations now allow a veteran to refer to circumstantial evidence to establish "markers" of psychological trauma. This circumstantial evidence shows drastic changes in one's life that indicate the person was experiencing concealed, underlying trauma. Examples include evidence of (but not limited to):

- Unexplained positive diagnostic tests for sexually transmitted diseases
- Positive pregnancy test results
- Development of a drug or alcohol problem
- Primary relationship difficulties (break-up, divorce)
- Development of mental or physical health problems
- Counselor or therapist reports of suicidal thoughts, sexual dysfunction
- Sudden changes in social behavior (isolation from friends or family)
- Evidence of past reactions to trauma
- Sudden employment problems (poor work performance, inability to hold a job)
- Sudden disciplinary problems during service (physical violence, frequent unauthorized absences, going AWOL)
- Evidence of sudden behavioral changes during service (frequent requests for transfer, social isolation, anger outbursts, unexplained anxiety, or depression)

If we see a drastic change in any of these areas, and the timeframe of that change coincides with the time of the sexual assault, then a forensic psychiatrist experienced in treating sexual trauma cases may conclude that those changes represent markers of sexual trauma. Depending on the tolerance and resilience of the MST survivor, and the circumstances surrounding the sexual assault, manifestations of MST can take days to years to develop, but any behavioral, mental, or physical change that occurred after the MST event can potentially serve as evidence of your reaction to trauma.

Shawn's Case

Unfortunately, the VA continues to have problems remembering that this circumstantial evidence is completely applicable to support an MST-related claim. For example, I recall one veteran who was drafted into the service in 1970. During boot camp, Shawn was coming out of the latrine when two members of his unit assaulted him, physically beating him, holding him down, and anally raping him. Extremely traumatized by this incident, Shawn was overcome with shame and concern about being labeled a homosexual and was too afraid to tell anybody about it. Instead, he kept the assault to himself and tried to cope with the resulting psychological trauma on his own.

Shawn tried to stay away from these two individuals as much as possible, but they were in the same unit. He made numerous requests to be transferred to other units. Since he had hurt his knee during service, he continually complained about his knee hurting during certain jobs to try to get a transfer. His continued requests for transfer were well-documented in his service personnel records.

Eventually, Shawn's father became ill. As his family owned a small business, Shawn requested a hardship discharge to go home and care for the family business. He was discharged early and tried to carry on with his life, eventually getting married and having children. Meanwhile, Shawn struggled with the psychological effects of the rape, holding it in and keeping it to himself for 30 years. He never even told his wife about the incident.

After three decades of keeping this secret and trying to cope alone, Shawn was finally forced to file a claim and go to the VA for help. Naturally, without specific documentation of a rape taking place, the VA denied the claim. The VA also denied the claim on the grounds that Shawn had waited almost three decades to file it.

Shawn then hired our law firm to represent his case in the U.S. Court of Appeals for Veterans' Claims. His VA psychologist offered a psychological opinion that our client was the victim of military sexual trauma related to service, confirming that he had the psychological presentation of a victim of military sexual trauma. Shawn also pointed to his multiple requests for transfer as evidence that he was experiencing psychological trauma in his unit.

The VA Board decision rejected the psychologist's medical opinion on the grounds that it held no weight because the stressor was not corroborated. The VA also disregarded Shawn's argument regarding transfer requests on the grounds that Shawn specifically stated his transfer requests were due to knee pain.

But we knew the VA's line of reasoning contradicted case law. Until recently, the U.S. Court of Appeals for Veterans' Claims held that a post-service psychiatric opinion could not be used to establish the occurrence of an in-service stressor. However, in *Menegassi v. Shinseki*,[240] the Federal Circuit held that under regulation 38 C.F.R. § 3.304(f)(5), medical opinion evidence may be used to help determine whether an in-service stressor is corroborated. The Federal Circuit observed that section 3.304(f)(5) allows a veteran claiming PTSD from an in-service personal assault to submit evidence other than in-service medical records to corroborate the occurrence of a stressor.

The provision states, in relevant part:

"If a posttraumatic stress disorder claim is based on in-service personal assault, evidence from sources other than the veteran's service records may corroborate the veteran's account of the stressor incident. . . Evidence of behavior changes following the claimed

assault is one type of relevant evidence that may be found in these sources. Examples of behavior changes that may constitute credible evidence of the stressor include, but are not limited to: a request for a transfer to another military duty assignment."

Under regulation 38 C.F.R. § 3.304(f)(5), the medical opinion of Shawn's VA treating clinician constituted a type of evidence. The case was overturned on appeal at the U.S. Court of Appeals for Veterans' Claims and went back to the Board of Veterans' Appeals for further adjudication.

On remand, we set out to establish the presence of MST and to show through expert testimony that Shawn's transfer requests did indeed constitute valid evidence that a stressful event had taken place during service. To do this, we hired a very well-known forensic psychiatrist who cited research studies showing that male sexual trauma victims typically do not report the trauma and explained that the shame associated with this type of event can prevent veterans from disclosing the real reasons behind transfer requests.

The forensic psychiatrist concluded that our client believed knee pain was a socially acceptable reason to seek transfer. In the timeframe involved, circa 1970, with the stigma surrounding homosexuality, our client was not going to risk being labeled a homosexual just to achieve a transfer away from the perpetrators. Rather, he looked to other benign and socially acceptable reasons for a transfer and cited those reasons to support his request.

Nevertheless, the Board of Veterans' Appeals denied the claim again. We again got the Board's decision overturned on appeal at the U.S. Court of Appeals for Veterans' Claims, successfully arguing that the Board completely misinterpreted and ignored key aspects of our forensic expert's medical opinion. The case was sent back to the Board again for readjudication.

With readjudication came the opportunity for us to submit yet more evidence to support the claim. We obtained further medical opinion from our forensic expert, who detailed why the Board had misconstrued his prior statements and provided sound arguments in support of his opinion. Several months later, the Board granted the claim. We were delighted that—after a decade of appeals—the veteran's claim was finally granted. He received a retroactive paycheck well into the six figures.

Shawn's case illustrates how critical the subtle details of a person's history can be in showing that a psychological trauma took place. Shawn's multiple requests for transfer, ostensibly for knee pain, were viewed in the context of the typical presentation of a male sexual trauma victim. Understanding the timeframe of the transfer requests versus the assault was also necessary to reach a proper conclusion.

Even the era in which the assault took place played a role in winning Shawn's claim for benefits. Society's views on homosexuality in the 1970s were drastically different than they are today. The possibility of being branded a homosexual was more than what our client could handle. Using this fact, along with medical literature reporting that male sexual assault victims tend not to report these events, our forensic medical expert was able to show that the veteran demonstrated a typical presentation of someone exposed to military sexual trauma.

The types of reports I find useful to establish service connection demonstrate that your symptoms match the profile of a victim of military sexual trauma. This evidence should be combined with evidence that highlights any of the circumstantial factors covered by 38 C.F.R. § 3.304(f)(5), listed above. The expert should give the opinion that the behavioral changes noted in the record represent the markers of a PTSD stressor.

Veterans' Varied Resilience to Trauma

In filing a claim for VA benefits related to MST, it is important to remember that not every veteran responds to trauma in the same way. While research links several mental and physical problems to MST, it is difficult to predict exactly how each veteran will respond. Many factors affect how each individual will react to a traumatic event. Gender, culture, religion, sexual orientation, general resilience, past exposure to trauma, the circumstances of the traumatic experience, and the frequency of abuse all play a role in how MST will play out. While some may be able to move through a traumatic event with little permanent damage, others may suffer lifelong mental or physical consequences that prevent them from gaining employment, having a family of their own, and leading a normal life.

Medical problems that develop and can be attributed to the onset of stress are important in MST-related claims. Unlike the sexual trauma itself, these medical concerns are often documented in service medical records. And even though they may have nothing to do with sexual trauma by themselves, their presence can be used as evidence of the onset of stress— and therefore, MST.

Stress can lead to all kinds of physical problems. Some develop ulcers; others break out in hives. Some develop insomnia, while others can't get out of bed. When preparing a claim for VA benefits relating to MST, understanding how your body reacts to stress and traumatic events, in general, can supply powerful evidence of MST and your need for treatment. Examining medical records for issues that can be attributed to stress is vital to winning cases like these.

Michael's Case

For example, our law firm represented a veteran, Michael, who grew up in New York City, in the Bronx—the only Jewish kid in an all-Irish neighborhood. During his childhood, he was picked on by the neighborhood kids, and he became hypersensitive to bullying behavior. By the time he reached high school, he seemed to be functioning normally, without any unusual fear of his peers.

Michael eventually joined the service. One day during boot camp, he was taking a shower, shampooing his hair with his eyes closed, when someone reached over and turned up the hot water. Michael immediately felt they were trying to scald him purposely. While he wasn't burned, the experience resulted in a tremendous amount of anxiety for him. From that point on, Michael felt he had to be on guard at every moment in case another service member played a dangerous prank on him. The anxiety became so overwhelming that he developed continuous angioneurotic edema and urticaria (hives).

Michael later filed a claim for VA benefits for the residual stress and anxiety caused by the shower incident. But because he never reported the incident, the VA denied his claim for lack of proof that the shower incident had taken place.

When helping Michael file his appeal for VA benefits, he mentioned that he often developed hives while under stress throughout his life. While this fact may seem insignificant, it isn't. The hives were Michael's body reacting to stress—hence a "marker" of trauma. His medical records of angioneurotic edema and urticaria could serve as strong evidence of psychological trauma. In addition, our forensic medical evaluator provided expert testimony concluding that Michael's physical symptoms were consistent with symptoms of psychiatric distress.

We presented this argument to the Board of Veterans' Appeals, who remanded the claim to the Regional Office, reasoning that there was no medical evidence that Michael was hypersensitive and could be traumatized by this mild shower prank incident—at least not enough to cause such drastic physical and psychiatric problems. Diving deeper into Michael's past, he described how years of pranks and bullying as a child had indeed made him hypersensitive to such conduct. After evaluating Michael, our forensic psychologist determined that he exhibited signs of an "eggshell plaintiff," one that can be traumatized by events that others can generally tolerate.

Our forensic psychologist diagnosed Michael with PTSD secondary to in-service trauma. Michael took this medical opinion with him to the VA medical examination. He told his story, and the VA doctor agreed with our forensic psychologist. Shortly thereafter, we received a favorable Rating Decision granting our client service connection and awarding a 70 percent rating plus a total disability rating.

While this case was not an MST case, the victory was profound given the significant lack of evidence, illustrating the importance of strong advocacy skills, medical expert opinion, and an analysis of response to trauma throughout the veteran's life in proving military sexual trauma cases. Our client received a nice retroactive check well into the six figures, a welcome reward after his long-standing fight against the VA.

Tom's Case

Another example of physical problems offering evidence of mental stress involves a veteran we represented who developed generalized anxiety disorder after service. Tom claimed that the problem began in service, but there were no records of any psychiatric complaints whatsoever. What we did have records of were Tom's skin problems. He developed a severe scratching problem that would not go away. He continued to scratch his skin until it bled. The doctors treated the symptoms without identifying what may have been causing this problem.

We theorized that the scratching was symptomatic of underlying anxiety that began during service. Our forensic medical expert who specializes in dermato-psychiatry determined that excessive itching of the skin is often a manifestation of underlying anxiety. Based on this, we were able to anchor our claim on the in-service medical records establishing excessive skin itching. This gave us the linkage we needed to establish the in-service onset of an anxiety disorder.

Conclusion

Our brave soldiers face unimaginable challenges during their service to our country. Sexual assault is a tragic and ongoing reality for these honorable men and women who have no one to tell of their abuse and suffer physical and psychological hardship from both the traumatic event itself and the years of holding their experience inside. While the military harasses MST victims and gives them other-than-honorable discharges, the perpetrators of these violent attacks continue their abuse with little to no repercussions.

Though the Department of Veterans Affairs offers benefits for service connection for psychiatric disabilities secondary to military sexual trauma, many veterans simply cannot win a claim with the sole support of a service officer. In most cases, an experienced veterans disability attorney who can supply substantial investigative resources and medical expert opinion is needed to win these claims. Fortunately, many veterans disability attorneys—including myself—know how difficult it can be for veterans to afford these services. As a result, we offer to cover the cost of these valuable resources until our clients win their claims.

Rehabilitation of MST victims is possible. With proper care, MST victims can overcome their mental and physical issues and lead productive and fulfilling lives. But for this to happen, treatment must begin as soon as possible. To prevent lifelong depression, homelessness, suicide, and physical illness, VA benefits must be available to every veteran who suffers MST without delay. Until that happens, we owe our best efforts as advocates to these veterans to help them obtain the benefits they need and deserve.

Traumatic Brain Injury

The nature of military veteran health care and combat-related injuries has changed over time due to multiple factors. Changes in combat arena weaponry, protective equipment, timing of evacuation into medical facilities, and advances in medical technology all play a role in the nature of post-war survivable injury for veterans. Soldiers with combat-related injuries that were often fatal in the past are now getting more advanced medical care and receiving that care faster than in prior conflicts.

According to the medical literature, in veterans from conflicts involving Afghanistan and Iraq, it is more common to have survivors of traumatic brain injury (TBI) and the wide range of medical sequelae associated with TBI than in previous conflicts.[241] The Department of Defense reports that in a tally from the years 2000 through 2017, approximately 400,000 military personnel were diagnosed with TBI.[242] In fact, TBI is considered the "signature" injury for veterans from the Afghanistan and Iraq conflicts.

Mild TBI

Traumatic brain injury, even when mild, has a significant negative impact on recovering veterans. The term "mild" can be quite misleading; it can create difficulty for veterans who are trying to obtain benefits for real medical problems associated with "mild" TBI. What determines whether a TBI is mild, moderate, or severe is also somewhat difficult to standardize. According to an in-depth review of the medical literature, TBI may be best rated using an assessment of the following factors: the score on the

Glasgow Coma Scale, the presence/absence of loss of consciousness (LOC), the duration of LOC, and any abnormal brain imaging (whether CT scan or MRI).[243] Rating TBI as "moderate" or "severe" is less challenging for medical professionals because the signs and symptoms are more graphic and obvious. Tragically, only a minority of veterans with this level of TBI return home and require immediate aggressive treatment.

However, when the criteria listed above are used, the vast majority of veterans diagnosed with TBI are classified as "mild."[244] Notably, a veteran can have no LOC and no abnormal imaging scans, yet still have a significant medical impact from a "mild" TBI.[245] While the sequelae of mild TBI and related post-concussion syndrome may eventually disappear completely, they linger and cause long-term problems in many patients. This aspect of the medical reality of TBI injuries in veterans is often overlooked, misunderstood, or downplayed.

The complexity of cases involving mild TBI cannot be overstated. Mild TBI symptoms often overlap with other medical issues common in veterans, such as PTSD or depression, and they can be difficult to tell apart. Symptoms such as headache may be obvious, but lesser symptoms, such as irritability or difficulty concentrating, are also associated with mild TBI. To make things more complicated, the medical literature is clear that veterans with TBI are at higher risk of developing PTSD and depression, which may actually be secondary to the TBI.[246] In spite of being secondary to the TBI, these problems may not fully develop until months or even years later.[247,248] The trip down the proverbial medical rabbit hole goes further; the medical literature reports that while the psychological issues of combat-related PTSD and depression are significant medical problems on their own, they have also been linked to cardiovascular problems, obesity, high blood pressure, and abnormal cholesterol. These associated problems also impact the expected medical outlook for veterans who have suffered a traumatic brain injury.

Association with Psychiatric Problems

Traumatic brain injury has a complex web of associated mental health problems and risk factors. It is considered a risk factor for tobacco use, alcohol misuse, and suicide.[249,250] Research has shown that even mild TBI has a significant association with psychiatric problems.[251,252] On the other hand, according to the medical literature, a significant number of veterans with a history of TBI suffer from major depression.[253,254] Studies have also shown that more than half of the veterans in the VA system who have a diagnosis of TBI also have PTSD, which is closely associated with residual TBI symptoms.[255,256]

Sleep disturbances are a major category of persistent long-term sequelae from TBI, and they are often missed as related to past, in-service TBI. Sleep disturbances associated with TBI are varied and include insomnia, excessive daytime sleepiness, nightmares, and broken sleep cycles.[257] According to the medical literature, insomnia may be more prevalent in mild TBI than in more severe forms of TBI, and sleep disturbances may occur years after mild TBI.[258] TBI is also associated with post-traumatic vertigo and dizziness.[259,260] Especially if there is more than one TBI, it may be associated with changes in personality and behavior.[261,262,263] Mild TBI is associated with double the risk for epileptic seizures for years after the TBI occurs.[264] There are medical studies that show a higher risk of mortality in patients with a history of mild TBI, more than a decade after the mild TBI occurred. [265,266]

There are many examples of veterans who suffered a TBI and later experienced changes in personality and behavior. Our client, Michael, illustrates how a veteran's life can change following TBI. Michael suffered an in-service motor vehicle accident (MVA) and head trauma, which was well-documented in his record. Before the accident, Michael was an exemplary airman who performed his duties with aplomb. His performance reviews noted that he was recommended for a career in the Air Force. But after the accident, Michael manifested drastic changes in his personality, judgment, and mental and social functioning. Behavioral changes after the accident included substance misuse, which was not present at all prior to the head trauma. Michael's conduct following the head injury was described in his service records as immature, impetuous, disorderly, dependent, and norm-violating. This stood in stark contrast with descriptions of him prior to the head trauma. Despite this evidence, the VA denied the claim on the grounds that Michael had not suffered a chronic injury to his brain. We hired several medical experts who properly understood that Michael exhibited classic symptoms of frontal lobe impairment directly attributable to the in-service MVA and head trauma.

Our medical experts further explained that Michael had a secondary psychological condition as a result of the physical trauma to his brain. They explained that reduced blood flow to the frontal lobe of the brain due to trauma is a well-known cause of depression. Thus, our experts opined that Michael suffered from depression due to the in-service head trauma. After many years on appeal, we finally won service connection for Michael. If it had not been for multiple medical experts that properly understood TBI, Michael might never have succeeded.

Many issues may occur secondary to a TBI and may be considered service-related if the TBI has been properly diagnosed. However, the true TBI may not be recognized for what it is and may be "missed." The medical issues, mental health problems, or sleep problems that occurred because of the TBI may also be "missed." The medical literature shows that an initial screening for mental health problems, shortly after a veteran's return, will frequently miss many mental health issues ("missed" diagnosis). Additionally, even if the TBI symptoms are found, properly characterized, and recorded in a medical exam, they may not be correctly identified as due to a TBI and may be misdiagnosed as something else ("misdiagnosis"). This creates many problems for veterans who are applying for benefits that are legitimately linked to TBI from their time in service.

The bottom line is that veterans who seek help with their medical problems related to mild TBI need an informed advocate who can help them address these issues, along with skilled medical experts with a thorough knowledge of the medical literature on TBI. Demonstrating the veteran's entitlement to benefits can be tricky. For example, many veterans may be denied appropriate benefits if they do not have an obvious head injury associated with their TBI. The medical literature does show that TBI often occurs due to head injury from physical contact with shrapnel or explosive fragments. Yet, it also states that veterans can develop significant sequelae from mild TBI without having any direct contact injury.[267] At first, this may seem like a skeptical theory, often overlooked by boards or agencies determining veterans' benefits. To an informed advocate, however, the explanation is clear and medically sound.

Most laypeople have enough knowledge of human anatomy to know the brain is seated within and protected by the skull. It would be easy (and highly inaccurate) to say that if the skull hasn't been fractured by a direct contact injury, the brain must be fine. The brain actually sits in liquid held around it by a membrane sac and the overlying skull. There is room for the actual brain tissue to move within the protective skull. Injury can occur if the brain is thrown against the skull with hard enough force. This may happen with a veteran exposed to a blast or explosion, a fall, or an MVA, without any object actually hitting the head. Medical professionals call this kind of brain injury "coup/contrecoup;" injuries caused by "acceleration/deceleration" of the brain within the skull. In this type of injury, no direct contact with shrapnel or other objects is involved. Forces such as an explosive blast cause the brain to basically crash up against the back or front of the skull and cause TBI, as shown in the diagram below.[268]

In addition to the damage done when the brain hits the skull, a second set of injuries occurs later with the brain swelling or having chemical changes that affect the blood vessels. This type of change from what is termed "secondary brain injury" may or may not show up clearly as anatomical abnormalities on CT scans or MRIs. The problem here is a disturbance in normal brain function, not a change in the brain structure as it appears in a medical image.[269] What is clear is that an assessment of a

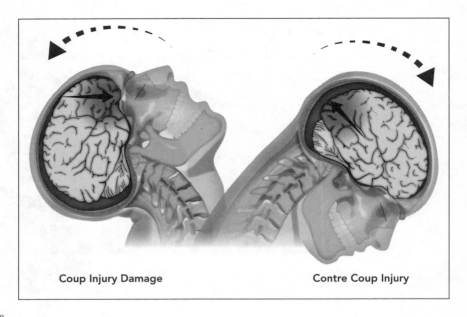

Coup Injury Damage   Contre Coup Injury

veteran's TBI requires more than just looking at the initial event and what hit them in the head. Veterans deserve to be appropriately compensated for all the sequelae of service-related TBI, even when there is no history of abnormal medical scans or direct hits to the head.

The case of one of our clients, named William, is an example of the gross inadequacy of the TBI evaluations many veterans receive, as well as the erroneous belief by VA examiners and regional office adjudicators that a skull fracture is required for there to be a TBI. William suffered a blow to the head from a crowbar. The resulting injury required multiple sutures. When he came to us, he was already service connected for the scars from this trauma—but not for the TBI or the psychiatric residuals. The records noted multiple lacerations and contusions on his head. A skull X-ray was negative for a skull fracture. He had symptoms that included seeing flashing lights. The medical corps performed an eye exam, which was negative. Against the medical standard of care, no brain scans were performed; despite William having been hit in the head and "seeing stars." In fact, a tragic and grossly ridiculous aspect of the case was that repeated eye exams were offered, despite the fact that they continued to show that the issue was not with William's eyes. Still, no further head imaging or brain scans were performed, as would have been appropriate. Yet, the VA predicated its denial of the TBI claim on the lack of a skull fracture. In fact, its own medical examiner opined that there was no TBI because there wasn't a skull fracture, and the examiner rendered this opinion in the face of a plethora of medical literature that indicates a skull fracture is not dispositive of head trauma.

To win William's case, we hired a top-notch forensic medical expert with M.D. and Ph.D. degrees who was able to establish the untenable position of the VA examiners and adjudicators. Ironically, the medical literature published by the VA itself contradicted their own position, a fact that our experts brought to light. Finally, after years of appeal, the Board of Veterans Appeals granted William's claim. William would not have been able to achieve this result without our assistance and our highly-qualified medical experts who understood TBI. The decisive factor was our firm's willingness to spend the necessary resources to hire such experts on behalf of William and others like him.

Veterans with service-related TBI are at high risk of missing out on the benefits they rightly deserve in a variety of circumstances, including the following:

- The TBI occurs without loss of consciousness
- The TBI occurs without direct impact of an object that hit the head and caused head injury (acceleration/deceleration injuries)
- The TBI occurs with a closed head injury (skull is intact)
- The TBI occurred due to chemical disruption of brain function (secondary brain injury) without obvious structural changes to the brain ("normal" CT scans and MRIs)
- The TBI is not properly assessed or diagnosed in service when it occurs—missed diagnosis
- The symptoms of TBI are noticed and recorded in medical files, but they are confused with unrelated mental health problems—misdiagnosis
- The TBI is diagnosed and classified as "mild," but the term "mild" traumatic brain injury is misunderstood and downplayed by VA adjudicators (it's still a brain injury!)
- The TBI causes mental health problems that are not properly assessed as secondary to the TBI

- The TBI causes other medical problems, such as cardiovascular issues, that are not properly assessed as secondary to the TBI
- The medical or mental health problems secondary to TBI are there, but they are missed specifically on the exam done upon leaving military service
- The medical or mental health problems secondary to TBI show up months or years after the TBI
- The medical or mental health problems secondary to TBI show up after active military service
- The TBI causes medical/psychiatric issues such as alcohol misuse, tobacco use, or suicidality that are not properly assessed as secondary to the TBI
- The TBI and secondary medical issues negatively affect the veteran's overall medical prognosis, and this is not properly assessed, resulting in a lower overall rating for the veteran

There are so many pitfalls associated with veterans getting proper benefits for service-related brain injuries, especially with the most common "mild" TBI, that many veterans miss out on benefits they more than earned in service. It takes a highly informed legal advocate with a strong team of knowledgeable medical experts to disentangle these cases and properly defend veterans' rights. With the proper analysis and logical breakdown, backed by strong references to current medical standards, many of these cases can be turned around to the veteran's benefit, translating into successful compensation for them and their families.

Service-Disabled Veteran-Owned Small Businesses Fraud

U.S. military service members return home with a unique arsenal of experience, discipline, reliability, leadership skills, organizational wisdom, and business savvy. As a result, veterans have founded some of the most successful businesses in the nation. Just look at FedEx, Nike, Walmart, and Enterprise Rent-a-Car. Many of the startups and small businesses that dominate the market are run by dedicated veterans, including service-disabled veterans.

Time and again, service-disabled veteran-owned small businesses (SDVOSB) come out on top, leading their industry into uncharted, upgraded territory using initiative and expertise acquired through their unique life experiences. But disabled veterans don't always have it easy getting their foot in the door.

Convincing investors and other financiers to look past a service-related disability is still, unfortunately, challenging. As a reward for their valuable service to our country and to help even the playing field, the federal government offers a percentage of contracting dollars to service-disabled veteran-owned small businesses every year.

However, while thousands of combat wounded and service-disabled men and women work hard to succeed in American business, corrupt business owners continue to defraud the U.S. government by falsely claiming they are eligible for SDVOSB contracts. Scores of dishonest entrepreneurs who don't qualify for these valuable funds will go to extravagant lengths to get them, lying about their eligibility, hiring veterans to pose as owners, even creating fake businesses to acquire SDVOSB funding. When these fraudsters illegally secure SDVOSB contracts, our nation's taxpayers and legitimate service-disabled veteran-owned small businesses suffer.

But there are ways to fight back and recover these stolen funds. Each year, the U.S. Justice Department pays whistleblowers hundreds of millions in award dollars to expose knowledge of fraud. For helping to uncover illegal contract procurement, our own whistleblower clients have received over $100 million in award monies. Veterans, military personnel, contracting officers, competitors, billing clerks, accountants, construction foremen, and anyone else with inside information about SDVOSB fraud can resort to the False Claims Act (FCA) to take action and stop the misconduct.

The SDVOSB Program

As far back as the late 1970s, legislators have been pushing for the Small Business Administration (SBA) to offer special consideration for veterans, but the ball didn't really start rolling until 1986. That year, Marine Corps Korean War veteran John K. Lopez and other members of the Palo Alto Disabled American Veterans chapter formed the Association for Service-Disabled Veterans (ASDV). The ASDV aimed to help disseminate opportunities for veteran-owned businesses, advocating "to create opportunities at all levels of government for these veterans to achieve and maintain their rehabilitation through enterprise development and managed employment."[270]

Lopez and ASDB greatly influenced the establishment of California's 1989 Disabled Veteran Business Enterprise (DVBE) legislation.[271] California Public Contract Code 10115 ensured that at least three percent of state contracting dollars went directly to certified disabled veteran-owned businesses annually, generating jobs and business opportunities throughout California.[272]

The idea was a good one, so good that the federal government decided to follow suit. In 1998, SBA Administrator Aida Alvarez initiated a veterans' task force (now VET-force) to examine the needs of veterans wishing to start their own businesses. Within three months, the SBA Veterans' Affairs Task Force for Entrepreneurship had prepared a report of 21 "high priority" recommendations,[273] and the Veterans Entrepreneurship and Small Business Development Act of 1999 was born. The Act created a three percent federal procurement goal for service-disabled veteran-owned businesses.[274]

Four years later, President Bush signed the Veterans Benefits Act of 2003, amending Title 38 of the United States Code to offer sole source and restricted competition contracts for service-disabled veteran-owned businesses in order to balance out the competition and help disabled veterans flourish amidst huge, more successful corporations.[275]

In October 2004, President Bush followed up by signing Executive Order 13360, which significantly increased federal contracting and subcontracting opportunities for service-disabled veteran-owned businesses. The legislation ordered agencies to more effectively implement the goal of not less than three percent for participation by service-disabled veteran businesses in federal contracting and subcontracting and gave agency contracting officers the authority to reserve certain procurements for service-disabled veteran businesses.[276]

At last count (2012), just over 2.5 million U.S. businesses (9.1 percent of all U.S. businesses) were majority-owned by veterans—pulling in over $1 trillion in total annual revenues. And veterans with service-connected disabilities owned an estimated 7.3 percent of veteran-owned businesses.[277]

SDVOSB Eligibility

To understand the brazen acts fraudsters use to access these set-aside funds, it is helpful to explain how service-disabled veteran-owned businesses become eligible for funding. Before you can bid on a set-aside contract, you must certify that you meet the eligibility requirements. To qualify for service-disabled veteran-owned small business contracts, the business must be a "small business" owned and controlled by a service-disabled veteran. Before October 1, 2018, the qualification criteria for service-disabled veteran-owned small business contracts included:

- Service-connected disability validated by the Department of Veterans Affairs or the Department of Defense
- < 500 employees and < $5 million annual revenue
- Service-disabled veteran is unconditional owner of 51 percent of the business
- Service-disabled veteran holds the highest officer position of the business
- Service-disabled veteran ownership must be direct (a company owned by another entity that is owned and controlled by a service-disabled veteran is not eligible)
- Service-disabled veteran must control decision-making, day-to-day management, and administration of business operations (in the case of permanent and severe disability, the veteran's spouse or caregiver may control the business)

Under the SDVOSB program, a "service-disabled veteran" is any person who served in the active military and was discharged or released under conditions other than dishonorable. The veteran must have a disability incurred or aggravated in the line of duty in the active military. There is no minimum disability rating, so veterans with a 0 to 100 percent disability rating are eligible.

SDVOSB Fraud

Unfortunately, somewhat vague eligibility criteria allowed corrupt companies and individuals to continually try and steal small business contracts meant for veterans by lying about veteran ownership and involvement, company size, or company earnings—resulting in millions of dollars being taken from veterans who deserve them.

For example, while 33-year-old Anthony R. Bilby was working as a sales representative for two SDVOSBs, one being Virginia-based ThunderCat Technology, LLC, he decided he would try to increase contract award dollars by creating an illusion of competition between companies. Bilby bid on contracts for his employer and then told the other SDVOSB to bid higher. The companies told each other what they bid each time, then proceeded to bid higher and higher until Bilby finally secured a $24.1 million contract.

How did Bilby know how high he could go and still win the fake bidding wars? He paid federal agents 10 percent of the profits in exchange for insider information on how much Customs and Border Protection officials would offer for his company's technology contract. In total, Bilby and his co-conspirators secured over $33 million in federal contracts through fraudulent procurement practices.

Bilby pleaded guilty in 2013 and was sentenced to 16 months in prison for conspiracy to commit wire fraud and major government fraud. Bilby was also ordered to forfeit $1,065,103.90, his personal proceeds from the fraud.[278] ThunderCat Technology agreed to pay $1 million to settle FCA, Anti-Kickback Act, and Procurement Integrity Act claims relating to bid-rigging and kickback schemes involved in a total of six awarded contracts. There was no determination of civil liability.[279]

In August 2017, in one of the largest settlements ever reached in a case of small-business contract fraud, ADS Inc. agreed to pay $16 million to settle False Claims allegations that it fraudulently obtained SDVOSB contracts through a similar scheme. Originally a diving supplies store, ADS provides a variety of equipment and logistics solutions for the U.S. military, from protective gear to combat supplies and robotic devices. The Department of Justice believes ADS allegedly used bid-rigging schemes to secure contracts with the Department of Defense and Homeland Security that were set aside for veteran-owned companies. The whistleblower responsible for prompting the investigation into ADS was awarded approximately $2.9 million for exposing the alleged fraud. No determination of liability was made in this case.[280]

Another common scheme used to steal contracts meant for disabled veterans is to create a sham company that appears eligible. On April 7, 2017, a San Diego federal grand jury named 54-year-old Andrew Otero of El Cajon, California, and 57-year-old, service-disabled veteran Roger Ramsey of Spring Valley, California and their companies, A&D General Contracting, Inc. and Action Telecom, Inc., in a 14-count indictment for allegedly defrauding the federal government out of $11 million in contracts set aside for service-disabled veteran-owned businesses.

Roger Ramsey was indeed a service-disabled veteran, but Otero was not. In order for Otero to be eligible for SDVOSB funds, the court alleged that Otero and Ramsey combined their two businesses to create a joint venture called Action-A&D. In their applications for the SDVOSB contracts, Ramsey said his company Action would manage the joint venture, hire project managers, and collect over 51 percent of the joint venture's profits. Based on these statements, Otero and Ramsey obtained $11 million in federal construction contracts and task orders with the Army Corps of Engineers and Department of Veteran Affairs.

Yet Otero and Ramsey allegedly made a secret side agreement that Otero's company A&D—not Ramsey's company Action—would manage the construction jobs. Under the secret agreement, A&D would also collect 98 percent of the joint venture's profits—not Action. Surprisingly, the side agreement also stated that Otero and Ramsey created the joint venture so that A&D could "use the Disabled Veteran Status of Action" to bid on contracts—a blatant admission of ineligibility under the SDVOSB program. Though the SDVOSB contracts listed Ramsey as president of Action and the joint venture Action-A&D, Ramsey actually worked for another company full time. Otero controlled the daily operations, hiring, management, and long-term decision-making of the joint venture. Otero allegedly paid Ramsey a small fee for letting him use Ramsey's disabled veteran status to obtain the SDVOSB contracts.

On November 21, 2018, a federal jury convicted Otero and A&D General Contracting, Inc. on charges that they fraudulently obtained $11 million in federal contracts specifically set aside for service-disabled veteran-owned businesses. The defendants are also facing civil charges alleging violations of the FCA based on the misconduct.

"One important way in which our country tries to repay the debt of gratitude we owe to our veterans is by setting aside some government contracts for those who have been disabled during their service," said acting United States Attorney Alana Robinson. "But unscrupulous contractors have abused this program through 'rent-a-vet' schemes, such as the one described in today's indictment. The Department of Justice will work to ensure that criminals who abuse important contracting programs such as the SDVOSB are held to account."[281]

In another case, while working for the Syracuse, New York-based construction company, Hayner Hoyt Corporation, John Rubar claimed he discovered Hayner Hoyt was working under an SDVOSB contract without being eligible. How were they getting away with it? Rubar alleged Hayner Hoyt had created a sham company called 229 Constructors LLC, which hired service-disabled veteran Ralph Bennett as president. Rubar alleged Bennett wasn't involved in making any Hayner Hoyt business decisions. Instead, Hayner Hoyt CEO Gary Thurston and his son Jeremy Thurston made all the decisions. Bennett merely handled the tool inventory and plowed snow on company property.

In addition, Rubar claimed Hayner Hoyt obtained its SDVOSB contract by making false statements and certifications that 229 Constructors met all SDVOSB requirements. John Rubar decided to file a whistleblower lawsuit against Hayner Hoyt. In March 2016, the lawsuit paid off. Because Rubar's information helped recover $5 million federal dollars through an FCA settlement with Hayner Hoyt, Rubar received a whistleblower cash award of $875,000. More importantly, he helped out all of the legitimate service-disabled veteran-owned small businesses that must compete for these valuable SDVOSB contracts.[282]

Then there is the case of Legion Construction. In 2006, in an effort to secure an SDVOSB contract, 41-year-old David Gorski of Chelmsford, Massachusetts, decided to recruit a disabled Korean War veteran to act as the owner of a company he had established, Legion Construction, Inc. When the veteran's health deteriorated, Gorski recruited another disabled veteran, Peter Ianuzzi, to be Legion's figurehead owner. By misrepresenting these veterans as owners, Legion acquired more than $113 million in federal contracts over a four-year period.

In March 2010, a competitor SDVOSB alleged Legion wasn't eligible for its contract with a Vermont VA medical center, saying it appeared that Gorski, not one of the veterans, was the person running things. Gorski apparently panicked. He filed an opposition using backdated documents containing false and misleading information. The SBA denied it. Gorski then started trying to siphon money to make things appear legitimate. Previously, he had been paying Ianuzzi more than regulations allow, had "gifted" himself $900,000 (from Ianuzzi), and had established private bank accounts into which Legion deposited $2.5 million for Gorski's benefit. But before he could open the bank accounts, a federal grand jury issued subpoenas to Legion and several witnesses.

In June 2016, a jury found Gorski guilty of conspiring to defraud the United States by "impairing the lawful governmental function of the Department of Veterans Affairs, the General Services Administration, the Army, and the Navy in the implementation and administration of the Service Disabled Veteran Owned Small Business Program." On September 27, 2016, a U.S. District Court Judge sentenced Gorski to 30 months in prison and a $1 million fine.

"We are pleased with today's sentencing, and it is quite satisfying to know that people who commit these types of crimes are held accountable," said Frank Robey, Director of the U.S. Army Criminal Investigation Command's Major Procurement Fraud Unit. "There is an important purpose for the Service-Disabled Veteran-Owned Small Business Program, and this individual attempted to exploit that program for his own personal gain while pushing those who deserve it aside."[283]

In another sham company case, the government alleges that W.G.

Mills, a Florida construction management company, created a company called Veterans Constructors Incorporated (VCI) merely as a contracting vehicle to qualify for a Coast Guard contract set aside for SDVOSBs. Two whistleblowers, Michael Jeske and Samuel McIntosh, filed an FCA lawsuit claiming that VCI did not qualify because it was owned by W.G. Mills, not by a veteran, and that W.G. Mills, not VCI, did most of the work performed for the Coast Guard contract.

On March 18, 2015, the Department of Justice announced that Gilbane Building Company (a Rhode Island company that merged with W.G. Mills in November 2010) agreed to pay $1.1 million to settle allegations that W.G. Mills allegedly violated the FCA by creating a sham company in order to qualify for SDVOSB contracts. There was no determination of liability.[284] For filing the FCA lawsuit and reporting their knowledge about the fraud, whistleblowers Jeske and McIntosh shared a six-figure whistleblower award.

In another case, engineering services company TTG joined with service-disabled veteran Jerome Schwab to form a company called Schwab Engineering, Inc. On paper, Jerome was the owner of the company, so the federal government awarded Schwab Engineering over a dozen SDVOSB contracts. But in reality, TTG provided the staffing and support, including financial and administrative services. TTG also collected up to 95 percent of the contract proceeds.

After TTG merged with Illinois engineering and construction services firm IMEG Corp., IMEG discovered the misconduct and reported it. In December 2018, IMEG Corp. agreed to pay $5.27 million to settle allegations that Schwab Engineering, Inc. had conspired to submit false claims for payment using SDVOSB contracts for which it was ineligible. There was no determination of liability.[285]

SDVOSB Eligibility Amendments

Due to the vast number of procurement fraud cases involving SDVOSBs, the government has tightened its eligibility criteria for SDVOSB contracts. In October 2018, the federal government implemented various additions and clarified definitions regarding eligibility. Since then, the SDVOSB must qualify as a "small business" under the North American Industry Classification System (NAICS) code assigned to each specific procurement contract. One or more service-disabled veterans must own at least 51 percent of the voting interest in the business, receive at least 51 percent of the company's annual distribution of profits, and hold the highest officer position in the business. Upon the veteran's passing, the veteran's spouse can take ownership of the SDVOSB if eligible.

The service-disabled veterans must also work at the company during regular business hours and control the company's decision-making, day-to-day management, and administration of business operations, including, but not limited to, "the marketing, production, sales and administrative functions of the firm, as well as the supervision of the executive team, and the implementation of policies."[286] The only control non-service-disabled veterans and other entities are allowed to exert is over "extraordinary actions," which are defined as:

- Adding new equity stakeholders
- Dissolution of the company
- Sale of the company
- Merger of the company
- Company declaring bankruptcy[287]

In addition to making changes to the SDVOSB eligibility criteria, the U.S. Department of Defense Office of the Inspector General (OIG) announced that it was initiating an audit to determine whether companies holding current SDVOSB contracts were meeting proper eligibility criteria and how agencies confirmed awardee eligibility.[288] According to the *National Law Review*, "These inquiries [might] range from requests for interviews and voluntary submissions of information relevant to the audit to requests for proof that the contractor is an eligible SDVOSB. To establish proof, OIG officials [might] request to visit SDVOSB facilities to determine whether a service-disabled veteran actually owns or controls the company and manages its daily business operations."[289]

In February 2020, the Inspector General for the U.S. Department of Defense published the audit's results. The government investigators concluded that $876.8 million in SDVOSB contracts were awarded to ineligible companies. After reviewing awards for 29 purported SDVOSBs, the DoD found that 16 of the contractors had misrepresented their status as small businesses owned by service-disabled veterans, thus securing DoD contracts valued at over $827 million between fiscal years 2017 and 2018. Hopefully, these shocking statistics will serve as a cautionary tale, and the government will stop handing out millions of taxpayer dollars without first ensuring that SDVOSB eligibility criteria are met.

Whistleblowing and the False Claims Act

Despite changes in eligibility criteria and other regulatory efforts, SDVOSB whistleblowers are still America's number one weapon against service-disabled veteran-owned small business fraud. It takes a lot of time and government resources to detect cases of fraud. To facilitate detection of illegal activities and recovery of stolen dollars, the government pays large cash awards to individuals with knowledge of SDVOSB fraud.

Enacted during the Civil War to expose overcharging and defective goods supplied to the Union Army, the False Claims Act,[290] or "Lincoln Law," pays cash incentives to urge those with information on fraud to come forward. Those whose knowledge of FCA violations leads to recovery of government funds receive between 15 and 30 percent of the total government recoveries. Penalties for violating the FCA continue to increase as the government suffers more and more related financial losses.

- Penalties for false claims made before August 1, 2016, are $5,500-$11,000 per false claim
- Penalties for false claims made between August 1, 2016, and February 3, 2017, are $10,781-$21,563 per false claim
- Penalties for false claims made between February 3, 2017, and January 29, 2018, are $10,957-$21,916 per false claim
- Penalties for false claims made between January 29, 2018, and June 19, 2020, are $11,181-$22,363 per false claim
- Penalties for false claims made after June 19, 2020, are $11,665-$23,331 per false claim

As fraud cases often involve hundreds—even thousands—of false claims, our whistleblower lawyers' veteran and active military clients often obtain cash awards that range in the hundreds of thousands to millions of dollars.

Most types of SDVOSB fraud involve a violation of the federal FCA. When a company obtains an SDVOSB contract that does not meet the required criteria and subsequently sends claims for payment to the government or causes claims for payment to be sent to the government, that business may be submitting claims to the U.S. government in violation of the FCA.[291] Common FCA violations committed by fraudulent SDVOSB contractors include:

- Misrepresenting company size or earnings
- Misrepresenting veteran company ownership
- Misrepresenting veteran company control
- Modifying corporate structure to indicate veteran owns controlling interest and manages day-to-day affairs
- Creating a business owned by a disabled veteran, then passing the work on to a non-qualifying business
- Claiming SDVOSB status when the owner is not a service-disabled veteran

Several activities occurring in your place of employment or your competitor's company serve as good indicators that the business may be committing SDVOSB contract fraud. These red flags may include:

- Payroll records show minimal SDVOSB work
- Minimal employee presence at "official" address
- Points of contact mostly through a larger company
- Corporate records altered to list veteran in controlling capacity
- Employees unaware that controlling member is a veteran
- Veteran has little on-site presence or contact with the contracting agency
- Payroll records show veteran does not receive top company pay
- Veteran receives one-time payment or ongoing, low salary payments

Whistleblowers don't have to be employees of a company. They just need to have unique, original-source information (information not available to the public via the media, online, or elsewhere). Of course, many SDVOSB whistleblowers are worried about employer retaliation. But FCA anti-retaliation provisions prohibit employers from firing, demoting, harassing, denying promotion, or otherwise discriminating against employees or other individuals because they choose to report a violation. SDVOSB fraud whistleblowers subjected to retaliation have the right to sue for damages, including double back pay, interest on lost wages, job reinstatement, and attorneys' fees and costs.

Defense Contractor Whistleblowers

Just as government funds set aside for service-disabled veteran-owned small businesses are susceptible to fraud, waste, and abuse, so are funds meant for eligible defense contractors—and veterans are in a unique position to report inside knowledge of defense contractor fraud. Data from the Bureau of Labor Statistics and Census Bureau data collected via the annual American Community Survey (ACS) suggests that certain employers hire more veterans than civilians—employers in management, construction, security, manufacturing, and transportation.[292] These occupations also happen to be frequent recipients of government defense contracts.

The U.S. Department of Defense supplies contractors with over $300 billion per year to produce safe, high-quality food, clothing, services, and equipment for our troops. As is the case with SDVOSB contracts, defense contract funds must be spent according to very specific rules and regulations that help ensure taxpayer dollars are spent properly. Unfortunately, billions of taxpayer dollars are lost to abuse of these valuable funds. Corrupt defense contractors continue to profit from government funds by breaking

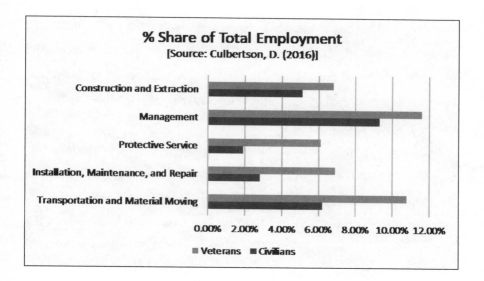

the rules, using cheap, substandard materials, overbilling, cross charging, and other schemes, in violation of the federal FCA.

For example, in July 2018, the Department of Justice announced that 3M Company (3M) agreed to pay $9.1 million to resolve claims that it knowingly sold its dual-ended Combat Arms Earplugs (CAEv2) to the U.S. military without disclosing known defects. 3M allegedly violated the FCA by selling (or causing the sale of) defective earplugs to the Defense Logistics Agency.

Specifically, the government alleged that 3M and its predecessor Aearo Technologies, Inc., knew the CAEv2 was too short for proper insertion into users' ears and that the earplugs could loosen imperceptibly. Despite knowing this, the U.S. alleged that 3M didn't disclose the design defect to the military. There was no determination of liability. The anonymous whistleblower who reported the wrongdoing came away with a $1.9 million cash whistleblower award.

"Today's settlement will ensure that those who do business with the government know that their actions will not go unnoticed," said Frank Robey, director of the U.S. Army Criminal Investigation Command's Major Procurement Fraud Unit. "Properly made safety equipment, for use by our Soldiers, is vital to our military's readiness. Our agents will respond robustly to protect the safety of our military." [293]

Corporate giants like Halliburton, Boeing, Honeywell International, L-3 Communications, KBR, Lockheed Martin, Northrop Grumman, Raytheon Company, SAIC, and United Technologies Corporation are repeatedly investigated and fined for FCA violations. They also hold the largest defense contracts in the nation. Common FCA violations committed by defense contractors include:

- Making fraudulent statements or misrepresentations in defense contract bidding
- Overbilling or submitting fraudulent invoices for defense contract labor, services, or goods
- Using defective, refurbished, or otherwise unsafe materials and parts
- Cross-charging from fixed-price contracts to cost-plus contracts
- Skirting design specifications or other contract requirements
- Failing to notify the government of product deficiencies upon discovery
- Failing to adhere to government environmental or worker safety standards
- Violations of best-price requirements
- Violations of Truth in Negotiations Act (TINA) obligations

Our defense contractor whistleblower lawyers have represented weapons manufacturers, military equipment mechanics, aircraft engineers, cybersecurity technicians, and other defense contractor employees who want to fight fraud, waste, and abuse of government funds. Evidence of intent to defraud the government is not required to file a False Claims Act whistleblower suit.

We are excited to see what service-disabled veteran entrepreneurs do in the business world, and with the SDVOSB program, anything is possible. However, corrupt, greedy entities who steal valuable government funds from deserving veterans continue to plague the system. Bureaucracy and lack of resources often make it difficult for law enforcement to spot these elaborate schemes. Without the invaluable assistance of whistleblowers, most fraudulent government contracts would never be exposed. Veterans and non-veterans alike, who use the False Claims Act as a tool to fight these thieves and recover stolen funds, are incredibly important to keeping this valuable program successful and enabling those who have served our country to improve our nation with high-quality business endeavors.

MILITARY SERVICE AND SUBSTANCE ABUSE

Substance abuse disorders result in the deaths of more than one in four U.S. military members each year. A chaotic military life of daily stressors and combat exposure surrounded by highly-addictive and easily obtained tobacco, alcohol, and prescription medications creates the perfect recipe for lifelong addiction. Veterans return home with heightened anxiety, post-traumatic stress disorder (PTSD), serious injuries, and pressure to quickly reintegrate into civilian society. Addiction only delays the difficult reintegration process and brings massive repercussions down the line, including debilitating health issues and an increased risk of unemployment, homelessness, incarceration, and accidental overdoses.

Military service members understand the very real dangers of addiction, yet many are unable to avoid it. Military society is rife with on-base tobacco use and binge drinking, more so than most civilians face. Drinking and smoking are the military's answer to generating camaraderie and alleviating boredom. When a soldier experiences combat trauma or a painful injury, he or she quickly learns to self-medicate with alcohol or by requesting prescription drugs long past the time they really need them. And the military is more than happy to oblige.

At home, veterans continue this learned trend of self-medication, only to realize they can't stop when they decide they want to. These addicted individuals return home with habits that make them ill-equipped to function in society. Addictions lead to relationship problems, divorce, unemployment, financial difficulties, and deadly diseases. Combine addiction with PTSD and other military-related physical and mental disabilities, and a veteran has slim chances of living a fulfilling life without fast and appropriate treatment.

The Department of Veterans Affairs does recognize the massive problem with addiction among veterans and offers a wide range of treatment protocols designed to help them recover fully from substance abuse disorders. Proper treatment can be extremely effective for veterans, providing new opportunities and a bright future. And while many veterans believe that the VA doesn't offer service-connected disability benefits for tobacco, alcohol, or drug abuse, this is not the case. Veterans are indeed able to collect VA benefits for disabilities associated with substance abuse disorders. They simply need the right advocates to guide them in the right direction.

Military Drug Use Through The Ages

Military service members and veterans have struggled with substance abuse and addiction throughout history. Between 1861 and 1865, Civil War medics took advantage of the recently invented syringe and a relatively new, highly addictive drug called morphine to relieve the pain of wounded soldiers. While morphine did indeed ease the pain, historians estimate that hundreds of thousands of military veterans went home suffering from debilitating morphine addictions.[294]

Between 1917 and 1919, World War I troops found respite in a new wave of pre-rolled cigarettes, replacing the more cumbersome pipe of years before. Tobacco companies supplied soldiers with free cigarettes as their "contribution to the cause." The military and the media encouraged American families to donate cigarettes as a way to boost soldier morale.

Even the YMCA and the American Red Cross collected mass quantities of cigarettes for troop rations.

In 1918, the U.S. government purchased all of Bill Durham Tobacco's output for the war effort, advertising patriotically, "When our boys light up, the Huns will light out." General John J. "Black Jack" Pershing, a senior United States Army officer and commander of the American Expeditionary Force (AEF) in World War I, reportedly stated, "You ask me what we need to win this war? I answer tobacco as much as bullets. Tobacco is as indispensable as the daily ration. We must have thousands of tons of it without delay."[295] By November 1918, the AEF was handing out 14 million cigarettes per day.[296]

Between 1939 and 1945, World War II soldiers took advantage of prohibition's 1933 demise to drink the readily available alcohol supplied on army bases and with military rations. Like the tobacco companies of WWI, distilleries and breweries advertised their products as patriotic cures for anxiety, pain, and boredom. WWII militaries, and notably Nazi Germany's armed forces, also supplied troops with plenty of methamphetamine tablets to help them stay awake and alert.

For Vietnam War soldiers, marijuana and heroin were in high demand, falling second behind alcohol use.[297] Vietnamese farmers grew and sold marijuana to troops as a new source of income, packing it in cigarettes for easy distribution. From 1967 to 1971, studies estimate that between 18 percent and 34 percent of American soldiers used marijuana.[298]

When the military began discouraging soldiers' use of marijuana, many turned to cigarettes laced with heroin. Dr. Norman E. Zinberg, Department of Defense consultant on drug abuse during the Vietnam War, reported, "More than one-third of the proven users begin during their first month in Vietnam, and probably 90 percent in their first four months."[299] In

June 1971, President Richard Nixon initiated a study to test every enlisted man for heroin addiction. Over a third of military veterans admitted to trying heroin during the Vietnam war, with 19 percent developing a heroin addiction.[300]

Substance Abuse in Modern War

In modern war, illicit drugs do not pose the same problems for service members as they did in the past. In fact, military veterans are less interested in illegal drug use than civilians, 2.3 percent compared to 12 percent, respectively,[301] largely because military policy began enforcing random drug testing in 1982. Today, the use of heroin, cocaine, marijuana, or opioids can lead to discharge and potential criminal charges.

Not to say that illegal drug use doesn't exist in the military. Between 2010 and 2011, eight soldiers died from heroin or morphine overdose, likely obtained from the mass quantities of opiates produced in Afghanistan.[302] Yet, most of today's service members and veterans are struggling with nicotine addiction, alcohol abuse, and the deadly temptation of highly available prescription drugs, all of which pose a significantly higher risk of addiction among veterans when compared with civilians.

Nearly 180 noncombat-related Army deaths were due to drug or alcohol overdose between 2006 and 2009.[303] In the 18 years between 1995 and 2013, treatments for substance abuse among veterans increased by 52.7 percent. Unfortunately, less than one out of every 10 veterans seek treatment for issues with alcohol or drug abuse.[304]

Soldiers exposed to combat are automatically at a higher risk for substance abuse. The National Institute of Drug Abuse reports that drug and alcohol abuse are highly correlated with exposure to violence and threats to personal safety. In addition, PTSD, traumatic brain injury (TBI), exposure to military sexual trauma (MST), and chronic pain significantly increase a veteran's risk for developing a substance abuse disorder.

Diagnostic Criteria for Substance Use Disorders

Substance use disorders present with two or more of the following symptoms over a 12-month period:

- Use of a substance in larger amounts or over a longer timespan than intended
- Unsuccessful attempts and/or persistent desire to reduce or stop use
- Substantial amounts of time spent obtaining, using, and/or recovering from the substance
- Strong craving for the substance
- Use causes significant interference with work, school, or home responsibilities
- Using despite repeated social or interpersonal consequences
- Missing important occupational or recreational activities because of the substance use
- Using in situations that could be physically hazardous
- Using despite repeated or persistent physical or mental consequences
- Developing tolerance to the substance
- Experiencing withdrawals when not using the substance

Tobacco and Nicotine Addiction

Tobacco use remains a continuous threat to the health and well-being of military service members and veterans. As the number one cause of preventable death in the U.S., tobacco use kills nearly half a million Americans each year. Over 16 million Americans currently suffer from diseases caused by smoking.[305] Along with alcohol, tobacco is currently the most widely used substance among U.S. military veterans.[306] Regular tobacco use among veterans is higher than that of civilians, causing debilitating, deadly health issues, including lung cancer, cardiovascular disease, and chronic obstructive pulmonary disease (COPD).

Military service is a known risk factor for smoking.[307,308] Not unlike during World War I, smoking is still permitted, even encouraged on military bases today. Smoking is a way for soldiers to relieve stress and boredom, generate a sense of camaraderie, and fight fatigue. Veterans continue to use tobacco products once they return to civilian life, to alleviate symptoms of depression, anxiety, and PTSD, and to ease themselves into a difficult transition.

A 2011 survey conducted by the U.S. Department of Defense reported that 49.2 percent of service members regularly used some form of nicotine. Smoking is reportedly highest among U.S. Marines (30.8 percent), followed by Army (26.7 percent), Navy (24.4 percent), and Air Force (16.7 percent) service members.[309] A survey of Iraq service members found that tobacco use increased from 51.9 percent before deployment to 58.3 percent during deployment. Most service members named stress as their reason for smoking (47.7 percent), while the remaining respondents said they smoked to relieve boredom (25.1 percent) or because they were addicted to nicotine (22.7 percent).[310]

A significant 25 percent of military veterans smoke regularly, compared to 19 percent of civilians. By 2015, approximately 17 percent of veterans enrolled in the VA health care system smoked cigarettes.[311] In 1997, research showed that those who suffer from PTSD smoke more heavily than those without PTSD,[312] eventually forcing the VA to implement smoking cessation assistance into PTSD treatment programs.[313] Yet, most veterans still find quitting extremely difficult. Cigarette smoking accounts for 50 percent of cancer-related deaths among veterans who are current smokers.[314]

Alcohol Abuse

Alcohol is currently the fourth leading cause of preventable death in the U.S. Despite the military discouraging alcohol use in combat theater beginning in 1986, both alcohol and tobacco remain the most easily obtained and widely used substances in the U.S. military. Binge drinking in the military increased significantly in the 10 years between 1998 and 2008. In 1998, 20 percent of military service members reported binge drinking every week, this rate rising to 27 percent with high combat exposure. By 2008, the number of service members who said they participated in binge drinking every week had risen to 47 percent.[315] Surveys suggest that service men and women in the Army, Navy, and Marine Corps are more likely to binge drink than Air Force service members.[316]

Alcohol problems among military service members cost the U.S. military billions of dollars each year. Data collected in 2006 showed that binge drinking in the military caused over 34,000 arrests every year (over 50 percent of these for driving while intoxicated) and over 320,000 lost work days—resulting in annual medical expenditures of over $425 million and total costs to the U.S. military totaling more than $1.12 billion per year.[317]

Issues with alcohol abuse don't end after service. Alcohol and tobacco remain the most widely used substances among U.S. military veterans.[318] Studies report that between 12 percent and 15 percent of Iraq and Afghanistan veterans struggle with alcohol abuse after three to six months of life back at home.[319] Combat exposure increases the rate of binge drinking among veterans significantly, with one study showing that 53 percent of veterans exposed to combat engage in weekly binge drinking.[320] Studies specifically focused on the effects of exposure to killing within combat theater show that alcohol abuse is independently linked to killing exposure, regardless of PTSD diagnosis, and that killing exposure may be a direct risk factor for alcohol abuse among combat veterans.[321] Among veterans, studies show that alcohol use increases the risk of life-limiting health issues, violent interactions, and death.[322]

Prescription Drug Abuse

Prescription drug abuse involving benzodiazepines, dextroamphetamine, and opioids, is epidemic among military members. These highly addictive drugs induce unbearable withdrawal symptoms, often after just two weeks of use. Many soldiers would rather continue taking the drugs than suffer withdrawal symptoms, and doctors and drug companies are more than willing to accommodate them. Medical monitoring and a carefully planned weaning-off protocol are required to overcome withdrawal symptoms and rehabilitate the patient.

Prescription drug abuse in the military tripled between 2005 and 2008.[323] The rate of military prescription drug abuse in 2008 was 11.7 percent, more than double the 4.4 percent rate for civilians.[324] A 2012 study conducted by the Department of Defense found that soldiers in Wounded Warrior Battalion units, created to facilitate the recovery of wounded service members, have a particularly high rate of prescription drug abuse, often taking multiple drugs at once.[325] As of 2009, over 3.8 million service members were using a prescribed pain medication.[326] Most of these medications are prescribed over long periods of time, increasing the risk of dependency.

VA doctors are prescribing opioids to veterans at higher and higher rates to ease problems with chronic pain, PTSD, and other mental health disorders. According to the VA, around 60 percent of Iraq/Afghanistan veterans and 50 percent of pre-Iraq/Afghanistan War veterans suffer from chronic pain, compared to just 30 percent of civilians over the age of 18. Between 2001 and 2009, the percentage of veterans who received opioid prescriptions rose from 17 percent to 24 percent. The average VA patient on prescription opioids is taking two different opioids from three different doctors, with the majority taking the infamous oxycodone (46.9 percent), hydrocodone (39.5 percent), or codeine (6.8 percent).[327]

Veterans with PTSD or other mental health disorders are more likely to receive opioid prescriptions than veterans without mental health issues, those with PTSD being more likely to get several different opioids and more frequent refills. Veterans with PTSD are also more likely to experience opioid addiction and opioid-related accidents or overdoses.[328] Many veterans combine both alcohol and prescription drugs, increasing the chances of overdose.

In 2012 the Army Surgeon General Office advised against treating PTSD with benzodiazepines after scientists noted that certain benzodiazepines, like Xanax and Valium, may impede the effectiveness of other forms of PTSD treatment and that discontinuing the drugs may increase symptoms of PTSD.[329] In 2013, the VA started its Opioid Safety Initiative. By mid-2016, the number of veterans given opioid pain medications and benzodiazepines each quarter had decreased by 25 percent. As of 2017, more veterans are receiving non-opioid pain therapies and treatment for substance use disorders.[330] Yet, the prescription drug abuse problem among soldiers and veterans remains widespread and dangerous.

Military Trauma Amplifies Addiction

Substance abuse in the military offers an easy and often inexpensive way for service members to bond in a foreign environment and cope with the horrifying trauma of war. It also results in a self-perpetuating cycle of mental and physical destruction for our soldiers. In addition to the military making addictive substances easily obtainable for soldiers, stigma and zero-tolerance policies encourage military members to hide their addiction problems.

When soldiers return home, they may use their newfound addictions to cope with the very real stresses of reintegrating into civilian society. This difficult transition entails moving from a structured, routine existence surrounded by comrades who identify with service into a free, independent reality where family and friends cannot fathom military life. They expect the veteran to quickly morph into a "normal" civilian who picks up hobbies, earns an income, and provides emotional support. A lack of psychological support, combined with readily available drugs, alcohol, and tobacco, only prolongs addiction problems.

The PTSD-Addiction Cycle

One of the most unfortunate and troubling aspects of substance abuse among active military and veterans is its ability to augment the symptoms of PTSD and vice versa. PTSD is one of the most prevalent mental complications seen among soldiers. Military veterans are 15 times more likely to develop PTSD than civilians.[331]

According to the VA, those receiving PTSD treatment include 31 percent of Vietnam War veterans, 20 percent of Iraq War veterans, 11 percent of Afghanistan War veterans, and 10 percent of Gulf War veterans. These numbers are likely much higher since many with PTSD do not report symptoms or seek treatment.[332] Over 20 percent of veterans with PTSD have a substance abuse problem. Nearly 33 percent of veterans who seek treatment for substance abuse also have PTSD. Researchers believe that veterans with PTSD turn to alcohol, tobacco, and prescription medications to alleviate problems with insomnia, depression, and traumatic memories.

Addiction among veterans with PTSD generates a snowball effect. While the initial trauma of service causes the PTSD, concurrent substance use causes the disorder to spiral out of control, adding the further trauma of life-threatening health problems, relationship difficulties, depression, failure to hold employment, and an ever-dwindling social support system. This inability to lead a fulfilling life while struggling with alcohol or drug

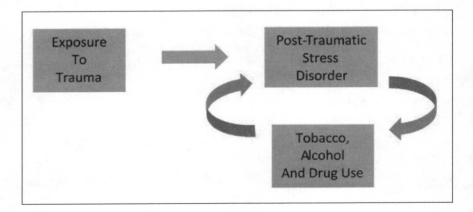

addiction only enhances PTSD symptoms, including insomnia, agitation, paranoia, and social isolation. In turn, the veteran's addiction only grows worse as they rely more and more on drugs or alcohol to cope. Addiction also delays recovery from PTSD, allowing the veteran to continue suppressing traumatic memories.

Unfortunately, veterans diagnosed with PTSD are more likely to receive highly addictive opioid prescriptions from VA hospitals, further exacerbating the problem.[333] Prescription opioid use among veterans can lead to depression, chronic health problems, injuries, and overdose. Researchers have found that the accidental overdose rate for VA patients is double that of the U.S. civilian population.[334]

TBI and Substance Abuse

Another issue associated with substance abuse among veterans is traumatic brain injury. As discussed in earlier chapters, TBI can result from a blow to the head or from exposure to severe shock waves from explosives, and symptoms may not appear for months after the injury. Up to 30 percent of veterans returning from Iraq or Afghanistan reportedly suffered a TBI during service. Studies suggest that between 10 percent and 20 percent of individuals with TBI develop substance abuse disorders.[335] Veterans who are victims of TBI have a 2.6 (mild TBI cases) to 5.4 times (more severe TBI) higher rate of alcohol and drug addiction than civilians with TBI.[336] This discrepancy may be caused by military veterans being less likely to seek or receive proper medical care for their TBI than civilians.

Traumatic brain injuries can damage the release of neurotransmitters that affect the pleasure centers of the brain.[337] Many TBI victims turn to alcohol and drug abuse to alleviate symptoms of anxiety and depression.

In addition, most health care professionals prescribe addictive opioid painkillers to TBI patients, leading to more problems with addiction.

When PTSD and TBI are combined, the risk of substance abuse and addiction increases. And this combination is common. A study examining risk factors for PTSD found that TBI was by far the strongest predictor of post-deployment PTSD among service members and veterans—even more significant than the intensity of trauma experienced during combat.[338] Up to 44 percent of veterans who reported loss of consciousness during service also exhibited PTSD symptoms.[339]

MST and Alcohol Abuse

In addition to TBI increasing the risk for substance abuse among veterans, exposure to military sexual trauma (MST) is also a predetermining factor for addiction. Studies show that military members who suffer from MST have elevated rates of alcohol abuse when compared to those not exposed to MST.[340]

Consequences of Addiction in Veterans

Should soldiers have to sacrifice their chances of leading a productive and fulfilling life in exchange for choosing to serve our nation and protect our rights and freedom? Injuries and illness contribute to enough difficulties after service. Our war veterans don't deserve to reenter civilian life battling addiction by themselves.

Veterans with substance abuse disorders face a future of health problems, social isolation, and financial difficulties. They may experience the realities of loneliness, frequent hospitalization, homelessness, and incarceration. They may neglect their loved ones, put themselves and others in danger by driving while intoxicated, be unable to hold down gainful employment, and turn to criminal activity to feed their addictions. The addiction takes control of their lives. Without proper treatment, it can destroy their opportunities.

Numerous health problems are associated with tobacco, alcohol, and prescription drug abuse. Nine out of 10 lung cancers are caused by smoking. Eight out of 10 COPD deaths are the result of smoking. Smoking is associated with cancers of the bladder, esophagus, kidney, pancreas, stomach, and throat. Smokers are also between 30 and 40 percent more likely to develop type 2 diabetes than nonsmokers.[341]

Excessive alcohol use (15 or more drinks per week) caused over 88,000 U.S. deaths between 2006 and 2010, accounting for one in 10 deaths among adults aged 20 to 64 years. Alcohol addiction increases a veteran's chances of injury, violence, alcohol poisoning, and risky sexual behavior. Over the long term, alcohol addiction can lead to high blood pressure, heart disease, stroke, liver disease, digestive problems, cancer, memory problems, dementia, severe depression, and suicide.[342]

Veterans who struggle with prescription drug abuse face the risk of accidental overdose and are often unable to perform in social or professional environments over the long term. Veterans who rely on prescription opiates also often have co-occurring medical conditions, including chronic pain, insomnia, and obesity, problems forming and maintaining relationships, a lower overall quality of life, and higher levels of aggression compared to veterans with mental health diagnoses but no substance use disorder.

Unemployment is a major issue for many veterans. In 2011, up to 30 percent of young veterans reported issues finding employment after leaving the military.[343] Criminal records can make finding a job even more difficult to find work. Studies show that 9 percent of Iraq and Afghanistan veterans have been arrested for a crime since returning home. Most of these arrests were due to alcohol intoxication, drug abuse, and violent outbursts.[344] Data from the National Inmate Survey conducted between February 2011 and May 2012 shows that 181,500 veterans were incarcerated in state and federal prison in 2011-2012. More veterans (64 percent) were sentenced for violent offenses than non-veterans (48 percent), and 43 percent of veterans in prison had four or more prior arrests.[345]

Studies on homelessness among veterans have shown that 11 percent of U.S. veterans are homeless, often due to difficulty finding and keeping gainful employment while struggling with PTSD and addiction.[346] A 2014 study showed that 27 percent of homeless veterans suffered from mental illness and addiction and that 21 percent of veterans in treatment for substance abuse were homeless.[347] Treatments for addiction in the case of homeless patients can be difficult as their surroundings often contribute to their addictions.

Some veterans know they are struggling, while others may be so affected by their addiction that they are unable to see their lives spiraling out of control. Some choose to seek help, but the majority feel that they can handle things on their own or will take care of it later. While close friends and family members often try to get a veteran help, addiction often causes individuals to push help away. When veterans choose to accept help, many of them have extreme difficulty recovering, especially when addiction is paired with PTSD.

Available Treatments for Substance Abuse Disorder

Proper and timely treatment for substance abuse disorder is vital in helping veterans lead quality, productive lives after service. The VA offers several successful treatment methods, both behavioral and pharmacological, that help rehabilitate veterans from addictive disorders. The VA offers both inpatient and outpatient programs, and several VA hospitals offer residential housing for those who live far from treatment facilities or are homeless. The VA also offers care through outside community providers when a local VA hospital or clinic is not available. Marriage and family counseling, relapse prevention, and continuing care are also available.

Tobacco cessation programs offer regular nicotine substitutes (patches, gum, medication), weaning schedules to help patients taper off the use of these substitutes, and counseling programs to help adapt to the lifestyle changes that come with quitting cigarettes. Alcohol abuse and opioid addiction treatment programs offer medical detoxification and monitored withdrawal support. Three craving-reduction medications, acamprosate, disulfiram, and naltrexone, are currently approved by the U.S. Food and Drug Administration (FDA) for alcohol use disorders. Similarly, buprenorphine, methadone, and naltrexone are FDA-approved for the treatment of opioid use disorders. Recent studies have investigated the use of prazosin, topiramate, and N-acetylcysteine in the treatment of coexisting substance abuse disorder and PTSD.[348,349]

The VA offers motivation and cognitive therapy programs that involve weekly meetings with a therapist over the course of 12 weeks. Motivational therapy helps veterans "reset" their thinking around productive habits by emphasizing why they desire freedom from addiction and the benefits that come along with sobriety. Cognitive behavioral therapy helps veterans recognize the real threats of substance abuse and works to shift their thinking in a positive direction.

Service Connection for Substance Abuse Disorders

One of the biggest misconceptions about winning VA claims is that veterans cannot claim service connection for their alcohol or drug abuse problem. While the VA does not grant direct service connection for substance abuse disorders, veterans are indeed able to service-connect their alcohol or drug abuse problem as secondary to other service-connected conditions.

In 1990, Congress enacted the Omnibus Budget Reconciliation Act (OBRA 1990), which implemented a partial ban on benefits when alcoholism or drug abuse were involved because it felt that alcohol and drug abuse constituted "willful misconduct." Under OBRA 1990, any injury or disease caused by willful alcohol or drug use during service cannot be considered as having occurred in the line of duty. After OBRA 1990, the VA started denying any claims remotely involving alcohol or drug abuse.

But things changed in 2001 after a veteran wanted an increased rating for his PTSD because of the social and occupational issues he suffered from his substance abuse. At first, the VA denied his request, saying that substance abuse could not be service connected as it was considered willful misconduct. However, the Federal Circuit court disagreed, ruling that OBRA 1990 "does not preclude a veteran from receiving compensation for alcohol or drug-related disabilities arising secondarily from a service-connected disability, or from using alcohol or drug-related disabilities as evidence of the increased severity of a service-connected disability."[350]

In *Allen v. Principi*, the court went on to explain that veterans must "adequately establish that their alcohol or drug abuse disability is secondary to or is caused by their primary service-connected disorder," and must provide "clear medical evidence establishing that the alcohol or drug abuse disability is indeed caused by a veteran's primary service-connected disability," and that the "alcohol or drug abuse disability is not due to willful wrongdoing."

This means that if a veteran can prove that their substance abuse disorder and any associated health problem were caused by PTSD or some other event that occurred during military service, that veteran has a right to VA benefits. For example, if (1) you are service connected for PTSD as a result of your time in service, and (2) you develop an addiction to alcohol, which (3) eventually leads to cirrhosis of the liver, your cirrhosis can be service connected since it was a result of your alcohol addiction—as long as you can show that the alcoholism was caused by the PTSD you developed as a result of serving in the military. A veteran who is service connected for PTSD and develops hepatitis C from a contaminated needle after developing a heroin addiction would also be eligible to file a claim for benefits by secondary connection of the hepatitis C.

When a veteran's alcoholism or drug abuse disability is determined to be caused or aggravated by a service-connected disability, the VA may grant secondary service connection and pay disability compensation for the alcoholism or drug abuse disability. VA benefits also extend to survivors of military veterans who lose their lives to alcohol or drug abuse. If a veteran dies from cirrhosis, eligible family members may qualify for Dependency and Indemnity Compensation (DIC), Dependent's Educational Assistance (DEA), Civilian Health and Medical Program of the Department of Veterans Affairs (CHAMPVA) medical care, loan guaranty benefits, and accrued benefits.

One of the most difficult aspects of winning these claims is showing that the alcohol or drug use is not due to willful wrongdoing but caused by the service-connected disability. In general, organic diseases and disabilities that are a secondary result of the chronic use of alcohol "will not be considered of willful misconduct origin."[351] Veterans with mental health disorders, PTSD, TBI, and MST are all at high risk for developing a substance abuse disorder. In turn, researchers have consistently shown that substance abuse disorders can cause a wide array of disabilities. The National Comorbidity Survey has reported that 51.9 percent of lifetime PTSD patients have lifetime alcohol abuse/dependence diagnoses and 34.5 percent have lifetime drug abuse/dependence diagnoses.[352]

I recently had the privilege of working on an appeal for a veteran who developed a neurological seizure disorder secondary to alcoholism. The veteran's PTSD led to self-medication via heavy use of alcohol. This, in turn, led to a neurological impairment that resulted in the development of epileptic-type seizures. Alcohol consumption can also lead to liver disease and cardiomyopathy, not to mention an increased risk for accidents associated with driving under the influence, pulmonary aspiration, and hypothermia.

Examples of disabilities commonly associated with alcohol and/or prescription drug abuse:

- Anemia
- Arrhythmia
- Brain damage
- Breast cancer
- Cardiomyopathy
- Cirrhosis
- Colon cancer
- Dementia
- Diabetes
- Esophageal cancer

- Fatty liver disease
- Heart disease
- Hepatitis
- Hepatitis C infection
- Hepatocellular carcinoma
- HIV infection
- Hypertension
- Insomnia
- Myopathy
- Oral cancer
- Peripheral neuropathy
- Seizure disorders
- Sleep apnea
- Stroke
- Sudden cardiac death
- Wernicke-Korsakoff disease

Regardless of the 2001 Federal Circuit decision in *Allen v. Principi*, the VA still tries to deny claims for secondary service connection and compensation for alcohol and drug abuse disabilities. Some adjudicators still interpret OBRA 1990 as ruling out all alcohol and drug use claims. Some systematically ignore claims that a veteran's alcohol or drug abuse resulted from, or aggravated, their service-connected disability. The VA may say that a correlation between drug abuse and PTSD is not sufficient to support causation.

It is important to remember that most VA claims require an appeal. Veterans can argue that the VA's interpretation of OBRA 1990 was too restrictive, or they may wish to submit new evidence that their condition

BETRAYAL *of* VALOR

is related to their primary service-connected disability. The opinion of a highly-credible medical expert is vital for showing that a science-backed relationship does indeed exist between substance abuse disorders and the service-connected disability. Veterans filing for these benefits can also use statements from civilian family and friends about their level of alcohol or drug use prior to service compared to after service. Military records and witness statements from comrades during service can also help verify any increases in alcohol or drug use following a particular injury or traumatic event.

Benefits for Smoking-Related Disabilities

While nicotine addiction is recognized as a disease, the VA does not recognize nicotine addiction as a service-connected disability, largely due to the astronomical costs of paying for all of the veterans who need medical care for ailments associated with smoking. Beginning in 1998, Congress used the enactment of the Transportation Equity Act for the 21st Century (Public Law 105-178) to restrict the VA's ability to grant service-connected compensation to veterans who claimed their tobacco use, which began during service, caused their smoking-related disabilities. Fiscal year 1999 budgets estimated that the savings resulting from prohibiting the VA from awarding compensation to veterans for adverse effects of tobacco use could surpass $16.9 billion over five years.

However, as it is the case with VA benefits for alcohol and drug abuse, veterans may obtain VA benefits for smoking-related disabilities, as long as they can demonstrate an association with a service-connected disability. For example, the National Comorbidity Survey reports that over 45 percent of American PTSD patients are smokers, compared to just 23 percent

230

of the general adult population. Although half of all smokers eventually stop using tobacco, only 23 percent of smokers with PTSD quit smoking, placing people with PTSD third from the bottom in quit-rate rankings for 13 mental disorders. Peer-reviewed studies show a 31.7 percent 10-year cumulative incidence of smoking among PTSD patients, compared to 19.9 percent in non-PTSD sufferers with a history of trauma and 10.5 percent in those with no history of trauma.[353]

If a veteran can show that their service-connected PTSD has led to increased smoking, and the increased smoking led to COPD, the VA may find service connection for the COPD. When a veteran's smoking habit is determined to be caused by or aggravated by a service-connected disability, the VA may grant secondary service connection and pay disability compensation for the smoking-related disability. These VA benefits also extend to survivors of military veterans who lose their lives to a smoking-related illness. Eligible family members may be able to collect DIC, DEA, CHAMPVA medical care, loan guaranty benefits, and accrued benefits.

Conclusion

The current state of affairs regarding substance abuse among veterans is tragic. Our nation's veterans end up risking a life of opportunity and growth to serve America. They put themselves on the battlefield to help us. It is now our turn to help them. Powerful advocates are necessary to ensure that your VA claim regarding substance abuse disorder is granted. While VA service officers are excellent at what they do, winning benefits for disabilities caused by addiction requires a legal expert who has access to the credible medical experts and robust investigative resources required to prove secondary service connection. Many of our clients' claims were denied by the VA multiple times. Only when the veteran or a veteran's family consulted us for help were they able to win their addiction-related claims.

Rarely does a veteran chose to engage in drinking, smoking, or drug abuse without having served on a military base that encourages the use of all three or without having suffered some form of trauma that resulted in the development of a mental illness like PTSD, problems associated with TBI, MST, or other military-related experiences. Addiction in veterans is merely one part, one symptom, of the disability they are experiencing due to service. And we owe our beloved heroes the treatment and care they deserve.

As long as tobacco, alcohol, and prescription drugs are inexpensive and easily obtainable on military bases, service men and women will continue to fall into the trap of addiction and suffer from the life-threatening diseases that ensue. Do we not care enough for these heroes to keep them safe and healthy both during service and after? The military must start controlling the vast, discounted supply of tobacco, alcohol, and pills on military bases. It must give our soldiers powerful incentives to stay away from these harmful substances. Until then, it is vital that veterans learn how to service-connect their substance abuse disorders so that they can obtain the VA benefits they need to get their lives back on track.

Veteran Homelessness

After five years with the U.S. Air Force, John Adelman returned home expecting to reconnect with family, start a new job, get his own place, and begin a new life. Yet somehow things aren't going as planned. He arranged to stay with his parents for a few months while he looked for work, but after five years of being away, relationships had changed. He decided he'd be better off with friends. An old high school buddy let him crash on the couch. Soon after, he secured a great job as an aircraft mechanic. He figured he would have enough money to get an apartment of his own within a month or two.

John worked hard, but he seemed to be losing his temper a lot. He was always cool, calm, and collected before joining the Air Force and never had any anger issues during service, but now he had zero patience—and coworkers were complaining. Within five weeks, he'd been in one fight too many. He lost his job. Meanwhile, his buddy was getting married. The new wife was moving in, and John had to go. Not wanting to move back in with his parents, John decides to take his savings and relocate to Houston, Texas—1,000 miles away, but better job prospects.

Fast forward six months. John has lost another job due to his sudden anger problem, can't afford another week in the motel, and is having constant pain in his knee. An injury from service is acting up, and he can hardly walk without severe pain. He starts sleeping in his car, using the remainder of his savings to numb his pain with alcohol. He knows no one in Houston. He doesn't have enough money to get back home. This life is nothing like what John expected when he left service. He is losing hope.

Just over 9 percent of all homeless adults in the United States are military veterans. Data collected by the Departments of Veterans Affairs and Housing and Urban Development (HUD) reports that 37,878 veterans were living on the streets (38.5 percent) or in shelters (61.5 percent) in January 2018. It's a problem across the U.S.; the states with the highest populations are also home to the highest number of homeless veterans. Nearly one-third of homeless veterans reside in California (28.6 percent), followed by Florida (6.7 percent) and Texas (5.1 percent).[354]

While the majority of homeless veterans are male (91.5 percent),[355] female veterans are more than twice as likely as civilian females to experience homelessness.[356] And the number of elderly homeless veterans is rising. Veterans age 62 and over increased 54.3 percent from 2009 through 2016, and approximately 60 percent of homeless veterans are already over age 51.[357]

Our nation's veterans deserve better. They've spent years serving our country with the promise that they would be well cared for when they got back home. Most leave service with a number of emotional, mental, and physical issues. The majority aren't prepared for the challenges of shifting into civilian life. Without an understanding support network and adequate transitional assistance, many turn to crime or substance abuse, making it difficult to maintain employment or acquire housing—a tragic yet common downward spiral.

Unfortunately, many veterans aren't aware that treatment and housing assistance are available to them. Rarely do they seek help without it being offered. The VA and government programs fail to reach out, and the public remains uneducated about the many ways they can help. Veterans living in unstable housing, shelters, or on the streets simply go unnoticed.

Decades of research have shown that the transition from service to civilian life is an incredibly difficult one. Still, military transitional training is severely lacking. While civilians have years of support, guidance, and mentorship in seeking and obtaining higher education, securing financial aid, getting in on internships, accessing finances to start a small business, and caring for personal finances, veterans exit service with none of these tools. In addition to locating veterans in need and providing them with stable housing and amenities, we must work to eliminate the problem of veteran homelessness before it begins.

Risk Factors for Homelessness

Identifying what puts a veteran at high risk for experiencing homelessness can provide helpful insight into how best to attack the problem. One major risk factor for homelessness among all Americans is economic background. As the military recruits service men and women largely from working-class backgrounds, service members are already at higher risk for homelessness than the general public.

Aside from economic background, the risk of becoming homeless for civilians and veterans alike increases with unemployment, economic difficulties, trauma, mental health disorders, substance abuse disorders, imprisonment, relationship problems, and social isolation.[358] For veterans, in particular, several factors contribute to the risk of experiencing homelessness at some point, including:

- Unemployment
- Service-related disabilities
- Mental health disorders
- Substance abuse problems

- Criminal activity
- Poor transition preparation

Unemployment and Service-related Disabilities

Unemployment is an obvious risk factor for experiencing homelessness among both veterans and non-veterans. Data from the Bureau of Labor Statistics suggests that unemployment rates for U.S. veterans and non-veterans are currently similar. In 2018, the U.S. unemployment rate was 3.9 percent,[359] compared to the 3.5 percent unemployment rate for veterans.[360] Similar unemployment rates exist for both genders and the various age groups among veterans and non-veterans.

However, certain aspects differ for veterans. Unemployment rates are higher for those with disabilities, and the veteran population has a disproportionately higher rate of disabilities than the civilian population. Approximately 19.3 percent of U.S. civilians have a disability,[361] compared to 24.5 percent of all veterans with a service-connected disability (note that thousands of veterans suffer from service-related disabilities for which they haven't been able to establish service connection—so 24.5 percent is a low estimate of the number of veterans actually struggling with a disability as a result of service). Over half (55 percent) of homeless veterans have a disability. Of the homeless veterans who received VA health care between 2009 and 2016, 39 percent were diagnosed with an alcohol or drug abuse problem, 28 percent had a chronic medical condition, 28 percent had a diagnosis of depression, and 13 percent had a PTSD diagnosis.[362]

In 2018, the unemployment rate for veterans with a service-connected disability was 5.2 percent, compared to a 3.5 percent unemployment rate for those without a disability. How does age factor in? Forty-one percent of

Gulf War II (GWII) veterans have a service-connected disability. Of Gulf War II vets with disabilities, 73.5 percent are employed. Of those without disabilities, 85.8 percent are employed. For Gulf War I (GWI) veterans, 27 percent have a service-connected disability. Of Gulf War I vets with disabilities, 67.9 percent are employed. Of those without disabilities, 85.4 percent are employed. Twenty-one percent of WWII/Korean/Vietnam veterans have a service-connected disability. Of those WWII/Korean/Vietnam vets with disabilities, 12.6 percent are employed. Of those without disabilities, 20.7 percent are employed.[363]

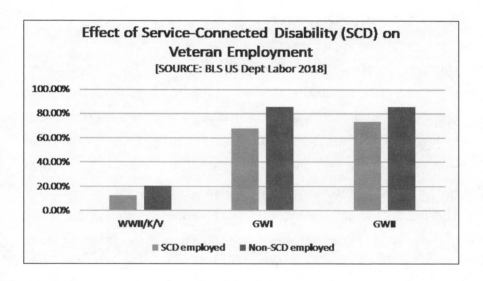

The higher the disability rating, the higher the unemployment rate. Unemployment rates for veterans with a 60 percent disability rating or higher were at 6.1 percent in 2018, while unemployment rates for those with disability ratings of less than 30 percent were 4.2 percent. Many of our nation's veterans suffer a lifetime of mental, physical, and emotional disabilities as a result of their service. And with disabilities putting such a dent in one's ability to be employed, unemployment is a very real possibility for veterans.

Of course, unemployment alone doesn't always lead to homelessness. After losing a job, many individuals are able to relocate to find new employment, join the family business, or pursue a new career through furthering their education. A strong support network of friends, family, and coworkers facilitates this transition. Rather than unemployment alone, homelessness is most often the result of a combination of factors, one of which is unemployment.

Mental Health Disorders

One of the most common traits of individuals experiencing homelessness is the presence of mental illness. While only 4.2 percent of U.S. adults have been diagnosed with severe mental illness, studies show that at least 45 percent of homeless individuals in the U.S. suffer from mental illness, with 25 percent having a severe mental illness. The most common types of mental disorders seen among people experiencing homelessness are bipolar disorder, depression, schizophrenia, and generalized anxiety disorder.[364]

Mental illness is common among veterans, a result of one-time or repeated exposure to military combat, abuse, sexual assault, life-threatening circumstances, or the death of comrades during service. Veterans with bipolar disorder experience exaggerated highs and lows— long periods of 'lows' characterized by inaction, hopelessness, and despair, followed by manic episodes of hyperactivity, insomnia, and aggressiveness. Depression can cause constant fatigue and frequently leads to substance abuse disorder. The most debilitating diagnosis, schizophrenia, can cause a complete disconnect from reality, including delusions, hallucinations, and extreme social isolation. Anxiety disorder can cause constant muscle tremors, heart palpitations, jumpiness, anger, and incessant paranoia.

Research shows that approximately 25 percent of all active-duty soldiers exhibit symptoms of a mental health condition, including post-traumatic stress disorder, mental complications due to traumatic brain injury, and mental side effects of chronic pain. The rate of depression in military veterans is five times higher than that in civilians, and military veterans are 15 times more likely to develop post-traumatic stress disorder than civilians.[365] Because those struggling with mental illness often exhibit behavioral and/or cognitive difficulties, maintaining employment, housing, and functional relationships becomes problematic. In many cases, the symptoms of these mental illnesses are further amplified by the trauma and shock of the homelessness experience itself.

Military sexual trauma has been associated with higher rates of homelessness in veterans. Studies suggest that nearly one in 10 veterans who report military sexual trauma experience homelessness within their first five years out of service (more than double the rate of homelessness in veterans who have never reported military sexual trauma). The risk of homelessness is shown to be slightly higher for men who suffer military sexual trauma (11.8 percent) than for women (8.9 percent).[366,367]

In both veteran and civilian women, intimate partner violence is also associated with the risk of homelessness. One analysis of VA medical records showed that women veterans who had experienced intimate partner violence within the past 12 months were three times more likely to be homeless or living in unstable housing than women veterans who hadn't screened positive for intimate partner violence.[368] Some reports suggest veteran women are at a higher risk for intimate partner violence than civilian women.[369]

Substance Abuse Disorders

When an individual remains under the influence of alcohol, opiates, or other drugs due to an addiction, holding a job, maintaining relationships, and even taking care of simple daily tasks can become impossible. Alcohol and drug abuse are unfortunately common among survivors of trauma and those who suffer from mental illness. Over 20 percent of veterans with PTSD have a substance abuse problem, and nearly 33 percent of veterans who seek treatment for substance abuse also have PTSD.

Opiate abuse is especially common among veterans, whether they are obtaining the drug from the streets, being prescribed opioid painkillers for service-related injuries, or receiving them to manage chronic pain. Studies report that the rate of homelessness among veterans seeking VA treatment for opioid addiction (10.2 percent) is over 10 times higher than that of veterans receiving other VA care. Male veterans seeking VA treatment for opiate abuse are most likely to be currently homeless, but female veterans seeking treatment are at a higher risk of eventual homelessness than men (11.8 percent and 4.9 percent, respectively).[370]

Criminal Activity

Tragically, veterans suffering from post-traumatic stress disorder, behavioral issues associated with traumatic brain injury, substance abuse disorders, and other difficulties commonly find themselves wrapped up in the criminal justice system. Involvement in criminal activity is a definite risk factor for homelessness, and vice versa. In 2016, U.S. prisons and jails housed nearly 2.2 million adults.[371] According to the Bureau of Justice Statistics, military veterans account for 8 percent of these 2.2 million adults.[372] Since leaving service, approximately 9 percent of Gulf War veterans have been arrested.[373]

In 2015, 41 percent of veterans receiving aid from the Veterans Justice Outreach program (which provides legal aid for veterans) reported they were having difficulties with housing. Twenty-two percent said they were homeless, 13 percent said they were in an unstable housing situation, and 6 percent reported they were at imminent risk of losing their home.[374] Similarly, nearly half of all veterans participating in VA homeless assistance programs are involved in the criminal justice system. [375]

Data from the U.S. Department of Justice shows that the majority of veterans in prison in 2015 were there for committing violent crimes (64 percent). Drug crimes made up around 14 percent of prison veteran arrests, followed by property crimes (12 percent). For veterans in jail in 2015, violent crimes were the main cause of arrest (28 percent), followed by property crimes (21 percent) and drug crimes (18 percent). Data showed that more veterans than non-veterans were sentenced for violent crimes (64 percent versus 48 percent respectively).[376]

Once a person is released from jail or prison, it can be very difficult to stay out of the system. Finding a job is difficult upon release, housing can become a problem, and association with others involved in criminal activity is common—often leading to probation violations or additional arrests. Studies show that nearly 50 percent of federal offenders are rearrested for new crimes or probation violations, half of those being rearrested within two years of release from incarceration.[377]

Estimates suggest that 43 percent of veterans and 55 percent of civilians have had at least four prior arrests.[378] Among veterans, contributing factors to arrest are often substance abuse disorders, behavioral difficulties associated with PTSD, and interpersonal relationship difficulties. Studies also show that difficulties adjusting to civilian life after military service, economic challenges, unemployment, and homelessness contribute to a veteran's risk of arrest for criminal activity.[379]

Interestingly, veterans with other-than-honorable military discharges are less likely to be incarcerated. The Bureau of Justice Statistics reports that 77 percent of incarcerated veterans received honorable discharges. In addition, veterans involved in combat during service were less likely to be incarcerated than those who hadn't experienced combat. Just 25 percent of veterans in prison and 31 percent in jail said they had been in combat. [380]

Poor Transition Preparation

Approximately 1,300 military service members and their immediate families transition into civilian life each day, and the majority find it challenging to adjust to the unstructured civilian world after military life.[381] Studies have shown that difficulty adjusting to civilian life can lead to mental health disorders, issues with substance abuse, unemployment, and homelessness. Yet, the military continues to offer inadequate transitional training and resources to sufficiently help our military men and women adapt to this necessary change.

Recent research from the University of Southern California showed that over 70 percent of post-9/11 veterans had no employment lined up upon discharge from service. More than 35 percent had no permanent housing plans.[382] Upon discharge from service, veterans have to secure housing, employment, transportation, health care coverage, and all the other life necessities that civilians have spent their adult years learning to acquire and maintain. The stress of this transition is a major contributor to the depression, substance abuse problems, relationship difficulties, and social isolation experienced by veterans.

Even harder than tackling daily life upon leaving military service can be trying to interact and connect with others. More often than not, a veteran will be the only one in the room who has served in the military. While most friendships, work relationships, and family discussions have been about the military for a veteran's entire time in service, now, out of the military, people simply can't relate.

Lack of daily routine can also be a shock for many new veterans. While an active-duty day is mapped out from start to finish, no one is laying out the routine for veterans in civilian life. If a veteran doesn't have a plan upon exit from the military, it can be rough to keep moving. Service members with plans for education or a family to attend to often have an easier time transitioning after discharge.

Veterans need transitional training long before leaving service, not only in general life skills, but training in soft skills—social skills, flexible attitudes, emotional navigation, and personal goal setting tools. They must be equipped to adapt to the upcoming change, emotionally and psychologically. Currently, military members who have been on active duty for at least 180 days must participate in the Department of Defense's Transition Assistance Program (TAP) to prepare for exit from service. The TAP program requires service members to identify their career planning needs, what benefits they are eligible for, how to obtain those benefits, how to prepare a resume, and how to interview for a job. Service members can take the entire program, lasting one to five days, either online or in a classroom.

One to five days is hardly enough to ensure an immersive and interactive learning environment where students will have the time to question the material and absorb the information necessary to make a successful transition. The TAP also fails to include a number of important skills in its curriculum, like how to handle personal finances, how to budget a household, how to avoid credit card debt. Some TAP modules are optional. One two-day TAP module, "Accessing Higher Education," aims to inform service members on how to pursue a college degree. Reports suggest that only around 40 percent of veterans elect to participate in this module.[383]

Misperceptions About Veterans

Society's perceptions and expectations regarding veterans can also impact unemployment rates, mental well-being, and risk of experiencing homelessness. A 2018 survey of 4,945 Americans showed that 65 percent of non-veterans, veterans, educators, and employers feel veterans have poor "well-being,"—defined as having financial stability, mental and physical health, meaningful relationships, and a desirable job or career.[384]

Of employers participating in the survey, 60 percent said they feel veterans need further education or training before they could qualify for a job in the public or private sector. Nearly half (46 percent) said they don't think veterans have vocational or college degrees, and 53 percent felt that veterans don't typically have successful careers after the military. In addition, 75 percent of civilians, 80 percent of employers, and 81 percent of veterans felt that the average civilian has difficulty relating to and understanding veterans. Over 65 percent said they feel the media portrays veterans as different from the average civilian, and 71 percent of veterans said they have an easier time relating with the military community.

Regarding perceptions of veterans' mental health, the survey reported that "fewer than 25 percent of non-veterans (18 percent) and employers

(23 percent) believe that veterans have good or excellent access to mental health support and more than 70 percent believe that their communities could do more to support veterans with mental health challenges."

The study concluded that "misperceptions about veterans continue to exist and may impede veterans' transitions back into the civilian world." All of these preconceived notions about the veteran community can impact many aspects of that transition, including employment, social integration, and overall well-being.

Historical Progress

Historically, veterans themselves are largely responsible for achieving the government aid for the homeless that exists today. Back in the mid-1500s, returning English soldiers made up a majority of the homeless population in Britain. In the 1640s, after years of suffering, these "vagabonds" banded together and helped topple the monarchy. Similar activities helped shape aid for the homeless in the U.S. In 1783, after the end of the American Revolutionary War, unemployed soldiers living in poverty assembled in Philadelphia to protest.[385]

After World War I, veterans again endured poverty and unstable housing. In 1932, as part of the "Bonus Army," thousands of veterans assembled in Washington to protest with their families. The impoverished veterans were demanding cash payment of bonus certificates they had received in lieu of a salary. Toward the end of World War II, Congress passed the G.I. Bill, which became the United States' first successful attempt at caring for veterans after service. World War II veterans received two years of unemployment pay, giving them time to adjust, receive an education, find employment, and get on their feet.

However, the success of the G.I. Bill wasn't long-lived. Many Vietnam veterans ended up homeless within 10 years of leaving service. By 1987, there were as many as 300,000 homeless veterans.[386] Twenty-two years later, President Barack Obama and U.S. Secretary Eric Shinseki announced a five-year plan to end veteran homelessness by offering accessible mental health care and affordable housing for veterans with the participation of the Department of Housing and Urban Development.

In 2009, the VA had set up call centers to help veterans access help with housing. That same year, the numbers had dropped to 154,000, nearly half of those being Vietnam veterans.[387] However, accessibility to government aid for homeless veterans began falling in 2014, when reports showed that

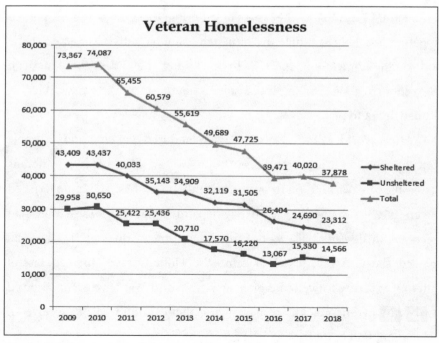

Source: U.S. Department of Housing and Urban Development, 2018

nearly half (47 percent) of the veterans who contacted call centers received no support services.[388]

Several programs working together were able to help bring homeless veteran levels down to less than 40,000 by 2018, including the American Legion, HUD, the Supportive Services for Veteran Families (SSVF) program, the National Coalition for Homeless Veterans, and Veterans of America. One of the most successful programs has been the HUD-VA Supportive Housing Program (HUD-VASH), which offers Section 8 subsidized housing vouchers to eligible veterans. HUD reports that, by 2018, the program had helped to completely eliminate veteran homelessness in Connecticut, Delaware, and Virginia. Between 2010 and 2018, veteran homelessness fell 49 percent (from 74,087 cases to 37,878 cases). The rate of decline has slowed since 2015, going from finding stable homes for 1,600 veterans per year to an average of 800 per year.[389]

Needed Changes

Strong, effective military transitional training and education are key in helping veterans obtain and maintain stable households and employment upon release from service. Throughout their military careers, service members should also be made aware of the risk factors and difficulties of transition, how to prepare for those challenges, and how to pursue goals and ambitions upon separation from active duty.

Programs designed around higher education, like DoD TAP's Accessing Higher Education module, should involve training designed by educators to ensure service members understand admission requirements and how to secure financial aid. Early access to plans for higher education well in advance of leaving service could give interested service members the necessary tools to be ready to enter school upon their leave date.

Many veterans express interest in starting their own business. Yet, unlike many civilian entrepreneurs, they lack the networking time, contacts, mentorship, and access to financial capital upon leaving service. A survey revealed that among post-9/11 veterans, 62 percent had either started or considered starting their own business after the military. Many were inspired by other veterans who started their own businesses or by financial assistance available to veteran entrepreneurs. However, nearly 50 percent of veterans who considered starting their own business reported a lack of access to necessary capital. [390]

Surveys also suggest that 82 percent of veterans would be interested in participating in veteran-focused apprenticeships and internship programs. These veterans felt such programs would help them acquire new skills and certifications and would better prepare them for job opportunities outside of the military. Three out of four employers surveyed felt veteran-focused apprenticeships and internship programs would benefit their businesses. Both veterans and employers stated they were interested in apprentice/internship programs focused on skilled trades and Information technology.[391] Employers felt such programs would help attract and retain veteran employees and ensure veterans develop the skills (both technical and soft skills) necessary to succeed in their companies.

In addition, government officials and the public must work to highlight the skills, experience, and discipline veterans can bring to the workplace and community. We must address the issues that tend to separate military families and the civilian community so that both benefit from the presence of the other. Both civilians (79 percent) and employers (87 percent) have expressed an interest in developing relationships with veterans through community projects. And 90 percent of veterans feel such projects would help them integrate into their communities.[392]

As we work to bring down the number of veterans living on the streets and in unstable housing, we must also work to lower the risk factors for homelessness among veterans, improve employment opportunities, and enhance their overall well-being. Improved data collection is essential. Most data on veteran homelessness and mental health is limited to those veterans in veteran-specific housing assistance programs and VA health care. Regular data collection that incorporates veteran status outside of the VA system is vital to gaining an accurate picture of the current state of veteran well-being. With this data, we can work to establish programs that target all veterans in need and prevent housing challenges for service members transitioning into civilian life.

Suicide Among U.S. Veterans

Throughout 2018, at least 19 veterans committed suicide[393] at a VA hospital—a clear plea for much-needed improvements to the program's mental health treatment facilities. Our heroic veterans and their families are literally begging the VA for help. But despite repeated promises of an overhaul, we aren't seeing much progress.

Long appointment wait times and inadequate staffing are atrocious and inexcusable in a hospital system that knows its patient population exhibits a risk of suicide 1.5 times greater than that of the civilian population.[394] On average, over twenty veterans commit suicide every day.[395] Veterans are reaching out for help. They are calling crisis hotlines, seeking treatment, and telling loved ones about their issues. And VA hospitals are turning them away.

In the Fall of 2015, the VA canceled yet another appointment for 51-year-old Gulf War vet Charles Ingram. They never followed up to reschedule, so Ingram went in to make an appointment himself. They penciled him in for three months later. Just before his March 2016 appointment, Ingram set himself on fire in front of the New Jersey VA clinic. An investigation into Ingram's death discovered the clinic's staff repeatedly failed to follow up on cancellations and no-shows, inaction the inspector general says led to "a lack of ordered therapy and necessary medications. . ."[396]

Five months later, 76-year-old Navy veteran and former police officer Peter A. Kaisen shot himself in the parking lot of Long Island's Northport Veterans Affairs Medical Center after the Center denied emergency treatment for his mental health condition.[397] In November 2016, 32-year-old Afghanistan veteran David Toombs hanged himself at Alvin C. York VA Medical Center in Murfreesboro, Tennessee, after being dismissed from a 90-day inpatient PTSD and substance abuse treatment program. Medical records show he was kicked out for being late to pick up his prescriptions and not following instructions.[398] "Earlier today, I was discharged for trivial reasons," Toombs says in a video on his Facebook page. "I came for help, and they threw me out like a stray dog in the rain."[399]

In February 2018, 33-year-old Marine and Iraq veteran Justin Miller shot himself in the parking lot of the Minneapolis Department of Veterans Affairs hospital after staff failed to schedule a follow-up appointment and properly assess his access to firearms.[400] Miller had called the Veterans Crisis line about his suicidal thoughts. The crisis hotline responder said he needed to have someone hold onto his guns and get to the VA hospital. But a nurse discharged him after just four hours, saying Miller was an intermediate/moderate suicide risk and "does not currently meet dangerousness criteria for a 72-hour hold."[401]

In March 2018, 62-year-old Marine Corps Vietnam veteran Philip Crews committed suicide in the waiting room of the John Cochran VA Medical Center in St. Louis. Reports suggest he was having financial difficulties after becoming addicted to opioid painkillers (prescribed for his severe stomach pains).[402] In December 2018, 55-year-old retired Marine Col. Jim Turner shot himself in the parking lot of the Florida Bay Pines Department of Veterans Affairs in St. Petersburg. He was found sitting on his VA and military records. His ex-wife and brother believe Turner ended his life after repeatedly having to wait for appointments and being refused treatment. "I bet if you look at the 22 suicides a day, you will see VA screwed up in 90 percent," a note found near his body said. "I did 20+ years, had PTSD, and still had to pay over $1,000 a month health care."[403]

The current state of the VA mental health system is appalling. The VA's new executive director for suicide prevention, Keita Franklin, recently told the *Washington Post* that the agency "now trains parking lot attendants and patrols on suicide intervention." Is this really the type of improvement our nation's veterans are asking for? Between 2001 and 2014, suicide rates among veterans rose by 32 percent.[404] Patrolling the VA parking lot isn't the answer. So, what is the solution? A first step to answering this question is to gain a better understanding of veteran suicide rates and what exactly leads veterans to take their own lives.

Suicide in Veterans vs. Civilians

Suicide is the tenth leading cause of death among U.S. civilians. It is the second leading cause of death among U.S. veterans.[405] Though veterans make up only 8.3 percent of the adult U.S. population, they account for 14.3 percent of all U.S. adult suicide deaths. Veteran suicide rates stood at 30.1 per 100,000 population in 2017 (45 per 100,000 population in veterans ages 18-34).[406] Compare this to the 16.8 per 100,000 population U.S. deaths from prescription or illicit opioid overdose,[407] and it's easy to see the enormity of the crisis.

On average, one Iraq or Afghanistan soldier died in combat every 36 hours. Meanwhile, there was one veteran suicide every 80 minutes. As New York Times columnist Nicholas Kristof put it, "More than 6,500 veteran suicides are logged every year—more than the total number of soldiers killed in Afghanistan and Iraq combined. . ."[408] After adjusting for age and gender, the veteran suicide rate is 1.5 times greater than that of civilian adults. In 2016, age- and gender-adjusted suicide rates were 26.1 per 100,000 for veterans and 17.4 per 100,000 for civilian adults.[409]

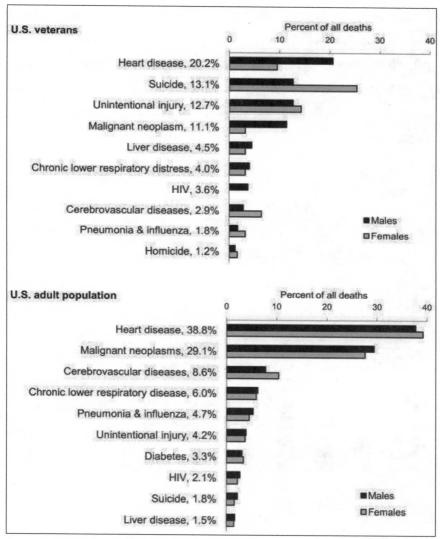

SOURCE: *Weiner J, Richmond TS, et al. (2011) BMC Public Health.*

A male veteran's risk of suicide is 19 percent higher than that of a male adult civilian, while female suicide rates are 1.8 times higher than female civilian suicide rates after adjusting for age.[410] Suicide rates among younger veterans are increasing markedly in recent years. Suicide rates for veterans ages 18-34 increased from 40.4 deaths per 100,000 in 2015 to 45 deaths per 100,000 in 2016. Overall, suicide rates are highest among male veterans ages 18-34 and lowest among male veterans ages 55-74, though the Department of Veterans Affairs reports veterans age 55 and up accounted for 58.1 percent of suicide deaths in 2016.[411]

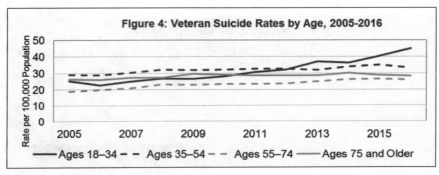

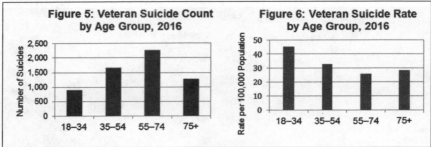

SOURCE: VA Natl. Suicide Data Report (2018)

Interestingly, VA data for 2016 shows that veterans who have recently used Veterans Health Administration (VHA) services (had a VHA encounter in the year of death or previous year) have higher suicide rates than veterans who have not recently used VHA services, veterans overall, and civilians.[412] The Department of Veterans Affairs explains this by stating,

"Veterans who use VHA have physical and mental health care needs and are actively seeking care because those conditions are causing depression in their lives. Many of these conditions—such as mental health challenges, substance use disorders, chronic medical conditions, and chronic pain—are associated with an increased risk for suicide."[413]

That may be true, but U.S. soldiers have been suffering from mental health challenges, substance use disorders, chronic medical conditions, and chronic pain since the 1600s. So, the VA's statement doesn't explain the discrepancy.

Let's take a look at another statistic. According to the VA, prior to 2016, the veterans in VHA care had a 13.7 percent increase in suicide rate compared to 26 percent among veterans who weren't in VHA care.[414] In other words, veterans receiving VA care used to be less at risk for suicide. The key words here are "used to be." Things have gotten so bad at the VA since 2016 that veterans who are seeking care are more likely to commit suicide than those who stay away from VA hospitals. And that is inexcusable.

Why Higher Suicide Rates Among Veterans?

The Department of Veterans Affairs and VHA's tragic incompetence in developing and implementing effective suicide prevention programs is obviously problematic. But let's take a step back and discuss why veteran suicide rates are so much greater than that of civilians in the first place. There are several possible explanations.

Some of the most common causes of suicide among U.S. civilians[415] are:

- **Mental illness:** depression, anxiety, insomnia, post-traumatic stress disorder (PTSD), obsessive-compulsive disorder (OCD), bipolar disorder, schizophrenia
- **Exposure to trauma:** physical abuse, mental abuse, sexual abuse, life-threatening experience, involvement in combat, exposure to death of a loved one, severe injury
- **Substance abuse:** alcohol dependence, illicit or prescription drug dependence, withdrawal symptoms
- **Financial burdens:** Unemployment, debt, gambling addiction, bankruptcy
- **Social isolation:** loneliness, disconnect, introversion, lack of purpose, retirement
- **Family history:** genetic history of mental illness, genetic history of suicide
- **Terminal illness:** feelings of hopelessness, fear of pain or death
- **Chronic pain:** impaired function, pain-associated depression, prescription drug dependence

Just one of these factors alone can contribute to a higher risk of suicide. Veterans often leave service with a dangerous combination of them. Research suggests that mental illness is a factor in at least 90 percent of U.S. suicides.[416] According to data from the Centers for Disease Control and Prevention, an estimated 25 percent of U.S. adults report having a mental illness, or one in four. It is estimated that around 8.1 percent of men and 20.4 percent of women who experience trauma will develop PTSD,[417] while 16.1 percent of Americans are diagnosed with clinical depression in their lifetime, and 12.3 percent with generalized anxiety disorder (GAD).[418]

Among active duty service members, the U.S. Department of Defense

Health Related Behaviors Survey shows, 17.9 percent of active service members screen positive for at least one of these three disorders (PTSD, clinical depression, or GAD), with 9.7 percent screening positive for at least two of them.[419] The question then becomes, is mental illness a result of military service? Or are individuals at risk for developing mental illness more likely to join the military? This is difficult to answer, but there are several variables to consider.

An individual's socioeconomic upbringing can contribute to their risk for developing mental illness. Several studies suggest that mental illness is higher among individuals coming from a lower socioeconomic status.[420] The majority of military participants appear to come from lower or middle-class families, and military personnel from high-net-worth families is rare.[421]

A 2008 report from Syracuse University's Department of Sociology found that those who served in the military came from slightly lower-income families than those who never served, with the highest income quartile significantly less likely to have served than the lowest income quartile, and the second and third income quartiles not significantly different from the lowest in their likelihood to serve.[422] The majority of individuals who served in the military attended public high schools (96.6 percent), with 3.4 percent attending private high schools.[423] Among civilians, 10 percent of U.S. students attend private school.[424]

While these data provide only indirect evidence that military personnel are at a slightly higher risk for developing mental illness than the general community, that is possibly the case. The VA must take these factors into consideration, address them head-on, and keep on top of the mental health issue throughout—and after—each service member's time with the military.

So, what happens to a population of individuals that is thrust into a world of strict regimen, war, and death? As human beings, none of us come out of exposure to death without some change in our mental makeup. Whether a soldier must kill an enemy, witnesses an enemy getting killed, witnesses a comrade dying, or loses a friend without witnessing the actual death—the soldier is impacted. There aren't many service members, whether in combat or working at base, who don't experience death in one form or another.

When a civilian loses a loved one, they may have friends and family who can relate. Many times, friends, family, or coworkers will suggest they seek grief counseling. It's something we in the real world feel free to console each other about. We know death is incredibly difficult to deal with, and we want to help each other get through it.

Unfortunately, this is not the case for service men and women. In fact, they are taught quite the opposite—that death is a part of war. Suck it up and deal with it. Sure, the guys at base might give you a pat on the back and an "I'm sorry" when you lose your best friend, but that's about the extent of it. Grieving over death can be considered a weakness in a soldier. Superiors encourage soldiers to be tough and carry on. Pretend as though it never happened. And in ignoring the grieving process, the seed of mental illness is often planted.

Similarly, when a civilian experiences a life-threatening event or is exposed to sexual, physical, or mental abuse, family, friends, and physicians often suggest they seek counseling. Without adequate therapy, rape victims, school shooting victims, or airplane crash survivors can develop post-traumatic stress disorder (PTSD) and suffer a lifetime of nightmares, depression, and survivor's guilt. Even with therapy, many people exposed to life-threatening events may never fully recover—but they can acquire tools to help them function in society.

Yet when trauma and abuse occur in the military, the problem is often swept under the rug. Again, being affected by trauma or abuse is still considered a sign of weakness. Rape and other forms of abuse typically go unreported for fear of retaliation by comrades and superiors. Surviving a hail of bullets and bombs makes you a hero in the military, while in civilian life, you would be considered a victim or survivor in need of support, encouragement, and mental health rehabilitation.

The death, trauma, and abuse most civilians experience only a handful of times in their lives; service members experience numerous times within just a few months or years. Soldiers often turn to drugs or alcohol to numb this heavy dose of mental and physical pain. Whether a veteran has a genetic or environmental predisposition to addiction or not, the chances of turning to self-medication increase with service.

In addition, prescription drug addiction is becoming a national crisis, as doctors prescribe highly-addictive opioids to patients after injuries or routine surgeries. Withdrawal symptoms are unbearable, and patients will "doctor shop" to obtain more and more pills to simply exist comfortably, rather than suffering excruciating withdrawals. After arriving home with chronic pain issues, veterans who are prescribed opiates may quickly fall into this trap.

Besides the health dangers of drug and alcohol abuse, addiction limits a veteran's ability to function in daily life. Addicts may have difficulty holding a job. They may struggle with friendships and long-term relationships. We often see a snowball effect of addiction leading to unemployment, financial instability, isolation, introversion, loneliness, enhanced substance abuse, even eventual homelessness. The extreme difficulty of attempting to live with these issues leads many to suicide. Without the right treatment and a solid support group, many veterans simply lose hope.

Even for those veterans who return home sober and have high hopes for a healthy and successful life after service, the immediate and jarring change in lifestyle that occurs upon returning home can prove incredibly difficult. Many service members thrive in the regimented, structured military world. They enjoy the early mornings, physical challenges, strong camaraderie, and systematic routine that the U.S. military provides. Whether a soldier serves in the military for a year or 20 years, suddenly going from military life to the completely unstructured civilian world can be overwhelming. Many hard-working, successful soldiers who've returned home quickly find themselves turning to alcohol or drugs to combat the loneliness, lack of routine, and lacking a sense of purpose.

OTH Discharges Not Informed of Benefits

One of the biggest problems with veteran suicide in the recent past has been the lack of access to VA benefits for veterans who received other than honorable (OTH) discharges. Though data shows that service members with OTH discharges are at the highest risk of suicide, the VA did not offer benefits for the more than 500,000 former service members with these discharges until recently.

One problem is that many veterans receive other than honorable discharges for misconduct when the misconduct itself is the result of an underlying mental illness. Many veterans begin to exhibit behavioral problems associated with post-traumatic stress disorder, traumatic brain injury, and other medical conditions after being exposed to mental or physical trauma during service. Military commanders anxious to rid their ranks of problematic personnel incorrectly view the behavior in isolation, failing to acknowledge that it is merely symptomatic of an underlying pathology.

A recent Government Accountability Office analysis of Department of Defense data showed that 57,141 of the 91,764 service members (62 percent) separated for misconduct between 2011 and 2015 had been diagnosed (within their last two years in service) with PTSD, TBI, or other conditions associated with misconduct. Specifically, 16 percent had been diagnosed with PTSD or TBI. Other conditions like adjustment and alcohol-related disorders were more common. Of the 57,141 servicemembers, 13,283 (23 percent) received an other than honorable discharge.[425]

While the acting Assistant Secretary of Defense for Health Affairs has questioned the accuracy of the reported data on PTSD and TBI case numbers, I can say that, as a VA appeals lawyer, the number of cases involving other than honorable discharges for misconduct stemming from underlying PTSD or TBI is escalating. Our office represents scores of veterans with other than honorable discharges who have been denied VA benefits. In almost all of these cases, the underlying "misconduct" is simply a manifestation of underlying brain pathology or psychiatric illness that goes unrecognized by untrained observers.

When an other than honorable discharge cuts off a veteran's eligibility for VA health benefits, that veteran may never receive the health care they need. This is particularly problematic because veterans suffering from PTSD or TBI can experience severe impairments that make it difficult or impossible to hold full-time employment and handle interpersonal relationships, commonly leading to depression, drug and alcohol abuse, and suicidal thoughts.

The government accountability office agrees that the Department of Defense needs to consider these issues when responding to misconduct charges and has made several recommendations for executive action,[426] including:

- Air Force and Navy need to address inconsistencies with DoD policies related to screening service members for PTSD and TBI, and with DoD policies related to reviewing the results prior to separation for misconduct
- Air Force and Navy need to address inconsistencies with DoD policies related to training service members, including officers, on how to identify mild TBI symptoms in the deployed setting
- Military services should routinely monitor adherence to policies related to screening service members for PTSD and TBI prior to separation for misconduct
- Military services should routinely monitor adherence to policies related to training service members on how to identify mild TBI symptoms in the deployed setting
- Military services should routinely monitor adherence to policies related to counseling about VA benefits and services during the process of separating certain servicemembers for misconduct

I also feel it's important for military commanders and the Department of Defense to adjust their protocols and regulations as emerging neuroscience requires. Scientists now recognize that subtle behavior and personality changes can occur as a result of TBI, often leading to misconduct and making a service member unfit for continued service.[427] Scientists are also learning more about how PTSD impairs judgment, a problem that can also lead to incompatibility with service. An awareness of neuroscience and how it affects behavior, judgment, and ability to function in a military environment would be helpful in providing proper care and exerting appropriate compassion for these individuals.

On March 7, 2017, Veterans Affairs Secretary David Shulkin stated that his new initiative, "Getting To Zero," was his top clinical priority. The program marked the first time a VA Secretary had set forth an initiative to expand benefits to former OTH service members who may be at risk for suicide. Getting To Zero aimed to bring veteran suicide rates to zero.

"We know the rate of death by suicide among veterans who do not use VA care is increasing at a greater rate than veterans who use VA care," Shulkin said. "This is a national emergency that requires bold action. We must do all that we can to help former service members who may be at risk. When we say even one veteran suicide is one too many, we mean it."[428] Shulkin's initiative included several plans to help bring down veteran suicide rates, including:

- Proving mental health care for 90 days post-discharge regardless of discharge status
- Expanding Vet Center or VA Emergency care to OTH service members
- Hiring 1,000 additional mental health providers
- Increasing calling centers and staff in rural areas
- Analyzing veterans' health records to identify and contact those at highest risk

Shulkin also hoped to implement programs to help prevent veteran homelessness, another cause of veteran suicide. But the word isn't getting out. Sixteen months after "Getting to Zero" launched, reports showed that only 115 veterans of the 500,000 OTH vets had used the program.[429] Veterans aren't being informed about it, and if they don't know they are eligible for mental health care, the program is a failure.

Recent Developments in Veteran Suicide Prevention

On January 9, 2018, President Trump signed an Executive Order titled, "Supporting Our Veterans During Their Transition from Uniformed Service to Civilian Life." This Executive Order directs the Departments of Defense, Veterans Affairs, and Homeland Security to develop a plan to ensure all new veterans receive mental health care for at least one year following their separation from service—even those ineligible for care.[430] The three departments will work together and develop a Joint Action Plan to ensure "seamless access to mental health treatment and suicide prevention resources for transitioning uniformed service members" for one year following their separation from service.[431]

In his fiscal year 2018 budget, President Trump proposed $186.5 billion for the Department of Veterans Affairs. While the VA's budget proposal set aside $8.4 billion for veterans' mental health care, up 6 percent from 2017,[432] it simply wasn't enough to provide the volume of care that could result from expanding benefits to OTH veterans.

The VA also received $6.2 million to spend on a national suicide prevention outreach campaign. The $6.2 million was meant to go towards saturating the media with information on the VA's suicide crisis hotline via paid advertisements, public service announcements, and social media exposure. Unfortunately, those government dollars just sat on the shelf. Nearly one year later, the VA had spent less than 1 percent of its suicide prevention budget—a total of $57,000[433]—completely ignoring veterans in dire need of help.

The 2019 budget requests $8.6 billion for veterans' mental health services, an increase of 5.8 percent above the 2018 current estimate and directs $190 million for suicide prevention outreach.[434] But whether this money will be spent as intended—on increased staff numbers, outpatient clinics, and suicide prevention campaigns—is yet to be seen.

Conclusion

It is estimated that one U.S. veteran commits suicide every 65 minutes. Is this the best the United States of America has to offer? We have the largest and most technologically advanced military in the world, yet our veterans come home only to suffer from severe mental disabilities that continue to take lives long after the war is over—and we do very little about it.

As a veterans disability benefits attorney, I have received numerous devastating phone calls from family members of veterans who have committed suicide. I recently received a letter from a veteran stating: "I'm not a whiner. I'm begging you for help and benefits. I'm on suicide watch and have nowhere to turn next to homelessness." The veteran went on to explain the difficulties he has experienced in receiving proper care at the VA. Shortly after receiving this letter. I got a telephone call from his ex-wife. They had been divorced for years, but she was the only family he had. She informed me he had committed suicide. This should never happen. My staff are not therapists. Lawyers shouldn't be filling in for missing health care treatments. Yet desperate, suicidal veterans often turn to attorneys as a last resort after years of being denied critical treatment.

We were deeply saddened to hear this news and further frustrated by the unacceptable VA claims process backlog, treatment wait times, and claims denials for deserving veterans in need. Continued delays and repeated denials of care only fuel the sense of despair and hopelessness that veterans with PTSD and other mental disabilities endure. I am not surprised that veterans keep citing the mantra, "Deny Until You Die," as the VA's governing motto.

The VA's failure to promptly grant veterans' claims and provide immediate, quality care only amplifies the mental trauma these veterans experience. The Department of Veterans Affairs must prioritize claims for mental disabilities. We must provide a surplus of staff, not skimp on funds and ignore veterans' needs. Suicide prevention is the key. We must act early, helping new veterans address their issues before things get out of hand.

We must also provide awareness of the mental health care available to veterans who may have received an other than honorable discharge. I have represented scores of veterans who have received a dishonorable discharge for alleged misconduct that was, in hindsight, just the early manifestations of PTSD or some other mental illness. We must spend whatever it takes to inform our veterans that they indeed do qualify for mental health benefits. The longer we wait, the more lives we lose.

We must provide therapeutic care for veterans who have been suffering from PTSD, traumatic brain injury, and other mental illnesses for years. Veteran suicide is a national crisis. Short staffing and poor resources are inexcusable. We can no longer afford to ignore these brave men and women who fought for our freedom and our rights. Their rights matter too. We can no longer afford one more veteran suicide that could have been prevented by proper access to mental health care.

THE OBESITY EPIDEMIC: AN EMERGING NATIONAL CRISIS

Obesity is an emerging crisis looming over the veteran community, potential military recruits, and the nation at large. Today, over one in every three adults is obese, around 36 percent of the U.S. population. Obesity rates in the U.S. have nearly tripled since 1975, rising from 30.5 percent in 1999 to 41.9 percent in 2020, with rates of severe obesity increasing from 4.7 percent to 9.1 percent. Adults aged 40-59 show the highest levels of obesity (44.3 percent), followed by those aged 60 and up (41.5 percent).[435] U.S. veterans are particularly vulnerable; the VA estimates that around eight out of ten military veterans are overweight or obese.[436]

Not only do veterans have higher risk factors for obesity, but they are also more likely to develop the adverse health conditions associated with obesity, including increased risk of disease, diminished quality of life, and abbreviated lifespan.

Military service exposes service members to numerous events that most civilians never experience. Many of these events are associated with the development of obesity, including psychological trauma and exposure to toxins from burn pits, herbicides, water contamination, and others. Chemical toxins can alter the body's metabolic pathways, leading to inefficient metabolism. Obesity can also be caused by medications, including medications used to treat PTSD, depression, and other service-related health conditions. Like alcohol and drug abuse, overconsumption of calories can serve as a coping mechanism in patients suffering from depression, anxiety, PTSD, and other mental conditions. Excessive weight gain is also one of the side effects of various medications used to treat service-related mental health conditions.

In addition, the locations targeted by military recruitment campaigns typically have a higher prevalence of obesity. For example, southern states and rural areas have high rates of obesity due to a sedentary lifestyle; high-calorie, poor nutrition diet; and lower socioeconomic status.[437] Service members recruited from these areas may get in great shape during service but will likely find it challenging to maintain a healthy lifestyle upon returning home.

What is Obesity?

The World Health Organization and the American Medical Association recognize obesity as a disease characterized by an accumulation of adipose tissue in the body to a level that presents a health risk. Excess fatty tissue places metabolic, hormonal, and physical restraints on body function, adversely affecting multiple body systems.

Most commonly, excess fat accumulation is caused by an individual consuming more calories than are needed for body function. Various factors, including eating disorders, poor access to healthy foods, and low physical activity, can cause overconsumption of calories. Mental and physical factors can also lead to lower metabolism. While genetics may play a role, environmental and behavioral factors are considered the leading contributors to obesity.

Being overweight and obese are distinct diagnoses, obesity being the more severe condition in terms of adverse health effects. Obesity is typically diagnosed using body mass index (BMI). Individuals with a BMI of at least 30 are considered obese. BMI is calculated by dividing an individual's weight (in pounds) by their height (in inches) squared, and multiplying the result by 703. For example, a 5-foot 6-inch tall (66-inch) individual who weighs 190 pounds would have a BMI of 30.9.

- 66 x 66 = 4,356
- 190 / 4,356 = 0.044
- 703 x 0.044 = 30.9 (BMI)

Data suggests the adverse health effects of obesity are more severe in people with Class II (BMI 35–39.9) and Class III (BMI >40) obesity.[438] Approximately 16 percent of VA patients are diagnosed with Class II or Class III obesity.[439]

The Consequences of Obesity

Obesity-related health conditions are among the leading causes of premature, preventable death, including stroke, heart disease, cancer, and type 2 diabetes. Individuals diagnosed with obesity are at a higher risk for numerous health problems, including:

- Varicose veins
- Type 2 diabetes
- Stroke
- Sleep apnea
- Prostate cancer
- Polycystic ovaries
- Plantar fasciitis
- Osteoarthritis

- Metabolic syndrome
- Lower back pain
- Knee pain
- Hypertension
- Herniated disks
- Hernias
- Heart disease
- Gout
- Gall bladder disease
- Fatty liver disease
- Esophageal cancer
- Depression
- Colon cancer
- Chronic pain
- Chronic Fatigue
- Cataracts
- Breast cancer
- Acid reflux

Obesity also leads to impaired earning capacity. The associated limitations in walking, balance, cadence, rising from a sitting position, range of motion, endurance, breathing, and maintaining personal hygiene mean difficulty gaining and maintaining employment. Studies have shown that overweight individuals earn less money and there is often prejudice against employing overweight people. [440,441] As obesity and other metabolic disorders correlate with reduced cognitive function,[442] evidence suggests that overweight individuals are not functioning optimally from a mental perspective, which further impacts their earning potential.

As a nation, obesity costs the U.S. healthcare system billions of dollars each year. Medical costs for adults with obesity are nearly $2,000 higher than for healthy-weight individuals. The estimated annual healthcare costs of Americans with obesity are approaching $150 billion per year.[443] Healthcare costs quadruple as obesity worsens from Class II to Class III. These numbers don't include the indirect costs of obesity, like greater workers' compensation claims, more missed workdays, and higher life insurance premiums.

A Leading Threat to National Security

The obesity epidemic is also detrimentally affecting our military. The strength of our national security relies on an ongoing pool of qualified military volunteers. In the 2022 fiscal year, all branches of the U.S. military failed to meet their recruiting goals, experiencing record lows unseen since 1973. Around 77 percent of Americans ages 17-24 do not meet the qualifying standards for military service, up from 71 percent in 2019. A Qualified Military Available Study by the Department of Defense revealed that just 23 percent of American youth are qualified to serve without a waiver.[444] An inability to meet weight requirements is partially responsible for these low recruitment numbers.

In 1973, at the end of the draft, the military consisted of 1.9 million active-duty members, just under 0.9 percent of the U.S. population. Today, 0.4 percent of the U.S. population is active-duty military.[445] All five military branches require recruits to meet specific eligibility requirements to ensure that service members are mentally and physically fit to cope with the pressures and potentially traumatic exposures of military service. These eligibility requirements include the following:

- U.S. citizen or resident alien
- At least 17 years old
- High school diploma
- Pass a physical and medical exam
- Pass a vocational aptitude battery test

As part of the physical assessment, different military branches have different height and weight requirements. Physical requirements are designed to reduce preventable injuries and ensure mental and physical strength, balance and coordination, flexibility, and muscular and aerobic endurance. The height range for new Army recruits is 5' to 6'8" for men and 4'10" to 6'8" for women. Maximum weight requirements are based on height for Army and Air Force recruits, on body fat percentage for Navy recruits, and on body mass index (BMI) for Marine (BMI range: 19-31.7) and Coast Guard recruits (BMI range: 19-27.5). Unfortunately, a record number of young people across the nation (including many potential recruits) are currently overweight or obese. Among U.S. adolescents, 22.2 percent of adolescents ages 12-19 are obese, and 39 million children under age 5 are overweight or obese.[446]

The connection between socioeconomic status and obesity only adds to its impact on military recruitment. The factors that lead to obesity disproportionately affect low- to mid-level income households.[447] In lower socioeconomic sectors, obesity results from an overabundance of pre-prepared, inexpensive, high-calorie foods combined with diminished physical activity. Stressors, time restraints, and financial limitations lessen the perceived priority of seeking healthy food options or participating in physical and recreational activities. Between 1999 and 2018, researchers found a 4.2 percentage point increase in obesity prevalence among U.S. youth ages 10-19 living in low-income households. Low head-of-household education levels correlate with a 9 percentage point increase in obesity rates,[448] while heads of household with college degrees tended to have lower obesity rates.[449]

The Department of Defense focuses its recruitment efforts on the nation's lower socioeconomic sectors—particularly in public high schools made up of young adults who gravitate toward otherwise scant opportunities for travel, independence, living accommodations, college tuition, and a fast-tracked citizenship status. Sixty-four percent of service members come from areas with household income levels ranging from $41,692 to $87,850, 19 percent from neighborhoods with average income levels up to $41,691, and 17 percent from areas with income levels above $87,850.[450]

Around 40 percent of Army Junior Reserve Officers' Training Corps (JRTOC) programs are stationed in inner-city schools and over half of the nation's JROTC programs are in southeastern states. In 2018, South Carolina provided the highest military recruitment numbers per capita, followed by Florida, Hawaii, Georgia, and Alabama. States contributing the fewest recruits per capita included Washington, DC; North Dakota; Massachusetts; Utah; and Rhode Island.[451]

According to the CDC, obesity is most prevalent in the southern U.S. (36.3 percent), followed by the midwestern states (35.4 percent), northeastern states (29.9 percent), and western states (28.7 percent). Kentucky and West Virginia show the highest obesity rates (over 40 percent). States with obesity rates at or over 35 percent include Alabama, Arkansas, Indiana, Kansas, Kentucky, Louisiana, Michigan, Mississippi, Oklahoma, South Carolina, Tennessee, and West Virginia.[452]

It makes sense to direct military recruiting efforts toward the individuals most likely to sign up for service, but our nation is creating health problems that extinguish our ability to recruit from these sectors. With the obesity epidemic disproportionately affecting military recruiting target sectors, the obesity epidemic is effectively compromising U.S. national defense.

One potential solution to these low recruitment numbers is to conduct mandatory military service across all socioeconomic sectors. According to military and defense officials, the Pentagon is currently relocating recruiting offices to higher-income areas[453] where obesity rates are lower. However, these communities have little incentive to join the military, and this can potentially drain recruitment resources. Meanwhile, mandatory military drafts are politically unpopular, and they have only been enacted in states of emergency.

Another possibility is to incorporate pre-induction health and fitness camps, allowing the military to relax maximum-weight requirements for entry and work to bring recruits within an acceptable weight range prior to service. However, obesity is accompanied by numerous health problems that can hardly be fixed in a few weeks or months, including diabetes, bone and joint disorders, and heart disease. Rarely will an obese individual meet medical requirements for military eligibility. In these cases, a waiver might be necessary, and the recruit would remain ineligible for service at the military's expense.

Imposing a regulatory excise tax on unhealthy food products is another potential solution that could drive dietary behavior. Taxing unhealthy food has been examined in recent years. In March 2015, Berkeley, California, placed a penny-per-ounce tax on sugar-sweetened beverages. Thus, a 2-liter soda costing $2.00 would now cost $2.68, a 34 percent price increase. Studies conducted one year after the tax was implemented showed that sales of sugar-sweetened beverages had fallen by up to 21 percent, whereas bottled water sales had increased by 63 percent.[454] Taxing fast-food products, foods containing high-fructose corn syrup, and other unhealthy processed foods would not eliminate our nation's obesity problem. However, it would help curb behaviors, particularly in communities with tighter budgets.

Ultimately, military recruiting requirements are designed to ensure that service members are mentally and physically fit to handle the physical and mental pressures of military service. The Department of Veterans Affairs and U.S. veterans benefits lawyers have clearly characterized mental and physical health trends that have risen out of military service over the past 75 years. Through World War II, the Vietnam War, and the Afghanistan and Iraq Wars, thousands of service members who entered the military with a healthy weight had great difficulty reintegrating into civilian society. PTSD, substance abuse disorder, physical disabilities, traumatic brain injury, diabetes, hypertension, and diseases caused by toxin exposure are common among these veterans.

The potential for increased health problems resulting from accepting recruits with preexisting physical ailments like obesity is high. Obesity is likely to recur, particularly in veterans who were obese as children. Placing obese recruits in pre-induction weight-loss camps and ensuring they maintain a healthy weight throughout service creates a ticking time bomb that may go off once the recruit is reintegrated into civilian life, where diet and exercise are not regulated.

Veterans Benefits for Obesity

In August 2021, the U.S. Federal Circuit Court of Appeals held that veterans may claim obesity as a service-connected disability for VA benefits as long as the obesity impairs their earning capacity. In the landmark *Larson v. McDonough* decision,[455] the Court held that a disability can be service connected even when it isn't listed on the VA rating schedule. The only requirement is that the condition causes a "functional impairment of earning capacity," making it possible for veterans to collect VA benefits for obesity and other conditions left off the rating schedule.

This means veterans can also use obesity to establish secondary service connection for several related conditions, including diabetes, heart problems, sleep apnea, depression, and PTSD. If veterans can obtain service connection for obesity, they may be able to obtain secondary-service connection for any health condition associated with the service-connected obesity. For example, if a veteran is service-connected for obesity but has been denied benefits for heart disease, they can file a claim for heart disease benefits secondary to the obesity.

Establishing service connection for obesity is critical to getting the health care benefits and financial compensation veterans deserve. The VA estimates that treating patients with obesity costs around $370 per year per patient.[456] Because of the numerous body systems affected by obesity, including musculoskeletal, endocrine, cardiovascular, and respiratory issues, the cost of treating veterans with obesity is extreme.

To collect VA benefits for obesity, veterans must show that they currently have a BMI of 30 or greater, that the obesity is associated with their time in service, and that the obesity functionally impairs their earning capacity. Associating obesity with service can be difficult. In most cases, a veteran will need to provide a medical expert's written opinion that includes references to scientific literature showing that an injury, traumatic event, or exposure to a chemical toxin is "as much as likely as not" to have caused the obesity.

To show functional impairment of earning capacity, veterans must provide evidence that their obesity affects their ability to perform certain tasks required to earn a paycheck. In terms of earning capacity impairment, prejudice toward obese employees is a relevant factor. As such, some reference to the research literature on how obesity affects earning capacity could be helpful.

It is also important to demonstrate the upward trajectory in weight when trying to establish an in-service onset to the obesity issues. In most cases, a veteran does not develop full-blown obesity during service. They may begin to gain weight during service, and then the weight gain continues steadily after service until the veteran begins developing health problems.

Often, obesity is part of metabolic syndrome. We have had many cases in our office where our theory for winning service connection was based upon the in-service origins of metabolic syndrome, characterized by high blood pressure, high triglycerides, and being overweight. These issues often lead to type 2 diabetes and heart disease in the years following service.

In fact, we use the metabolic syndrome theory to service connect many type 2 diabetes cases involving non-Agent Orange veterans. If someone was exposed to Agent Orange, type 2 diabetes is presumptively service connected. But for veterans who were not in Vietnam or exposed to Agent Orange, another theory must be used to service-connect type 2 diabetes. As such, the early signs of metabolic syndrome in service are often revealed through weight gain and high cholesterol.

Potential Solutions

Obesity is a multifaceted disease with a myriad of contributing factors. Rural versus urban locations, cultural norms, socioeconomic status, access to physical recreational activities, fast-food marketing, and the affordability of healthy foods all play a role.

Agricultural policy should be adjusted more dramatically to address the emerging obesity problem. There is a blatant contradiction between the foods our government recommends that we eat and the foods our government supports. For example, the U.S. Department of Agriculture (USDA) suggests our diet should consist of 50 percent fruits and vegetables and recommends limiting our sodium and saturated fat intake from processed meats. [457] Meanwhile, just 4 percent of U.S. federal agriculture subsidies fund the production of fruits and vegetables,[458] and the government pays meatpacking monopolies millions of dollars each year.[459]

Today, the U.S. government offers a majority of its farm subsidies to soybeans, corn, and other commodity crops grown to generate cheap, high-calorie food ingredients like starches, sugars, and oils—ingredients needed to generate processed junk foods. In 2019, over 25 percent of agricultural spending went to the industrial poultry and meat industries. The system revolves around producing corporate profits, with no concern for public health. The USDA labels vegetables, fruits, and healthy proteins as "specialty crops." As a result, most Americans perceive them as luxury food products. Estimates show that around 20 percent of Americans are receiving the recommended daily allowance for fruits, and just 10 percent are getting the recommended amount of vegetables.[460] Fifty percent of the average U.S. diet consists of highly processed foods made from the commodity crops the government funds.[461]   In the end, farmers must support their families; they will produce what they are paid to produce.

Agricultural policies and federal subsidies determine which foods American farmers will produce and which foods are the most marketed, accessible, and affordable. We must work to transition federal support toward the production of healthy foods and away from commodity crops. We must align our public investments with our public health goals. Since the health of our population impacts our ability to staff our military, our agricultural policies need to align with national security interests as well.

Likewise, U.S. public health policy should be grounded in science and not influenced by food industry lobbyists. Today, health policy is swayed toward the big food lobbyists' corporate objectives. The junk food industry is highly powerful and political. It influences public opinion and procedures for its benefit and systematically undermines efforts to thwart obesity and other diet-related diseases. When the food industry helps fund political parties, politicians are prevented from creating and enacting policies that promote public health at the expense of big food—even going so far as to cherry-pick data and cite industry-backed research to support the food industry's position. To address this problem, we must enforce disclosure of funding sources and enact more powerful conflict-of-interest policies to minimize the influence of commercial interests on public policy.

Intercepting the obesity epidemic would cut U.S. healthcare costs both directly and indirectly. Healthcare for individuals with Alzheimer's disease and dementia will cost Medicare and Medicaid approximately $206 billion in 2022. This cost is projected to hit $618 billion by 2050.[462] Research shows that obesity is linked to an increased risk for neurodegeneration, Alzheimer's disease, and other types of dementia.[463]

Obesity is, in my opinion, the next big crisis. It will take decades to solve. Due to immediate national security concerns and the cost to taxpayers in funding VA healthcare, policymakers must tackle this problem aggressively. Obesity treatment and prevention programs are currently inefficient. Veterans' advocates must be prepared for the health challenges and staggering healthcare costs associated with future pools of veterans. If we want to control the obesity epidemic in our country, we must address agricultural policy, public health policy, education, poverty, and community development.

Community leaders and policymakers are working to address the problem, but their approaches could take decades to generate noticeable improvement. Education is vital in strengthening the youth of lower socioeconomic sectors. We need to improve the quality and availability of education, communicate with the youth of higher economic sectors, and ensure that education is effective at improving lifestyle. Investments in physical activity and recreation programs, subsidized staple foods, food programs offering pre-prepared meals, and other assistance is needed.

Attorney Representation and Access to Advocates

Just as access to adequate medical care has been a problem for disabled veterans, so has access to high-quality legal representation. Historically, the federal government has discouraged attorneys from representing veterans on VA claims. As far back as 1862, Congress limited attorney fees to just $5. This limitation was raised to $10 in 1864. Congress wanted to keep the VA claims process from becoming adversarial, and they didn't think attorney representation was really necessary. This institutional bias against attorney involvement persists today. A $10 fee may have been reasonable in 1864, considering that the VA claims process was simpler and the cost of living was much lower than today.

However, this limitation on attorney fees remained in effect for more than 120 years. Because $10 would not even cover the cost of a FedEx package, the limitation on attorney fees prevented any attorney from being able to afford to represent a veteran.

In the late 1980s, Congress changed the law to allow attorneys to represent veterans—and charge reasonable fees—under certain circumstances. The law allowed for paid attorneys to get involved:

- Within one year after the denial by the Board of Veterans Appeals (called "BVA") to file a reopened claim with the Regional Office for the same benefit that the BVA denied.
- To file a reconsideration motion with the BVA.
- To file a motion with the BVA to revise a decision based on Clear

and Unmistakable Error (called CUE).

- To file an appeal with the U.S. Court of Appeals for Veterans Claims.

The law changed again in 2006 to provide veterans with easier access to the services of paid attorneys. The new legislation allowed a veteran to hire a paid attorney so long as his Notice of Disagreement had been filed after June 19, 2007. So, if a veteran filed a claim that was denied and filed a Notice of Disagreement on or after June 20, 2007, he can hire a paid attorney who can charge a reasonable fee.

If the BVA denies a veteran's claim where the Notice of Disagreement was filed before June 20, 2007, then a paid attorney can get involved in the case after a final BVA decision to file a reopened claim with the Regional Office for the claim that the BVA denied, or to file a reconsideration or clear and unmistakable error motion with the BVA. These are insider terms that are widely known by those familiar with the VA benefits system. Suffice it to say; the law provided for limited circumstances where a veteran could hire a paid lawyer.

So, the bottom line is that if a veteran's Notice of Disagreement was filed after June 19, 2007, he can hire a paid attorney to represent him at the Regional Office or the BVA.

The issue of attorneys charging legal fees again saw slight modification after the Appeals Modernization Act ("AMA") took effect in February 2019. Under the AMA, a veteran has three appeal options after an initial VA denial of his claim. He can file a Notice of Disagreement directly with the BVA, a Higher Level Review appeal, or a Supplemental Claim. Under the pre-AMA rules, veterans had a well-defined appeal track to follow. There was little strategic discretion as to how to handle a VA denial.

Now, under the current AMA, significant strategic thinking must take place after an initial VA denial. This means that the need for the advice and consultation of a skilled lawyer is more important than ever. As such, most practitioners agree that veterans can hire a paid lawyer after the initial VA adjudication.

The U.S. Court of Appeals for Veterans Claims and Attorney Fees

The Veterans Judicial Review Act of 1988 (VJRA) opened up the federal court system to veterans seeking redress of VA decisions. In doing so, it gave veterans far more opportunities to obtain legal counsel. The VJRA created the U.S. Court of Appeals for Veterans Claims (CAVC). This was created under Article I of the U.S. Constitution. Thus, it is referred to as an Article I or tribunal court. The VJRA gave the U.S. Court of Appeals exclusive jurisdiction to review final BVA decisions. It also allowed attorneys admitted to practice before the court to charge a reasonable fee for representation. The VJRA also transferred jurisdiction for challenges to VA regulations and other policies from the U.S. Federal District Courts to the U.S. Court of Appeals for the Federal Circuit. The Federal Circuit now has the power to review challenges to, among other things, VA procedural rules, regulations, and substantive rules of general applicability.

Accordingly, after the enactment of the VJRA, veterans now have two avenues to pursue federal court review of VA regulations and policies affecting their case. First, they can file an appeal administratively with the BVA. If the BVA denies the claim, then the veteran can file an appeal with the CAVC and challenge the VA policy or regulation as part of his appeal from the final BVA denial. If the CAVC affirms the BVA decision, the veteran could appeal the CAVC's decision to the U.S. Court of Appeals for the Federal Circuit. The second avenue would be for a veteran to challenge the VA regulation or policy in the Federal Circuit. In either case, the veteran would be wise to retain legal counsel. The VJRA created a system of federal court review for veterans, which created more opportunities to obtain legal counsel.

Can a Veteran Really Get an Attorney for Free?

More places to utilize legal counsel means little if a veteran cannot afford the "reasonable fee" that an attorney would charge. After all, veterans file claims because their disabilities impair their earning capacity and, in many cases, render them totally disabled and incapable of sustaining a gainful occupation. In short, disabled veterans usually do not have the money to hire private lawyers that charge rates as high as $500 per hour. Even a modest rate of $300 per hour would be more than most disabled veterans could afford.

Fortunately, the problem of not having money to pay an attorney at the CAVC has already been solved. Congress enacted the Equal Access to Justice Act in 1980. The attorneys often refer to this law simply as the EAJA. This law applies to cases before the U.S. Court of Appeals for Veteran's claims. This law levels the playing field and gives ordinary citizens easier access to the courts when fighting the federal government. The idea is that it is normally very expensive to fight a legal case against the U.S. government, and the average person would not be able to afford the legal fees to undertake such litigation. However, the EAJA allows the winning party to have his attorney's fees paid by the government. The primary rationale for its enactment was to "eliminate for the average person the financial disincentive to challenge unreasonable government actions."[464] Under the EAJA, "a court shall award to a prevailing party other than the United States fees and other expenses. . . incurred by that party in a civil action (other than fees sounding in tort), including proceedings for judicial review of agency action, brought against the United States in any court having jurisdiction of that action, unless the court finds that the position of the United States was substantially justified or that special circumstances make an award unjust."[465]

The EAJA was not initially deemed applicable to matters before the CAVC. In 1992 the CAVC held that the EAJA did not apply to appeals before the CAVC.[466] But in 1992, Congress acted to expressly make the EAJA applicable to the CAVC.[467]

In the case of a veteran, this means that if he prevails at the CAVC, his attorney can apply to have the VA pay the legal fees. To prevail, the attorney would have to get the claim remanded or reversed. The payment of attorney fees under the EAJA works like a contingency fee—that is, the attorney can collect a fee only if he prevails in the appeal at the U.S. Court of Appeals for Veterans Claims. So, there is no risk of owing an out-of-pocket attorney fee when a veteran hires a lawyer to represent him at the U.S. Court of Appeals for Veterans Claims.

Also, until recently, if an attorney represented a veteran at the Board or Regional Office level as well, and attorney fees were collected under the EAJA, then there was historically an offset of the amount already paid by the EAJA. Here's an example: The attorney gets paid $5,000 by the EAJA for winning the appeal at the CAVC. The attorney then gets the case sent back to the Board, where he wins the claim. The veteran eventually receives $100,000 in past-due benefits. Normally, a 20 percent contingency fee would equal $20,000, but the previous $5,000 payment under the EAJA would have been deducted or "offset." In our example, this would mean that the attorney fee for representation at the Board and Regional Office level would be only $15,000. ($20,000 minus $5,000 = $15,000).

The EAJA offset rules also saw modification in 2019 with changes in the law that no longer required an attorney to offset legal fees paid by the U.S. government in accordance with the EAJA.

The EAJA applies only to the part of the case at the U.S. Court of Appeals for Veterans Claims. All the talk about 20 or 33 percent of back pay only applies to representation at the Board or Regional Office level. So, a veteran can hire an attorney just to represent him at the Court, and there would be no charge—win or lose (assuming his net worth was less than $2 million). And the money paid to the attorney under the EAJA would not affect his potential back pay. If a veteran then hired the attorney *after* the U.S. Court of Appeals for Veterans Claims returned (or remanded) the case to the Board, then the attorney could charge a percentage of back pay as a contingency fee.

How Much Do Attorneys Charge?

As noted above, for representation at the U.S. Court of Appeals for Veterans Claims, there is no risk of owing an attorney fee. If a veteran hires a lawyer to represent him at the BVA or Regional Office level, there is no EAJA to pay the fee. The EAJA exists only at the U.S. Court of Appeals for Veterans Claims. So, at the BVA or Regional Office level, most attorneys charge a contingency fee. This means that there is no fee unless money is recovered for the veteran. But the VA regulations provide that an attorney fee can charge a flat fee, an hourly rate, a percentage of past-due benefits, or some combination of these types of fees. The main issue is that the fee must be reasonable.

As mentioned, at the BVA or Regional Office level, the most common type of fee arrangement between veterans and their attorneys is the contingency fee. A contingency fee is where the attorney charges a percentage of any past-due benefits (sometimes called the "back pay" or "retro") contingent upon winning past-due benefits. This means that the attorney will not charge an up-front fee but will get paid a percentage of the back pay only if he wins. So, if the attorney does not win back pay for the veteran, there is no fee owed. In other words, there is no money owed unless the attorney wins. This fee structure allows disabled veterans, who may be too disabled to work and earn an income, to retain legal counsel to help them win.

But what is considered a "reasonable fee"? Generally, the rules provide that a contingency fee of 20 percent is considered reasonable. And a contingency fee of more than 33 percent is deemed unreasonable. Thus, fees ranging from more than 20 percent to less than 33 percent could be considered reasonable. In practice, most attorneys charge from 20 to 33 percent as a contingency fee. In other cases, the VA determines the "reasonableness" of an attorney fee by several factors, such as:

- Rates charged by other attorneys
- Whether the fee is contingent upon the results achieved
- The complexity of the case
- The level of skill required
- The amount of time spent
- The results achieved

The VA will split a past-due-benefits check between the veteran and his attorney so long as the fee is no more than 20 percent. If the agreement between the veteran and his attorney charges a fee of more than 20 percent, then the VA will not split the check, and the veteran will pay his attorney directly himself. Usually, this means that once the veteran receives his back-pay check, he will then write a check to his attorney for the contingency fee plus any expenses.

At this point, let me say a word about expenses. In most cases, for an attorney to work on a case, there are certain expenses that he is required to pay. This could be the expense of hiring a medical expert or paying to reproduce medical records. Usually, the attorney will advance the cost of the expenses, and the veteran will pay him back once he receives his past-due benefits check. The attorney cannot charge "normal office overhead" as an expense, but anything paid directly to develop a veteran's case is considered an appropriate expense, and the veteran will re-pay the attorney. In most cases, the primary expense would be to pay for the services of a medical expert or travel costs to go to a hearing before the BVA or Regional Office. So, even if the VA splits the past-due-benefits check, the veteran will have to send the attorney a separate check to reimburse him for the expenses incurred in developing the veteran's case. The method of how expenses will be reimbursed is determined by the agreement between the attorney and his client. The VA will not withhold expense money and pay it to the attorney. The veteran will always have to pay the attorney separately for expenses.

What is "reasonable" in terms of expenses? Again, there are several factors that determine what is reasonable. For example:

- The complexity of the case
- Whether the expenses are consistent with what other representatives charge

- The potential size of any past-due-benefits check

Historically, I have been a big proponent of using top-notch medical experts. Our firm spends hundreds of thousands of dollars each year to hire experts for our clients. When we win the case, the client does have to reimburse our firm for that expense. However, without these expert witnesses, the odds of winning a case are poor. When we decide on an expert for a case, we want the best expert for the job, but we also consider the potential size of the retroactive award when determining which expert we hire. Some experts are more expensive than others. We do not spend $5,000 on an expert for a case that has the potential of only $30,000 in retroactive benefits.

On the other hand, in complex cases that have been on appeal for a long time and have the potential to pay the veteran a sizable retroactive benefit, our firm can justify spending whatever it takes to win. For example, I represented a veteran in a complex organic brain syndrome and multiple chemical sensitivity syndrome case. The case had been pending on appeal for 17 years. The veteran had been represented by various veterans' service officers and, just prior to hiring our firm, a nationally recognized white-shoe law firm in Manhattan. His case had been denied for the second time at the Board of Veterans Appeals, and he hired our firm to appeal his case to the U.S. Court of Appeals for Veterans Claims. His prior representatives, including the big New York City law firm, had advised him that his case was not winnable.

But we were determined to win his case. We hired a world-renowned expert from South Africa, who was only one of nine experts in the world with his level of credentials and expertise. The expert's curriculum vitae was over 80 pages long. Our law firm spent about $20,000 on this expert.

The strategy paid off, and we won a retroactive award for this client that exceeded $300,000 in back pay. Yes, the client had to reimburse our firm for the $20,000 payment, but had we not spent that money, we would never have won the case. In that sense, the $20,000 investment was certainly reasonable.

The lawyers cannot advance money to a veteran client in anticipation of winning the claim—except, as noted above, for case-related expenses. This means that a veteran cannot ask his lawyer for a loan to pay his rent. It is considered professionally unethical for lawyers to loan money to clients except for case-related expenses. In more than two decades of practicing law, I have had many deserving clients contact me for loans to pay rent or other such things. I genuinely felt bad for each of these clients and wished that I could have helped them. However, in each instance, the Rules of Professional Conduct prevented me from assisting these clients. I have to advise the client that the best thing I could do to help him was win his case.

Many lending firms offer financial products for people with pending lawsuits. A client could obtain money for non-case expenses from one of these firms, and it would not run afoul of the rules of ethics. Almost all of these firms offer products to people with traditional civil lawsuits, usually personally injury cases. The client would essentially sell a portion of his future proceeds to the lender with exorbitant interest rates. This type of arrangement is known as a "non-recourse" loan, meaning that the lender would not be able to collect the debt from the client if the underlying lawsuit were not successful. Because of this risk, these lenders charge outrageous interest rates. As such, an initial "loan" of $3,000 could turn into $15,000 by the time a case resolves. I historically have advised clients against using these lending firms. Fortunately, there are not too many of these firms that lend to veterans in the VA administrative appeal process.

Such firms would, however, lend money to a veteran who has an active FTCA civil lawsuit for VA medical malpractice.

How Does a Veteran Know Which Lawyer is Right for His Case?

Frequently, a veteran struggles with his case with little or no significant help for many years. Then he files an appeal with the U.S. Court of Appeals for Veterans Claims, and he is suddenly made aware of attorneys and law firms from all over the country. A veteran often wonders why he did not know about the availability of legal representation sooner.

Veterans are frequently confused over which lawyer to pick. So there are some important criteria to consider when making a selection. Here's the reality: most of the attorneys that specialize solely in representing disabled veterans are highly competent. A veteran would be well-served and in good hands with most of them. I know many of my colleagues, and they are competent and effective advocates. If I were disabled and had a claim, I would feel confident in recommending many of my colleagues. So, a veteran must understand that the selection of an attorney has nothing to do with whether one law firm knows the law and the others don't. The selection is more personal, and it comes down to how comfortable the veteran feels working with a specific attorney. After all, in some situations, a veteran will be working with this lawyer or law firm for a long time, and the person he's working with must be someone he likes and someone with whom he feels comfortable working. The personal aspect must be at the center of this decision.

What Should Veterans Look for in an Attorney?

The first thing to consider is whether the attorney concentrates all or most of his practice on veterans disability law. If a lawyer practices primarily veterans disability law—and he's been doing it for a number of years—he is most likely going to be competent to get the job done in the average case. They will have the required knowledge and skill to assist a veteran. So, a veteran can determine competency by whether veterans' law is the majority of what a lawyer does. He should be cautious about hiring a lawyer who merely dabbles in veterans' cases on rare occasions. A veteran should find someone who primarily represents veterans all the time.

Second, although it's not a test of competency, I recommend considering a lawyer who is a member of the National Organization of Veterans Advocates or NOVA. The NOVA organization is like a trade organization, and attorneys who support this organization with their membership have demonstrated a commitment to representing disabled veterans.

Third, a veteran should consider experience. Although many brand new attorneys can handle cases with competency and effectiveness, it is recommended that a veteran consider someone who has been practicing law for a reasonable number of years and has a diverse legal background. I'm not suggesting an exact number of years of experience, but I am suggesting that experience is one of several factors to consider. In general, I would not hire a lawyer to represent me unless he has litigated at least 300 cases at the U.S. Court of Appeals for Veterans Claims. In fact, in my professional opinion, lawyers that litigate cases at the U.S. Court of Appeals for Veterans Claims are in the upper tier of the domain of veterans' law. Whether a veterans' benefits attorney regularly practices before the U.S. Court of Appeals for Veterans Claims is, in fact, a benchmark of an elite practitioner.

There are reasons why so many veterans' lawyers have little to no experience in practicing before the U.S. Court of Appeals for Veterans Claims. With the 2006 changes in the law regarding when paid attorneys could get involved to represent veterans, this practice area saw an influx of Social Security Disability lawyers. These lawyers had little to no experience in litigating at the U.S. Court of Appeals for Veterans Claims. As Social Security lawyers, they had administrative law experience but did not have the appellate law experience that comes with regular practice before the U.S. Court of Appeals for Veterans Claims. Lawyers with extensive appellate experience are knowledgeable in the case law that drives their practice area, and they are at the forefront of new cases that come out of the appellate court. Frankly, appellate lawyers in the VA world are in the *avant-garde* of the profession.

In addition, the mindset of Social Security lawyers typically differs from those that have been long-time VA practitioners. Usually, Social Security lawyers rely on a client's treating doctors. Social Security claimants typically have private treating physicians, and no rule prohibits private doctors from writing medical opinions for their patients. As such, Social Security lawyers usually do not have to spend money to hire outside experts. The treating doctors in the Social Security context will supply what medical information is needed for little or no extra cost. In addition, Social Security lawyers do not need to prove what caused their client's disability. In the VA context, to win service connection, a veteran must prove that his current disability was caused by something that happened on active duty. Proving this nexus with service requires a medical expert. These experts cost money. Veterans typically do not have extra money to pay for medical experts. This means that the law firm must advance the cost of the expert out of its own pocket and then wait to win the case and seek reimbursement from the client. Social Security law firms do not operate on the model of lending out money to clients and then waiting years to get reimbursed. Our law firm lends hundreds of thousands of dollars each year to help clients obtain the expert testimonies they need to win their cases. In my professional opinion, a veteran should be cautious in hiring a law firm with a long history as a Social Security Disability law firm.

Turning to the fourth factor to look for in a lawyer, a veteran should consider someone who has demonstrated a commitment to veterans' issues. Is he or she active in leading or contributing to organizations or causes that benefit disabled veterans? In other words, a veteran should consider whether the attorney or law firm has a sincere concern for disabled veterans. There are many personal injury or negligence attorneys who have decided to add veterans disability law to their menu of services. The problem is that these attorneys may be looking at disabled veterans simply as another revenue source, and they are not otherwise committed to veterans. A veteran should look into whether the attorney he is considering is a member of NOVA and other veterans' sections of bar associations, and whether he or she is involved in any nonprofit organizations dedicated to assisting disabled veterans.

What About Attorneys with Military Experience?

There is a difference between military law and veterans' law. An attorney who specializes in military law does not necessarily know much about veterans' law. Similarly, a veterans disability attorney may not know much about military law. Just because an attorney served as a military attorney does not mean that he also practices veterans disability law before the VA and the U.S. Court of Appeals for Veterans Claims. In our law firm, we do not handle cases involving the Uniform Code of Military Justice (UCMJ).

The UCMJ is the foundation of military law. We have a relationship with another law firm that is owned by a former JAG attorney. We refer all relevant cases to him, including UCMJ cases, discharge upgrade cases, and MEB and PEB cases. This allows us to help veterans in need of these services while at the same time maintaining our singular focus on veterans' benefits law.

Does a Veteran's Lawyer Need to Be in Washington, D.C.?

Representation at the Regional Offices, the BVA, and the U.S. Court of Appeals for Veterans Claims can all be done through the mail, over the telephone, by fax, and by internet and email. Distance is no problem. The Court of Appeals for Veterans Claims (CAVC) is national. It handles cases from Alaska to Puerto Rico and from Maine to Hawaii. The practice of veterans' law does not require a veteran to live near his attorney's office. In fact, veterans seldom need to go to an attorney's office. Again, everything can be done over the telephone, by mail, fax, or over the internet. Our law firm represents veterans worldwide. Not only do we have clients in almost every state, but we have clients in Europe, Australia, Thailand, the Philippines, Canada, Mexico, Peru, and Panama, just to name a few locations. We have even been contacted by veterans in Africa and China for assistance with their VA appeals. So, it does not matter how far a veteran lives from his attorney's office.

What About Lawyers That Used to Work For The VA?

Some lawyers received their initial training and experience in veterans' law by working for the VA. Whether veterans disability lawyers have always worked for veterans or have been employed by the VA at some point, they can be competent and professional. Good lawyers can argue both sides of a case. I would not hesitate to recommend any of my colleagues that used to work for the VA. Some lawyers get involved in veterans disability law by having worked for the government, and other lawyers get involved from the claimant's side. Either way, if the attorney concentrates most of his practice on representing disabled veterans, they will be competent, and veterans will be well served.

What About Veterans Service Officers or Organizations?

Historically, veterans' service organizations have been the primary source of assistance for veterans seeking help with VA claims. Many of these organizations are congressionally chartered by the laws administered by the Department of Veterans Affairs, as provided in 38 U.S.C. § 5902 and 38 C.F.R. § 14.628(a) and (c). These organizations are also recognized by the VA for purposes of representing claims for benefits under the law administered by the VA. There are also organizations that are congressionally chartered but not recognized by VA for purposes of representing claims for benefits; there are organizations that are not congressionally chartered but that are recognized by VA for purposes of representation of claims for benefits; and, finally, there are organizations that are not congressionally chartered and not recognized for purposes of representing claims for benefits.

List of Congressionally Chartered and Recognized Organizations:

African American Post Traumatic Stress Disorder Association

American Ex-Prisoners of War

American GI Forum of the United States

The American Legion

American Red Cross

Amvets

Army and Navy Union, USA, Inc.

Associates of Vietnam Veterans of America

Blinded Veterans Association

Catholic War Veterans, USA, Inc.

Disabled American Veterans

Fleet Reserve Association

Gold Star Wives of America, Inc.

Italian American War Veterans of the United States

Jewish War Veterans of the USA

Legion of Valor of the USA

Marine Corps League

Military Officers Association of America

Military Order of the Purple Heart of the USA, Inc.

National Association for Black Veterans, Inc.

National Association of County Veterans Service Officers, Inc.

National Veterans Legal Services Program

National Veterans Organization of America

Paralyzed Veterans of America

Polish Legion of American Veterans, USA

Swords to Plowshares: Veterans Rights Organization

TREA: The Enlisted Association

Veterans of Foreign Wars of the United States

Veterans of the Vietnam War, Inc. & The Veterans Coalition

Vietnam Veterans of America

Wounded Warrior Project

Congressionally Chartered but NOT Recognized Organizations:

Air Force Sergeants Association

American Gold Star Mothers, Inc.

American War Mothers

Blue Star Mothers of America, Inc.

Congressional Medal of Honor Society of the United States of America

Korean War Veterans Association, Inc.

Military Chaplains Association of the United States of America

Military Order of the World Wars

Navy Club of the United States of America

United States Submarine Veterans, Inc.

Women's Army Corps Veterans Association—Army Women United

NOT Congressionally Chartered but Recognized Organizations:

Armed Forces Service Corporation

Navy Mutual Aid Association

Vietnam Era Veterans Association

In addition, the VA recognizes the State Veterans Affairs organizations. Each of the States and Territories have a Veterans Affairs organization. These organizations assist veterans in many of the same ways as the private service organizations do.

Given the historical limitations on a veteran's ability to retain paid legal counsel early in the process, the devoted men and women of the veterans' service organizations (VSO's) have handled frontline assistance to veterans. VSO's are the ones often helping a veteran file his initial claim. Paid lawyers were not allowed to get involved until later in the appeal process. Even now, paid lawyers cannot get involved until after an initial decision. The VSO is the place most veterans start, and if the VSO is successful, the veteran can win his claim at the initial filing. The assistance of the VSO does not cost the veteran anything. As a result, VSO's often have incredibly high caseloads and are often overworked.

Once the VA denies a claim, however, the case proceeds to appellate status. This means that the veteran appeals the denial. In most cases, to be successful on appeal, the veteran will have to obtain new evidence to strengthen any weaknesses in the case. This can be a challenge given that the most common reason for a VA denial is the lack of evidence of a nexus with service. Although there are several strategies for proving a nexus with service, the most effective is to obtain the opinion of a medical expert.

Veterans cannot easily obtain expert medical opinions. First, most veterans obtain their medical care through the VA. The VA discourages treating doctors from writing medical nexus opinions for their patients in connection with claims for compensation benefits. Moreover, even if the veteran's VA primary care physician did write a letter, it is often insufficient to establish the appropriate nexus. Treating doctors are proficient in treating patients, and most lack the skills of forensic doctors that specialize in serving as expert witnesses in legal disputes. If the veteran cannot use his treating VA physician, then he is left trying to find a private physician to do an expert evaluation. But good medical experts cost money. Most veterans who are unable to work due to their service-connected disabilities do not have the money to hire expensive medical experts to fight the VA's compensation and pension exam doctors. Even if the veteran did have the extra money, he would have a hard time finding the right expert. In most cases, the veteran is unable to obtain the appropriate expert medical opinion and resorts to submitting his own lay opinion as to what caused his disability. The VA will always reject such opinions on the grounds that the veteran is not a physician and lacks the competency to opine on complex matters of medical etiology.

The VSO's will submit any favorable evidence a veteran can obtain and supply. But the service organizations are not equipped to find and fund the cost of private medical experts. If the veteran cannot afford to obtain an expert medical opinion, then his case proceeds without the evidence needed to win. Thus, even with a VSO, his case is often doomed on appeal.

This is where the VSO's and the private law firms can work together to help veterans. Skilled veterans' benefits attorneys are not at odds with the VSO's. We recognize that VSO's play a valuable role in the veterans claims ecosystem. VSO's play a huge role in getting the claims started and helping veterans win claims that do not need high-powered medical experts. However, in cases where the complexity of the issues demands a sophisticated private medical expert or complicated legal argument, the veteran is best served by retaining a private law firm.

In most cases, when a veteran hires a private law firm, he can leverage the law firm's resources to obtain the medical expert evidence he needs to win his case. The law firm will advance the cost of the expert, thus solving the veteran's lack of money problem. Moreover, the veteran can leverage the law firm's connections with medical experts, thus solving the veteran's lack-of-connections problem. The experts that are the most experienced as witnesses in legal cases are not the mainstream treating doctors a veteran would find in the Yellow Pages. They are a group of forensic-oriented physicians with an understanding of legal proceedings. They are rarely known outside legal circles. They are known to lawyers, who generally have scouting reports on the various experts available. Lawyers know which experts to use depending on the case and how good their reports are. This valuable knowledge is intangible at first blush but pays dividends in winning results. Often, just the lawyer's ability to navigate the medical expert arena alone is worth the fee he charges the client—because most cases are denied due to the lack of a medical nexus.

So, instead of viewing law firms as competition or entities that are unnecessarily taking veterans' money, VSO's can see law firms as strategic partners. VSO's can view themselves as the first leg of a two-legged relay race. The VSO starts off the claim and does what he can to win the claim at the initial stage. If not successful, then he can hand the proverbial baton off to the law firm to run the final leg of the race and win the claim on appeal. This makes sense because most cases should have medical experts if the case is going to be developed properly. Granted, many attorneys will argue that clever legal arguments alone can win cases. I respectfully disagree. Hard-hitting legal arguments are needed, but they should not be a substitute for strong expert medical opinions in cases where the dispositive issue is the absence of a medical nexus. As such, the most viable means of creating a seamless system to ensure veterans' claims are maximized would seem to be for VSO's to create strategic partnerships with law firms.

Another reason why strategic partnerships between VSO's are important—whether they are private, congressionally chartered, or state/county organizations—concerns the changes in the law that occurred in 2019. With the implementation of the Appeals Modernization Act ("AMA"), veterans now have three distinct appeal lanes to choose from when undertaking an appeal. Each option has its pros and cons, and which lane to choose requires expert legal guidance. Before AMA, the appeal process had no real options. It was automatic that an appeal should get a Notice of Disagreement within one year. The only strategic thinking that existed involved whether to choose a traditional appeal or a Decision Review Officer.

Now, however, the veteran can choose Higher Level Review, Supplemental Claim, or Notice of Disagreement directly to the BVA.

Further, after a BVA denial, an appeal to the CAVC is no longer automatic in the sense that the veteran could obtain new and relevant evidence within one year and file a Supplemental Claim and still preserve his original retroactive effective date. Which lane a veteran chooses is dependent on the unique facts of his case, his ability to obtain new evidence, and the legal issues at stake. One-size does not fit all anymore. My concern is that veterans need legal counsel now more than ever immediately following an initial VA denial.

Further, the AMA treats these cases like traditional appellate cases in other contexts. This means there is no longer the ability to continue to submit new evidence and argument right up until the time that the BVA makes a decision. There are deadlines for the submission of evidence and argument. After that point, the record is closed. Therefore, the preservation of records for appeal is extremely important. Similar to a case on appeal from a jury trial, issues not raised below on the record will generally not be entertained on appeal at the appellate court. This means that expert legal guidance on which theories to raise is now critical. Frankly, it is difficult for non-lawyers without a strong understanding of the CAVC's jurisprudence to know what issues and theories to raise on appeal.

This is why VSO's should be moving in the direction of forming strategic partnerships or relationships with law firms. For instance, let's say that the XYZ Service Organization receives initial denials on claims for its veteran clients, which it invariably will. Instead of automatically filing a random appeal using one of the three appeal lanes, it could contract with a law firm to review and advise on the various denials. Expert legal review will increase the chances that the appropriate appeal lane is chosen, and the outcomes will improve. The law firm could then represent the veterans in the complex appeals that require medical experts. Overall, the rate of success would go up, and the VSO would have provided a better service to its veteran clients. In other words, instead of viewing law firms as competitors, VSO's can see themselves as project managers who are astute enough to contract with a law firm to ensure that the client gets the best legal advice possible. The VSO assists the client in availing himself of the services of a predetermined law firm with which the VSO has a contract. This means a veteran doesn't have to search for the proverbial needle in the haystack of lawyers. The number of lawyers truly skilled in VA benefits law is minuscule compared to the number of lawyers in practice. The VSO could ease this daunting task by having its own law firm on retainer to assist its veteran clients.

As a veteran seeking VA benefits, whatever avenue you chose to file or appeal your claim, know that there is hope. The VA's tactics to deny valid claims are well known, but with expert medical advice and in-depth knowledge of legal precedents and the intricacies of the VA claims process, it is possible to beat the system and secure compensation. As a veterans disability lawyer, I have made it my life's mission to assist our courageous service members in obtaining the benefits they deserve. Our government may have betrayed your valor, but we are on your side, and as we advocate for system reform, we will defend your rights as fiercely as you defended our country and our way of life.

GLOSSARY

BVA Board of Veterans' Appeals

"A part of the Department of Veterans Affairs (VA), located in Washington, D.C. The Board's mission is to conduct hearings and decide appeals properly before the Board in a timely manner." This is where you file an appeal if your claim for benefits has been denied. If you don't succeed, you can then appeal to the CAVC (see below).

CHAMPVA Civilian Health and Medical Program of the Dept. of Veterans Affairs

For spouses, surviving spouses, or children of veterans with disabilities or veterans who passed away, if they don't qualify for TRICARE, they may resort to CHAMPVA. This cost-sharing health insurance program partially covers the cost of health care services and supplies.

CAVC Court of Appeals for Veterans Claims

"The United States Court of Appeals for Veterans Claims is a national court of record, established under Article I of the Constitution of the United States. The Court has exclusive jurisdiction to provide judicial review of final decisions by the Board of Veterans' Appeals, an entity within the Department of Veterans Affairs."

COPD Chronic Obstructive Pulmonary Disease

A progressive, obstructive lung disease that causes long-term breathing problems and poor airflow. Its main symptoms include shortness of breath, cough, and sputum production. U.S. veterans are at higher risk of COPD than the general population.

DEA Survivors' and Dependents' Educational Assistance

The DEA program "offers education and training opportunities to eligible dependents of Veterans who are permanently and totally disabled due to a service-related condition or of Veterans who died while on active duty or as a result of a service-related condition."

DIC Dependency and Indemnity Compensation

"A tax free monetary benefit paid to eligible survivors of military service members who died in the line of duty or eligible survivors of Veterans whose death resulted from a service-related injury or disease."

EAJA Equal Access to Justice Act

"The Equal Access to Justice Act (EAJA) (5 U.S.C. § 504; 28 U.S.C. § 2412) provides for the award of attorney fees (up to $125 per hour) and other expenses to eligible individuals and small entities that are parties to litigation against the government. An eligible party may receive an award when it prevails over the government, unless the government's position was 'substantially justified' or special circumstances make an award unjust." Under certain circumstances, EAJA can cover attorney's fees for cases filed by veterans at the Court of Appeals for Veterans Claims.

FCA False Claims Act

The False Claims Act enables whistleblowers to expose fraud against the government and receive a share of any monetary recoveries. Veterans with information about SDVOSB fraud (see below) or military contract fraud can use the False Claims Act (FCA) to file a lawsuit and stop the misconduct.

GAO *General Accountability Office*
A legislative agency in charge of monitoring and auditing government spending and operations. The GAO tracks the use of taxpayer dollars, for example, by the VA, and then reports to Congress.

HUD-VASH *Housing and Urban Development VA Supportive Housing Program*
"A collaborative program between HUD and VA combines HUD housing vouchers with VA supportive services to help Veterans who are homeless and their families find and sustain permanent housing."

MPN *Myeloproliferative Neoplasms*
Known collectively as MPNs, Myelofibrosis (MF), Polycythemia Vera (PV), and Essential Thrombocythemia (ET) often result from exposure to Agent Orange. The MPN Education Foundation is currently running a survey of Vietnam veterans, who are heavily affected.

MST *Military Sexual Trauma*
As per the VA, "Sexual assault or harassment experienced during military service. MST includes any sexual activity that [a veteran was] involved with against [their] will."

Section 1151 Benefits
Disability benefits available to veterans injured at VA facilities. Section 1151 refers to the U.S. Code's section of veterans' law, which refers to

compensation for this type of injury. Under this legislation, injuries at VA facilities are considered to be service connected.

OTH *Other Than Honorable Discharge*

An OTH discharge poses problems to obtain certain VA benefits. The Department of Veterans Affairs recently implemented two programs to make "mental health care treatment available to former service members with other-than-honorable (OTH) administrative discharges."

SDVOSB *Service-Disabled Veteran-Owned Small Businesses Program*

"The federal government's goal is to award at least three percent of all federal contracting dollars to service-disabled veteran-owned small businesses each year."

TAP *Transition Assistance Program*

VA-provided "comprehensive" support to help veterans transition to civilian life. As a rule, it falls short of its commendable mission.

TCDD *2,3,7,8-Tetrachlorodibenzodioxin*

One of the components of the infamous Agent Orange, an herbicide used tactically during the Vietnam War between 1961 and 1971. It has been responsible for causing major health problems for a large number of exposed veterans.

TDIU *Total Disability based on Individual Unemployability*

TDIU "allows VA to pay certain Veterans at the 100-percent disability rate even though their service-connected disabilities are not rated as 100-percent disabling. Veterans may be eligible for this rating increase if they are either unemployed or unable to maintain substantially gainful employment as a result of their service-connected disability (or disabilities)."

VA OIG U.S. Department of Veterans Affairs Office of Inspector General
Its mission is "to serve veterans and the public by conducting effective oversight of the programs and operations of the Department of Veterans Affairs (VA) through independent audits, inspections, reviews, and investigations."

VSO Veterans Service Officer/Veterans Service Organization
If you are filing a claim for VA benefits, you can appoint an attorney, claim agent, or VSO "to act on your behalf in the preparation, presentation, and prosecution" of your claim. VSO also refers to advocacy organizations providing the same services.

About the Author

Eric Gang is a recognized speaker and legal analyst. Coming from a lineage of WWII and Vietnam veterans, he has litigated close to 1,000 appeals at the U.S. Court of Appeals for Veterans Claims, recovering millions of dollars on behalf of disabled veterans. He lectures widely on veterans benefits' litigation, for such prestigious organizations as the New Jersey State Bar Association,  the National Business Institute, and Lawline. He has authored influential publications for The National Business Institute and The Federal Lawyer and has been a commentator on veterans' issues for WRNJ radio. Eric's expertise and legal victories have been featured in the Miami Herald, Fox News, CBS, the Dallas Morning News, The Sacramento Bee, and the Cincinnati Enquirer. In 2019, he delivered a keynote speech at the annual conference of MENSA, the High IQ Society.

Learn more about Eric Gang at www.EricGangESQ.com

REFERENCES

(Endnotes)

1   38 U.S.C. §101(2).

2   38 U.S.C.. § 101(24)(B).

3   Idem

4   38 U.S.C. § 101(24)(C).

5   Idem

6   38 U.S.C. §101(2).

7   38 U.S.C. § 1110.

8   *See McClain v. Nicholson*, 21 Vet. App. 319 (2007).

9   *Buchanan v. Nicholson*, 451 F.3d 1331 (Fed. Cir. 2006).

10   *Collette v. Brown*, 82 F.3d 389 (Fed. Cir. 1996).

11   *See* 38 C.F.R. § 3.309(a).

12   *See* 38 C.F.R. § 3.307(a)(3), 3.309(a).

13   *Id.*

14   38 C.F.R. § 3.309(b).

15   38 C.F.R. § 3.309(c).

16   *See* 38 C.F.R. § 3.317.

17   *See* 38 C.F.R. 3.309(d).

18   *See* 38 C.F.R. 3.309(e).

19   *Vanerson v. West*, 12 Vet. App. 254 (1999).

20   *See* 38 C.F.R. § 3.310.

21   *See Allen v. Brown*, 7 Vet. App. 439 (1995).

22   Baran M. Timeline: Mental illness and war through history. Minnesota Public Radio. Feb 2010. Retrieved from http://minnesota.publicradio.org/projects/2010/02/beyond-deployment/ptsd-timeline/index.shtml

23   Tierney J. What Is Nostalgia Good For? Quite a Bit, Research Shows. The New York Times. July 9, 2013. Retrieved from http://www.nytimes.com/2013/07/09/science/what-is-nostalgia-good-for-quite-a-bit-research-shows.html

24   Hochschild A. (2012). To End All Wars: A Story of Loyalty and Rebellion, 1914-1918. Boston, New York: Mariner Books, Houghton, Mifflin Harcourt. pp. xv, 242, 348.

25 Jones E, Fear N, Wessely S. Shell Shock and Mild Traumatic Brain Injury: A Historical Review. Am J Psychiatry 2007; 164:1641-1645. Retrieved from http://ajp.psychiatryonline.org/doi/abs/10.1176/appi.ajp.2007.07071180.

26 Mcleod AD. "Shell Shock, Gordon Holmes and the Great War" J. R. Soc. Med. 2004 February; 97(2): 86-89. Retrieved from https://www.ncbi.nlm.nih.gov/pmc/articles/PMC1079301/.

27 Friedman MJ. (2017) History of PTSD in Veterans: Civil War to DSM-5. VA National Center for PTSD. Retrieved from https://www.ptsd.va.gov/public/PTSD-overview/basics/history-of-ptsd-vets.asp

28 Shatanmay, Chaim F. Post-Vietnam Syndrome. New York Times. May 6, 1972

29 Baran M. Timeline: Mental illness and war through history. Minnesota Public Radio. Feb 2010. Retrieved from http://minnesota.publicradio.org/projects/2010/02/beyond-deployment/ptsd-timeline/index.shtml

30 Hoge CW, Castro CA, Messer SC, McGurk D, Cotting DI, Koffman RL. (2004). Combat duty in Iraq and Afghanistan, mental health problems, and barriers to care. New England Journal of Medicine, 351, 13-22. Retrieved from http://www.nejm.org/doi/full/10.1056/NEJMoa040603.

31 Kessler RC, Nock MK, Schoenbaum M. Mental Health and the Army. JAMA Psychiatry. 2014;71(8):967-968. Retrieved from http://jamanetwork.com/journals/jamapsychiatry/article-abstract/1895655.

32 Kessler RC, Nock MK, Schoenbaum M. Mental Health and the Army. JAMA Psychiatry. 2014;71(8):967-968. Retrieved from http://jamanetwork.com/journals/jamapsychiatry/article-abstract/1895655.

33 American Psychiatric Association. (2013) Diagnostic and statistical manual of mental disorders. 5th ed.

34 Yaffe K, Vittinghoff E, Lindquist K, Barnes D, Covinsky KE, Neylan T, Kluse M, Marmar C. Post-Traumatic Stress Disorder and Risk of Dementia among U.S. Veterans. Arch Gen Psychiatry. 2010; 67(6): 608-613. Retrieved from https://www.ncbi.nlm.nih.gov/pubmed/20530010.

35 Tanielian T, Jaycox LH, Schell T, Marshall GM, Burnam MA, Eibner C, Karney B, Meredith LS, Ringel J, Vaiana ME. Invisible Wounds of War: Summary and Recommendations for Addressing Psychological and Cognitive Injuries. (2008) RAND Corporation. MG-720/1-CCF. Retrieved from https://www.rand.org/pubs/monographs/MG720z1.html.

36 Yaffe K, Vittinghoff E, Lindquist K, Barnes D, Covinsky KE, Neylan T, Kluse M, Marmar C. Post-Traumatic Stress Disorder and Risk of Dementia among U.S. Veterans. Arch Gen Psychiatry. 2010; 67(6): 608-613. Retrieved from https://www.ncbi.nlm.nih.gov/pubmed/20530010.

37 Kessler RC, Nock MK, Schoenbaum M. Mental Health and the Army. JAMA Psychiatry. 2014;71(8):967-968. Retrieved from http://jamanetwork.com/journals/jamapsychiatry/article-abstract/1895655.

38 Department of Defense. Defense and Veterans Brain Injury Center. Worldwide Numbers for TBI 2001- 2016. Retrieved from http://dvbic.dcoe.mil/dod-worldwide-numbers-tbi

39 Tanielian T, Jaycox LH, Schell T, Marshall GM, Burnam MA, Eibner C, Karney B, Meredith LS, Ringel J, Vaiana ME. Invisible Wounds of War: Summary and Recommendations for Addressing Psychological and Cognitive Injuries. (2008) RAND Corporation. MG-720/1-CCF. Retrieved from https://www.rand.org/pubs/monographs/MG720z1.html.

40 Trotter BB, Robinson ME, Milberg WP, McGlinchey RE, Salat DH. Military blast exposure,

ageing and white matter integrity.Brain. 2015 Aug;138(Pt 8):2278-92. Retrieved from http://www.ncbi.nlm.nih.gov/pubmed/26033970.

41 Yurgil KA, Barkauskas DA, Vasterling JJ, Nievergelt CM, Larson GE, Schork NJ, Litz BT, Nash WP, Baker DG. Association between traumatic brain injury and risk of posttraumatic stress disorder in active-duty Marines. JAMA Psychiatry. 2014 Feb;71(2):149-57. Retrieved from https://www.ncbi.nlm.nih.gov/pubmed/24337530.

42 Charles W. Hoge, M.D., Dennis McGurk, Ph.D., Jeffrey L. Thomas, Ph.D., Anthony L. Cox, M.S.W., Charles C. Engel, M.D., M.P.H., and Carl A. Castro, Ph.D. Mild Traumatic Brain Injury in U.S. Soldiers Returning from Iraq. N Engl J Med 2008; 358:453-463 January 31. Retrieved from https://www.ncbi.nlm.nih.gov/pubmed/18234750.

43 Brenner LA, Ignacio RV, Blow FC. Suicide and traumatic brain injury among individuals seeking Veterans Health Administration services. J Head Trauma Rehabil. 2011 Jul-Aug;26(4):257-64. Retrieved from https://www.ncbi.nlm.nih.gov/pubmed/21734509.

44 Goldstein LE, Fisher AM, Tagge CA, Zhang XL, et al. Chronic traumatic encephalopathy in blast-exposed military veterans and a blast neurotrauma mouse model. Sci Transl Med. 2012 May 16;4(134):134ra60. Retrieved from https://www.ncbi.nlm.nih.gov/pubmed/22593173.

45 Cook DB, Stegner AJ, Ellingson LD. (2010). Exercise Alters Pain Sensitivity in Gulf War Veterans with Chronic Musculoskeletal Pain. Journal of Pain, 11:8, 764-772.

46 Veteran Suicide Statistics by State. September 15, 2017. Retrieved from https://www.va.gov/opa/pressrel/pressrelease.cfm?id=2951

47 Fernandez I, Solomon RM. Neurophysiological Components of EMDR Treatment. Retrieved from http://www.psicotraumatologia.com/pdf/neuroemdr.pdf.

48 Substance Abuse and Mental Health Services Administration. Veterans and Military Families. (2017) https://www.samhsa.gov/veterans-military-families

49 Department of Veterans Affairs Office of Public and Intergovernmental Affairs. (2017) Care and Benefits for Veterans Strengthened by $186.5 Billion VA Budget. Retrieved from https://www.va.gov/opa/pressrel/pressrelease.cfm?id=2909.

50 American Psychological Association. (2011) The Critical Need for Mental Health Professionals Trained to Treat Post-Traumatic Stress Disorder and Traumatic Brain Injury. Retrieved from http://www.apa.org/about/gr/issues/military/critical-need.aspx.

51 Ben-Zeev D, Corrigan PW, Britt TW, Langford L. (2012). Stigma of mental illness and service use in the military. Journal of Mental Health, 21(3), 264-273. Retrieved from https://www.ncbi.nlm.nih.gov/pubmed/22250849.

52 World Health Organization, Department of Mental Health and Substance Abuse. (2004). Promoting mental health: concepts, emerging evidence, practice: summary report.

53 Ironson G, Cruess D, Kumar M. (2007). Immune and neuroendocrine alterations in post-traumatic stress disorder. In Psychoneuroimmunology. Vol. 1, pp. 531-547. Elsevier Inc.

54 Sijbrandij M, Engelhard IM, Lommen MJ, Leer A, Baas JM. Impaired fear inhibition learning predicts the persistence of symptoms of posttraumatic stress disorder (PTSD). J Psychiatr Res. 2013 Dec;47(12):1991-7. Retrieved from http://www.ncbi.nlm.nih.gov/pubmed/24090716.

55 Brewerton TD. Eating disorders, trauma, and comorbidity: focus on PTSD. Eat Disord. 2007;15:285-304.

56 Gielen N, Havermans RC, Tekelenburg M, Jansen A. Prevalence of post-traumatic stress

disorder among patients with substance use disorder: it is higher than clinicians think it is. Eur J Psychotraumatol. 2012; 3:10.3402/ejpt.v3i0.17734. Retrieved from http://www.ncbi.nlm.nih.gov/pmc/articles/PMC3415609/.

57   Pagoto SL, Schneider KL, Bodenlos JS, et al. (2012), Association of Post-Traumatic Stress Disorder and Obesity in a Nationally Representative Sample. Obesity, 20: 200-205. Retrieved from http://onlinelibrary.wiley.com/doi/10.1038/oby.2011.318/full.

58   Vanden Brook T. Veterans' claims for sleep apnea soar. USA Today. May 21, 2014. Retrieved from http://www.usatoday.com/story/news/nation/2014/05/21/veterans-administration-sleep-apnea/9291425/.

59   US. Department of Veterans Affairs. 2016 Annual Benefits Report. Retrieved from http://www.benefits.va.gov/REPORTS/abr/ABR-Compensation-FY16-0613017.pdf.

60   Colvonen PJ, Masino T, Drummond SP, et al. Obstructive Sleep Apnea and Posttraumatic Stress Disorder Among OEF/OIF/OND Veterans. J Clin Sleep Med. 2015 Apr 15;11(5):513-8. Retrieved from http://www.ncbi.nlm.nih.gov/pubmed/25665698.

61   Tasali E, Mokhlesi B, Van Cauter E. Obstructive sleep apnea and type 2 diabetes: interacting epidemics. Chest. 2008 Feb;133(2):496-506. Retrieved from http://www.ncbi.nlm.nih.gov/pubmed/18252916.

62   Vaccarino V, Goldberg J, Rooks C, et al. Post-Traumatic Stress Disorder and Incidence of Coronary Heart Disease: A Twin Study. J. Am. Col. Card. Volume 62, Issue 11, 10 September 2013, pp. 970-978. Retrieved from http://www.sciencedirect.com/science/article/pii/S0735109713025060.

63   Coughlin SS. Post-traumatic Stress Disorder and Cardiovascular Disease. Open Cardiovasc Med J. 2011; 5: 164-170. Retrieved from http://www.ncbi.nlm.nih.gov/pmc/articles/PMC3141329/.

64   Yaffe K, Vittinghoff E, Lindquist K, et al. Post-Traumatic Stress Disorder and Risk of Dementia among U.S. Veterans. Arch Gen Psychiatry. 2010 Jun; 67(6): 608-613. Retrieved from http://www.ncbi.nlm.nih.gov/pmc/articles/PMC2933793/#__ffn_sectitle.

65   McFall M, Cook J. PTSD And Health Risk Behavior. PTSD Research Quarterly. Fall 2006. Vol. 17:4. Retrieved from http://www.ptsd.va.gov/professional/newsletters/research-quarterly/V17N4.pdf.

66   Carrillo-Vico A, Lardone PJ, Álvarez-Sánchez N, et al. Melatonin: Buffering the Immune System. Int J Mol Sci. 2013 Apr; 14(4): 8638-8683. Retrieved from http://www.ncbi.nlm.nih.gov/pmc/articles/PMC3645767/.

67   Moreno-Smith M, Lutgendorf SK, Sood AK. Impact of stress on cancer metastasis. Future Oncol. 2010 Dec;6(12):1863-81. Retrieved from http://www.ncbi.nlm.nih.gov/pubmed/21142861.

68   Segerstrom SC, Miller GE. Psychological stress and the human immune system: a meta-analytic study of 30 years of inquiry. Psychol Bull. 2004 Jul;130(4):601-30. Retrieved from http://www.ncbi.nlm.nih.gov/pubmed/15250815.

69   O'Donovan A, Cohen BE, Seal KH, et al. Elevated risk for autoimmune disorders in Iraq and Afghanistan veterans with posttraumatic stress disorder. Biol Psychiatry. 2015 Feb 15;77(4):365-74. Retrieved from http://www.ncbi.nlm.nih.gov/pubmed/25104173.

70   Boscarino JA. Posttraumatic stress disorder and physical illness: results from clinical and epidemiologic studies. Ann N Y Acad Sci. 2004 Dec;1032:141-53. Retrieved from http://www.

ncbi.nlm.nih.gov/pubmed/15677401.

71 McFall M, Cook J. PTSD And Health Risk Behavior. PTSD Research Quarterly. Fall 2006. Vol. 17:4. Retrieved from http://www.ptsd.va.gov/professional/newsletters/research-quarterly/V17N4.pdf.

72 Breslau N, Davis GC, Schultz LR. (2003). Posttraumatic stress disorder and the incidence of nicotine, alcohol, and other drug disorder in persons who have experienced trauma. Archives of General Psychiatry, 60, 289-294.

73 Kessler RC, Sonnega A, Bromet E, et al. Posttraumatic stress disorder in the National Comorbidity Survey. Arch Gen Psychiatry. 1995 Dec;52(12):1048-60. Retrieved from http://www.ncbi.nlm.nih.gov/pubmed/7492257.

74 Lu Y, Nyunt MS, Gwee X, et al. Life event stress and chronic obstructive pulmonary disease (COPD): associations with mental well-being and quality of life in a population-based study. BMJ Open. 2012 Nov 19;2(6). Retrieved from http://www.ncbi.nlm.nih.gov/pubmed/23166130.

75 Vozoris NT, Fischer HD, Wang X, et al. Benzodiazepine drug use and adverse respiratory outcomes among older adults with COPD. Eur Respir J. 2014 Aug;44(2):332-40. Retrieved from http://www.ncbi.nlm.nih.gov/pubmed/24743966.

76 Hall RCW. (ed). Psychiatric Presentations of Medical Illness, SP Medical and Scientific Books, NY, 1980

77 Koranyi EK. (1979) Morbidity and rate of undiagnosed physical illnesses in a psychiatric clinic population. Archives of General Psychiatry, 36, 414-419.

78 Tanielian T, Jaycox LH, Schell T, et al. (2008) Invisible Wounds: Mental Health and Cognitive Care Needs of America's Returning Veterans. RAND Corporation Research Brief. Retrieved from https://www.rand.org/pubs/research_briefs/RB9336.html.

79 Deller JJ, Smith DE, English DT, Southwick EG. Venereal Diseases. In: Ognibene AJ, Barrett O. (Ed) Internal Medicine in Vietnam. Vol II. General Medicine and Infectious Diseases. (1982) Washington: Office of the Surgeon General and Center of Military History United States Army.

80 Clark LL, Hunt DJ. Incidence of Syphilis, Active Component, U.S. Armed Forces, 1 January 2010 Through 31 August 2015. September 2015. Medical Surveillance Monthly Report. Vol. 22 No. 9. Armed Forces Health Surveillance Branch. Retrieved from http://health.mil/Reference-Center/Reports/2015/01/01/Medical-Surveillance-Monthly-Report-Volume-22-Number-9.

81 Lacy BE, Mearin F, Chang L, et al. Bowel disorders. Gastroenterology 2016; 150(6): 1393-1407.

82 Lacy BE, Mearin F, Chang L, et al. Bowel disorders. Gastroenterology 2016; 150(6): 1393-1407.

83 Palsson OS, Drossman DA. Psychiatric and psychological dysfunction in irritable bowel syndrome and the role of psychological treatments. Gastroenterol Clin North Am 2005; 34(2): 281 303.

84 Selnes OA, Gottesman RF, Grega MA, et al. Cognitive and Neurologic Outcomes after Coronary-Artery Bypass Surgery. N Engl J Med 2012; 366:250-257. Retrieved from http://www.nejm.org/doi/full/10.1056/NEJMra1100109.

85 Roytera V, Bornstein NM, Russell D. Coronary artery bypass grafting (CABG) and cognitive decline: a review. J. Neuro. Sci. Vol 229-230, 15 March 2005, pp. 65-67. Retrieved from http://www.sciencedirect.com/science/article/pii/S0022510X04004241.

86 Ho PM, Arciniegas DB, Grigsby J, et al. Predictors of Cognitive Decline Following Coronary

Artery Bypass Graft Surgery. Ann Thorac Surg 2004;77:597-603. Retrieved from http://www.annalsthoracicsurgery.org/article/S0003-4975(03)01358-4/pdf.

87   Deng, J. (2019, April 16). Veteran's 29-day wait for VA appointment too short to qualify for outsourced care. WISHTV. Retrieved from https://www.wishtv.com/news/local-news/veteran-s-29-day-wait-for-va-appointment-too-short-to-qualify-for-outsourced-care/1929368038

88   Bronstein S, Griffin D. (2014, April 23). A fatal wait: Veterans languish and die on a VA hospital's secret list. *CNN*. Retrieved from http://www.cnn.com/2014/04/23/health/veterans-dying-health-care-delays/index.html

89   Carney J, Kaper S. (2014, May 20). Who really broke veterans' affairs? *National Journal*. Retrieved from http://www.nationaljournal.com/defense/who-really-broke-veterans-affairs-20140520

90   VA health care: Restructuring ambulatory care system would improve services to veterans. (1993, October 15). GAO/HRD-94-4. Retrieved from https://www.gao.gov/products/GAO/HRD-94-4

91   Veterans' Health Care Eligibility Reform Act of 1996, P.L. 104-262, Sec. 104(b)(1).

92   More national action needed to reduce waiting times, but some clinics have made progress. (2001, August). GAO-01-953. Retrieved from http://www.gao.gov/assets/240/232610.pdf

93   Trends in the utilization of VA programs and services. (2013, August). National Center for Veterans Analysis and Statistics. Retrieved from https://www.va.gov/vetdata/docs/quickfacts/Utilization_trends_2012.pdf

94   Reliability of reported outpatient medical appointment wait times and scheduling oversight need improvement. (2012, December). GAO-13-130. Retrieved from http://gao.gov/assets/660/651076.pdf

95   Timeline: The road to VA wait time scandal. (2014, May 9). AZ Central. Retrieved from https://www.azcentral.com/story/news/arizona/politics/2014/05/10/timeline-road-va-wait-time-scandal/8932493/

96   Timeline: The road to VA wait time scandal. (2014, May 9). AZ Central. Retrieved from https://www.azcentral.com/story/news/arizona/politics/2014/05/10/timeline-road-va-wait-time-scandal/8932493/

97   Wagner D. (2014, June 5). Acting VA secretary: 18 vets on Phoenix wait list died. *USA TODAY*. Retrieved from https://www.usatoday.com/story/news/nation/2014/06/05/va-scandal-sloan-gibson-phoenix/10033543/

98   Bronstein S, Griffin D, Black N. (2014, June 23). VA deaths covered up to make statistics look better, whistle-blower says. Retrieved from https://www.cnn.com/2014/06/23/us/phoenix-va-deaths-new-allegations/index.html

99   Oppel RA. (2014, September 18). V.A. official acknowledges link between delays and patient deaths. *New York Times*. Retrieved from https://www.nytimes.com/2014/09/18/us/va-officials-acknowledge-link-between-delays-and-patient-deaths.html

100 Review of alleged consult mismanagement at the Phoenix VA health care system. (2016, October 4). VAOIG-15-04672-342. Retrieved from https://www.va.gov/oig/pubs/VAOIG-15-04672-342.pdf

101 Shabad R. (2016, May 23). Veterans Affairs secretary compares wait times to lines at Disneyland. *CBS News*. Retrieved from https://www.washingtonpost.com/news/powerpost/wp/2016/05/23/

va-chief-compares-waits-for-veteran-care-to-disneyland-they-dont-measure-and-we-shouldnt-either/

102 VA Commission on Care Final Report (2016, June 30). Retrieved from https://s3.amazonaws. com/sitesusa/wp-content/uploads/sites/912/2016/07/Commission-on-Care_Final-Report_063016_FOR-WEB.pdf

103 Review of alleged wait-time manipulation at the Southern Arizona VA Health Care System. (2016, November 9). VAOIG 14-02890-72. Retrieved from https://www.va.gov/oig/pubs/ VAOIG-14-02890-72.pdf

104 Omaha World-Herald. (2017). Editorial: Sen. Grassley continues to be Congress' watchdog. Retrieved from https://omaha.com/opinion/editorial-sen-grassley-continues-to-be-congress-watchdog/article_6728c03c-00ec-5c56-8e58-a733c9ebd9c4.html

105 Grassley presses VA on apparently misleading wait times for veterans at Des Moines, Iowa City facilities. (2017, June 6). Retrieved from https://www.grassley.senate.gov/news/news-releases/ grassley-presses-va-apparently-misleading-wait-times-veterans-des-moines-iowa

106 Bennett J. (2017, August 24). Phoenix VA whistleblower files new complaint alleging that hundreds of vets are waiting more than 150 days for care. *Daily Caller.* Retrieved from http:// dailycaller.com/2017/08/24/phoenix-va-whistleblower-files-new-complaint-alleging-that-hundreds-of-vets-are-waiting-more-than-150-days-for-care/]

107 Improvements needed to address access-related challenges as VA plans consolidation of its community care programs. (2018, June). GAO-18-281. Retrieved from http://www.gao.gov/ assets/700/692271.pdf

108 VA announces access standards for health care. (2019, January 30). Retrieved from https://www. va.gov/opa/pressrel/pressrelease.cfm?id=5187

109 Penn M, Bhatnagar S, et al. (2019, January 18). Comparison of wait times for new patients between the private sector and United States Department of Veterans Affairs medical centers. *JAMA Netw Open.* 2(1):e187096. Retrieved from https://jamanetwork.com/journals/ jamanetworkopen/fullarticle/2720917

110 Bakalar N. (2019, January 22). V.A. wait times now shorter than for private doctors. *New York Times.* Retrieved from https://www.nytimes.com/2019/01/22/well/live/veterans-affairs-doctor-wait-times.html

111 Rubio requests additional information from VA after investigation into Orlando VA Medical Center wait times. (2019, February 14). Retrieved from https://www.rubio.senate.gov/public/ index.cfm/press-releases?ContentRecord_id=EA75264F-63AC-49EA-BE50-1BE6E41F1357

112 Slack D, Kelly J, Sergent J. (2019, February 7). Death rates, bedsores, ER wait times: Where every VA hospital lags or leads other medical care. *USA TODAY.* Retrieved from https://www. usatoday.com/in-depth/news/investigations/2019/02/07/where-every-va-hospital-lags-leads-other-care/2511739002/

113 2016 Wounded Warrior Project Survey. (2016, October 6). Retrieved from https://www. woundedwarriorproject.org/media/2641/2016-wwp-annual-warrior-survey.pdf

114 Gately PJ. (2019, April 10). Veteran who killed self at Austin clinic was referred from local VA. KWTX News. Retrieved from https://www.kwtx.com/content/news/Suicide-inside-Texas-VA-clinic-closes-down-facility-508390211.html

115 VA ensures Veterans have same-day access to emergency mental health care. (2019, April 16).

Retrieved from https://www.va.gov/opa/pressrel/pressrelease.cfm?id=5234

116 Kassraie A. (2019, March 19). Veterans cheer push for private health care options but worry about funding. *AARP.* Retrieved from https://www.aarp.org/home-family/voices/veterans/info-2019/mission-act-funding-concerns.html#

117 VA needs to address challenges as it implements the Veterans Community Care Program. (2019, April 10). GAO-19-507T. Retrieved from https://www.gao.gov/assets/700/698392.pdf

118 Mission Act: Community Care (2019, March 1). USDS Discovery Sprint Report. Retrieved from https://www.documentcloud.org/documents/5766330-USDS-Mission-Act-Report.html

119 Rosiak L. (2015, December 17). VA paid $871M in medical malpractice deals in past decade. *The Daily Caller.* Retrieved from https://dailycaller.com/2015/12/17/va-has-paid-230m-in-medical-malpractice-settlements/

120 End of year hospital star rating (FY2016). Veterans Health Administration. Retrieved from https://www.va.gov/qualityofcare/measure-up/End_of_Year_Hospital_Star_Rating.asp

121 Slack D, Lowary J. (2017, September 7). Exclusive: Botched surgery, delayed diagnosis at a one-star 'house of horrors' VA hospital. *USA TODAY.* Retrieved from https://www.usatoday.com/story/news/politics/2017/09/07/memphis-va-botched-surgery-veteran-patient-safety-threats/637497001/

122 Slack D, Kelly J, Sergent J. (2019, February 7). Death rates, bedsores, ER wait times: Where every VA hospital lags or leads other medical care. *USA TODAY.* Retrieved from https://www.usatoday.com/in-depth/news/investigations/2019/02/07/where-every-va-hospital-lags-leads-other-care/2511739002/

123 Interim summary report. (2017, April 12). VAOIG-17-02644-202. Retrieved from https://www.va.gov/oig/pubs/VAOIG-17-02644-202.pdf

124 Davidson J. (2018, July 16). VA doctor shortage fueled by management issues, poor pay. *Washington Post.* Retrieved from https://www.washingtonpost.com/news/powerpost/wp/2018/07/16/va-doctor-shortage-fueled-by-management-issues-poor-pay/

125 Steps taken to improve physician staffing, recruitment, and retention, but challenges remain. (2018, June 21). VHA GAO-18-623T. Retrieved from https://www.gao.gov/products/GAO-18-623T

126 OIG determination of Veterans Health Administration's occupational staffing shortages (FY2018). (2018, June 14). VAOIG-18-01693-196. Retrieved from https://www.va.gov/oig/pubs/VAOIG-18-01693-196.pdf

127 Slack D. (2017, December 3). USA TODAY Investigation: VA knowingly hires doctors with past malpractice claims, discipline for poor care. Retrieved from https://www.usatoday.com/story/news/politics/2017/12/03/usa-today-investigation-va-knowingly-hires-doctors-past-malpractice-claims-discipline-poor-care/909170001/

128 Greater focus on credentialing needed to prevent disqualified providers from delivering patient care. (2019, February 28). VHAGAO-19-6 Retrieved from https://www.gao.gov/products/GAO-19-6

129 Roos R. (2015, February 25). CDC puts *C. difficile* burden at 453,000 cases, 29,000 deaths. CIDRAP. Retrieved from http://www.cidrap.umn.edu/news-perspective/2015/02/cdc-puts-c-difficile-burden-453000-cases-29000-deaths

130 Nearly half a million Americans suffered from *C. difficile* infections in a single year. (2015,

February 25). CDC. Retrieved from http://www.cdc.gov/media/releases/2015/p0225-clostridium-difficile.html

131 Kang YP. (2018, December 11). Feds settle suit claiming VA's medication error killed patient. *Law360*. Retrieved from https://www.law360.com/articles/1110345/feds-settle-suit-claiming-va-s-medication-error-killed-patient

132 Slack D, Estes A. (2018, November 14). Feds find 'blatant disregard' for veteran safety at VA nursing home among the nation's worst. *USA TODAY*. Retrieved from https://www.usatoday.com/story/news/politics/2018/11/14/va-nursing-homes-ratings-patient-care-veterans-affairs/1947406002/

133 Slack D. (2019, March 28). Veterans harmed at VA nursing homes in 25 states, inspections find. *USA TODAY*. Retrieved from https://www.usatoday.com/story/news/politics/2019/03/28/va-nursing-home-inspections-find-veterans-harmed-52-facilities/3276087002/

134 Tap Water Scalds. (2012, March). U.S. Consumer Product Safety Commission. Retrieved from https://www.cpsc.gov/PageFiles/121522/5098.pdf

135 28 U.S.C. § 2674.

136 28 U.S.C. §1346(b).

137 28 U.S.C. § 2401(b).

138 Cueto E. (2018, January 16). Man says VA hospital left scalpel in his abdomen. *Law360*. Retrieved from https://www.law360.com/medical-malpractice/articles/1002025/man-says-va-hospital-left-scalpel-in-his-abdomen

139 Liessi G, Semisa M, et al. (1989, August). Retained surgical gauzes: acute and chronic CT and US findings. *Eur J Radiol*. 9(3):182-6. Retrieved from https://www.ncbi.nlm.nih.gov/pubmed/2680489

140 Serra J, Matias-Guiu X, et al. (1988, February). Surgical gauze pseudotumor. *Am J Surg*. 155(2):235-7. Retrieved from https://www.ncbi.nlm.nih.gov/pubmed/3277472

141 38 U.S.C. 1151

142 Agent Orange Record. Retrieved 24 July 2019, from http://www.agentorangerecord.com/information/the_quest_for_additional_relief/P1/

143 Agent Orange's Long Legacy, for Vietnam and Veterans. (2014). Retrieved 24 July 2019, from https://www.nytimes.com/2014/05/12/us/agent-oranges-long-legacy-for-vietnam-and-veterans.html

144 Bulletin of the Atomic Scientists. (1971). Retrieved 24 July 2019, from https://books.google.com/books?id=agsAAAAAMBAJ&pg=PA36#v=onepage&q&f=false

145 Vietnam's war against Agent Orange. (2004). Retrieved 24 July 2019, from http://news.bbc.co.uk/2/hi/health/3798581.stm

146 Veterans and Agent Orange Health Effects of Herbicides Used in Vietnam. (1994). Division of Health Promotion and Disease Prevention, Institute of Medicine. Retrieved 24 July 2019, from https://www.nap.edu/read/2141/chapter/1

147 Deutsche Welle (2015). *Lighter than Orange* [Video]. Retrieved from https://www.dw.com/en/documentary-lighter-than-orange/av-18559152 on February 10

148 Kahn, P.C., Gochfeld, M., Nygren, M., et al. Dioxins and Dibenzofurans in Blood and Adipose Tissue of Agent Orange—Exposed Vietnam Veterans and Matched Controls. *JAMA*.

1988;259(11):1661-1667. doi:10.1001/jama.1988.03720110023029

149 Fleischer, D. (2012). *Disability Rights Movement.* Philadelphia PA: Temple University Press.

150 US Department of Veterans Affairs, V. (2019). Veterans' Diseases Associated with Agent Orange - Public Health. Retrieved 24 July 2019, from http://www.publichealth.va.gov/exposures/agentorange/conditions/index.asp

151 Agent Orange Increases Lethal Prostate Cancer Risk - U.S. Medicine. (2019). Retrieved 24 July 2019, from http://www.usmedicine.com/agencies/department-of-veterans-affairs/agent-orange-increases-lethal-prostate-cancer-risk/

152 Agent Orange blights Vietnam. (1998). Retrieved 24 July 2019, from http://news.bbc.co.uk/2/hi/health/227467.stm

153 US Department of Veterans Affairs, V. (2019). Spina Bifida and Agent Orange - Public Health. Retrieved 24 July 2019, from https://www.publichealth.va.gov/exposures/agentorange/birth-defects/spina-bifida.asp

154 Agent Orange's Possible Link to Rare Cancer Type Sparks Advocacy Efforts. (2017). Retrieved 24 July 2019, from http://www.curetoday.com/articles/agent-oranges-possible-link-to-rare-cancer-type-sparks-advocacy-efforts

155 Post-deployment surveillance report Dec. 2015. (2015). Retrieved 24 July 2019, from http://www.publichealth.va.gov/docs/epidemiology/PDSR-Vol1-No1.pdf

156 Veterans Disability Info. (2017). New Study Could Expand a List of Diseases Associated with Agent Orange Exposure. Retrieved 24 July 2019, from https://www.veteransdisabilityinfo.com/blog.php?article=va-disability-claims-new-study-expand-agent-orange-list_347

157 DIC Benefits for widow of deceased veteran. Retrieved 24 July 2019, from https://www.veteransdisabilityinfo.com/case-studies.php

158 Veterans and Agent Orange: Update 2014 : Health and Medicine Division. (2014). Retrieved 24 July 2019, from http://www.nationalacademies.org/hmd/Reports/2016/Veterans-and-Agent-Orange-Update-2014.aspx

159 Ornstein, C. (2016). The Agent Orange Widows Club—ProPublica. Retrieved 24 July 2019, from https://www.propublica.org/article/the-agent-orange-widows-club

160 Gang, E. (2015). The VA Population of Veterans Receiving VA Benefits Has Still Not Peaked. Retrieved 24 July 2019, from https://www.veteransdisabilityinfo.com/blog.php?article=va-population-veterans-receiving-va-benefits-has-still-not-peaked_275

161 2019 Wounded Warrior Project - Annual warrior survey results. Retrieved December 6, 2022, from https://www.woundedwarriorproject.org/media/gyvp3ns1/2019-annual-warrior-survey.pdf

162 Pittman, P. R., Norris, S. L., Coonan, K. M., & McKee, K. T. (2005). An assessment of health status among medical research volunteers who served in the project Whitecoat Program at Fort Detrick, Maryland. *Military Medicine, 170*(3), 183-187. doi:10.7205/milmed.170.3.183

163 Government denies health benefits for most U.S. troops who blame illnesses on burn pits. (2019, November 12). Retrieved December 6, 2022, from https://abc11.com/burn pit-illness-troops-denied-coverage-veterans-affairs/5689738/

164 Open Burn Pit Report to Congress. (2019). Retrieved from https://www.acq.osd.mil/eie/

Downloads/Congress/Open%20Burn%20Pit%20Report-2019.pdf

165 *Gulf War and health: Fuels, combustion products, and Propellants, volume 3.* (2005). National Academies Press. Retrieved from https://nap.nationalacademies.org/read/11180/chapter/1

166 National Academies News: Gulf War and Health. (2004). Retrieved December 6, 2022, from https://www.eurekalert.org/news-releases/470872

167 Guidelines for field and waste management. Technical Bulletin - Headquarters, Department of the Army. (2006). Retrieved from https://armypubs.army.mil/epubs/DR_pubs/DR_a/pdf/web/tbmed593.pdf

168 Defense Health Board Findings Pertaining to Health Risk Assessment, Bum Pit Exposures, Balad Air Base, Iraq. (2008). Retrieved from https://www.health.mil/Reference-Center/Reports/2008/06/26/Health-Risk-Assessment-burn pit-Exposures-Balad-Air-Base-Iraq

169 Senate Democratic Policy Committee "Are burn pits in Iraq and Afghanistan making soldiers sick?" - DPC. (2009). Retrieved December 6, 2022, from https://www.dpc.senate.gov/hearings/hearing50/szema.pdf

170 King, M. S., Eisenberg, R., Newman, J. H., Tolle, J. J., Harrell, F. E., Nian, H., . . . Miller, R. F. (2011). Constrictive bronchiolitis in soldiers returning from Iraq and Afghanistan. *New England Journal of Medicine, 365*(3), 222-230. doi:10.1056/nejmoa1101388

171 Long-term health consequences of exposure to burn pits in Iraq and Afghanistan. (2011). *The National Academies Press.* doi:10.17226/13209

172 Open Burn Pit Report to Congress. (2019). Retrieved from https://www.acq.osd.mil/eie/Downloads/Congress/Open%20Burn%20Pit%20Report-2019.pdf

173 VA enhances research and education efforts related to airborne hazards and burn pit exposure. (2019, July 26). Retrieved December 6, 2022, from https://blogs.va.gov/VAntage/63885/va-enhances-research-education-efforts-related-airborne-hazards-burn pit-exposure/

174 War Related Illness and Injury Study Center. Burn Pits (Trash and Feces Fires). (2013, December 13). Retrieved December 6, 2022, from https://www.warrelatedillness.va.gov/education/exposures/burn pits.asp

175 Viers, M., Gleason, P., & Copp, T. et al. (2019) STRICKEN: Military veteran cancer rates on the rise. *McClatchy DC.* Retrieved from https://www.mcclatchydc.com/news/nation-world/national/article236566228.html

176 Wallis, C. (2018, April 01). Why pancreatic cancer is on the rise. *Scientific American.* Retrieved December 6, 2022, from https://www.scientificamerican.com/article/why-pancreatic-cancer-is-on-the-rise/

177 Government denies health benefits for most U.S. troops who blame illnesses on burn pits. (2019, November 12). *WTVD-TV Chicago.* Retrieved December 6, 2022, from https://abc7chicago.com/burn pit-illness-troops-denied-coverage-veterans-affairs/5689738/

178 H.R.2436 - 117th Congress (2021-2022): Veterans burn pits exposure ... (n.d.). Retrieved December 6, 2022, from https://www.congress.gov/bill/117th-congress/house-bill/2436

179 VA - Office of Public and Intergovernmental Affairs. (2022). *VA establishes presumptive service connection for rare respiratory cancers for certain Veterans* [Press release]. Retrieved from https://www.va.gov/opa/pressrel/pressrelease.cfm?id=5786

180 VA Rule 87 FR 24421 - Presumptive Service Connection for Rare Respiratory Cancers Due to Exposure to Fine Particulate Matter. (2022, April 26). Retrieved December 6, 2022, from https://

www.federalregister.gov/documents/2022/04/26/2022-08820/presumptive-service-connection-for-rare-respiratory-cancers-due-to-exposure-to-fine-particulate

181 White House. (2022, August 10). *President Biden Signs the PACT Act and Delivers on His Promise to America's Veterans.*[Press release].

182 Summary of the water contamination situation at Camp Lejeune. (2017, April 18). *Agency for Toxic Substances and Disease Registry.* Retrieved December 6, 2022, from https://www.atsdr.cdc.gov/sites/lejeune/watermodeling_summary.html

183 Bove, F. J., Ruckart, P. Z., Maslia, M., & Larson, T. C. (2014). Evaluation of mortality among Marines and Navy personnel exposed to contaminated drinking water at USMC Base Camp Lejeune: A retrospective cohort study. *Environmental Health, 13*(1). doi:10.1186/1476-069x-13-10

184 Sass, J. B., Castleman, B., & Wallinga, D. (2005). Vinyl chloride: A case study of data suppression and misrepresentation. *Environmental Health Perspectives, 113*(7), 809-812. doi:10.1289/ehp.7716

185 Integrated Risk Information System (IRIS) U.S. Environmental Protection Agency. Chemical Assessment Summary National Center for Environmental Assessment. Vinyl chloride. Retrieved December 6, 2022, from https://iris.epa.gov/static/pdfs/1001_summary.pdf

186 Assessment of the Evidence for the Drinking Water Contaminants at Camp Lejeune and Specific Cancers and Other Diseases. (2017). *Agency for Toxic Substances & Disease Registry.* Retrieved December 6, 2022, from https://www.atsdr.cdc.gov/sites/lejeune/docs/ATSDR_summary_of_the_evidence_for_causality_TCE_PCE_508.pdf

187 Bove, F. J., Ruckart, P. Z., Maslia, M., & Larson, T. C. (2014). Evaluation of mortality among Marines and Navy personnel exposed to contaminated drinking water at USMC Base Camp Lejeune: A retrospective cohort study. *Environmental Health, 13*(1). doi:10.1186/1476-069x-13-10

188 Dahlgren, J., Klein, J., & Takhar, H. (2008). Cluster of Hodgkin's lymphoma in residents near a non-operational petroleum refinery. *Toxicology and Industrial Health, 24*(10), 683-692. doi:10.1177/0748233708100553

189 Wang, G., Wang, J., Ansari, G. S., & Khan, M. F. (2017). Autoimmune potential of perchloroethylene: Role of lipid-derived aldehydes. *Toxicology and Applied Pharmacology, 333*, 76-83. doi:10.1016/j.taap.2017.08.009

190 Aksoy, M. (1989). Hematotoxicity and carcinogenicity of benzene. *Environmental Health Perspectives, 82*, 193-197. doi:10.1289/ehp.8982193

191 Fedeli, U., Girardi, P., & Mastrangelo, G. (2019). Occupational exposure to vinyl chloride and liver diseases. *World Journal of Gastroenterology, 25*(33), 4885-4891. doi:10.3748/wjg.v25.i33.4885

192 Malaguarnera, G. (2012). Toxic hepatitis in occupational exposure to solvents. *World Journal of Gastroenterology,18*(22), 2756. doi:10.3748/wjg.v18.i22.2756

193 Cave, M., Falkner, K. C., Ray, M., Joshi-Barve, S., Brock, G., Khan, R., et al. (2009). Toxicant-associated steatohepatitis in vinyl chloride workers. *Hepatology, 51*(2), 474-481. doi:10.1002/hep.23321

194 Kim, K. (2015). Influences of environmental chemicals on atopic dermatitis. *Toxicological Research, 31*(2), 89-96. doi:10.5487/tr.2015.31.2.089

195 Watanabe, H. (2011). Hypersensitivity syndrome due to trichloroethylene exposure: A severe generalized skin reaction resembling drug-induced hypersensitivity syndrome. *The Journal of Dermatology, 38*(3), 229-235. doi:10.1111/j.1346-8138.2010.01155.x

196 Li, A. J., Pal, V. K., & Kannan, K. (2021). A review of environmental occurrence, toxicity,

biotransformation and biomonitoring of volatile organic compounds. *Environmental Chemistry and Ecotoxicology, 3*, 91-116. doi:10.1016/j.enceco.2021.01.001

197   Toxicological profile for vinyl chloride. (2006). *ATSDR's Toxicological Profiles.* Retrieved December 6, 2022, from https://www.atsdr.cdc.gov/ToxProfiles/tp20-a.pdf

198   Forand, S. P., Lewis-Michl, E. L., & Gomez, M. I. (2012). Adverse birth outcomes and maternal exposure to trichloroethylene and tetrachloroethylene through soil vapor intrusion in New York State. *Environmental Health Perspectives, 120*(4), 616-621. doi:10.1289/ehp.1103884

199   Veteran exposed to contaminated water at Camp Lejeune suffers skin lesions, loses teeth and legs. (2019, September 24). Retrieved December 6, 2022, from https://www.11alive.com/video/news/investigations/the-reveal/veteran-exposed-to-contaminated-water/85-28a79fed-a5af-40f8-9eee-dfc34c215347

200   National Research Council (US) Committee on Contaminated Drinking Water at Camp Lejeune. (2009). *Contaminated Water Supplies at Camp Lejeune: Assessing Potential Health Effects.* National Academies Press (US).

201   Institute of Medicine. (2003). *Gulf War and health. Volume 2: Insecticides and solvents.* Washington, DC: The National Academies Press. Retrieved from https://nap.nationalacademies.org/read/10628/chapter/1

202   Reif, J., Burch, J., Nuckols, J., Metzger, L., & Anger, K. F. (2003). Neurobehavioral effects of exposure to trichloroethylene through a municipal water supply. *Epidemiology, 14* (Supplement). doi:10.1097/00001648-200309001-00213

203   Who qualifies for PACT Act VA benefits? (2022, September 16). Retrieved December 6, 2022, from https://www.veteransdisabilityinfo.com/blog/482/who-qualifies-for-pact-act-va-benefits/

204   Toxicologic assessment of jet-propulsion fuel 8. (2003). Washington, D.C.: National Academies Press. Retrieved from https://www.ncbi.nlm.nih.gov/books/NBK207620/

205   Marker, B. R. (2007). Contaminants in the subsurface: Source zone assessment and remediation, National Research Council. The National Academies Press, Washington, D.C., 2005. ISBN 0 309 09447 X, XII + 358 pp. *Land Degradation & Development, 18*(4), 471-472. doi:10.1002/ldr.788

206   Follow-up Health Consultation: Anniston Army Depot. Anniston, Alabama. (2008, September 30). *U.S. Department of Health And Human Services. Public Health Service. Agency for Toxic Substances and Disease Registry.* Retrieved December 6, 2022, from https://www.atsdr.cdc.gov/HAC/pha/AnnistonArmyDepot093008/Anniston%20Army%20Depot%20HC%20093008.pdf

207   Health Consultation. Anniston PCB Air Sampling. (2015, February 4). *Department of Health And Human Services. Agency for Toxic Substances and Disease Registry.* Retrieved December 6, 2022, from https://www.atsdr.cdc.gov/HAC/pha/AnnistonPCBSiteAirSampling/Anniston%20PCB%20Site_Air%20Sampling_HC_02-04-2015.pdf

208   Department of Defense Annual Report on Sexual Assault in the Military Fiscal Year 2015 (2016). Retrieved from http://www.sapr.mil/public/docs/reports/FY15_Annual/FY15_Annual_Report_on_Sexual_Assault_in_the_Military.pdf

209   'DailyMail UK (2014) When a gunnery sergeant tells you to take off your clothes, you better take off your clothes': The male victims of military rape tell their heartbreaking stories. Retrieved from http://www.dailymail.co.uk/news/article-2757344/When-gunnery-sergeant-tells-clothes-better-clothes-You-don-t-ask-questions-The-male-victims-military-rape-tell-heartbreaking-stories.html

210 Holland, K.J., Rabelo, V.C., & Cortina, L.M. (2015). Collateral damage: Military sexual trauma and help-seeking barriers. Psychology of Violence, 1-9. doi: http://dx.doi.org/10.1037/a0039467

211 Title 38 U.S. Code 1720D

212 Department of Veterans Affairs, Military Sexual Trauma. May 2015. Retrieved from https://www.mentalhealth.va.gov/docs/mst_general_factsheet.pdf

213 University of Michigan Sexual Assault Prevention and Awareness Center (2011) Military Sexual Trauma. Retrieved from https://sapac.umich.edu/article/military-sexual-trauma-mst

214 Department of Veterans Affairs, Patient Care Services, Mental Health Services, MST Support Team, FY 2015 Summary of MST-Related Outpatient Care (2016)

215 Fischer, B. Son, men don't get raped. GQ Magazine August 2015. Retrieved from https://www.gq.com/long-form/male-military-rape

216 Fischer, B. Son, men don't get raped. GQ Magazine August 2015. Retrieved from https://www.gq.com/long-form/male-military-rape

217 Department of Defense Annual Report on Sexual Assault in the Military Fiscal Year 2015 (2016). Retrieved from http://www.sapr.mil/public/docs/reports/FY15_Annual/FY15_Annual_Report_on_Sexual_Assault_in_the_Military.pdf

218 Department of Defense Annual Report on Sexual Assault in the Military Fiscal Year 2016 (2017). Retrieved from http://sapr.mil/public/docs/reports/FY16_Annual/FY16_SAPRO_Annual_Report.pdf

219 Department of Defense Annual Report on Sexual Harassment and Violence at the Military Service Academies 2012 (2013). Retrieved from http://www.sapr.mil/public/docs/reports/FINAL_APY_12-13_MSA_Report.pdf

220 Human Rights Watch. Booted. Lack of Recourse for wrongfully discharged US military rape survivors. (2016). Retrieved from https://www.hrw.org/report/2016/05/19/booted/lack-recourse-wrongfully-discharged-us-military-rape-survivors

221 Department of Defense Annual Report on Sexual Assault in the Military Fiscal Year 2016 (2017). Retrieved from http://sapr.mil/public/docs/reports/FY16_Annual/FY16_SAPRO_Annual_Report.pdf

222 Department of Defense Annual Report on Sexual Assault in the Military Fiscal Year 2015 (2016). Retrieved from http://www.sapr.mil/public/docs/reports/FY15_Annual/FY15_Annual_Report_on_Sexual_Assault_in_the_Military.pdf

223 Department of Defense Annual Report on Sexual Assault in the Military Fiscal Year 2015 (2016). Retrieved from http://www.sapr.mil/public/docs/reports/FY15_Annual/FY15_Annual_Report_on_Sexual_Assault_in_the_Military.pdf

224 Brown, N. B., & Bruce, S. E. (2016). Stigma, career worry, and mental illness symptomatology: Factors influencing treatment-seeking for Operation Enduring Freedom and Operation Iraqi Freedom soldiers and veterans. Psychological Trauma: Theory, Research, Practice, and Policy, 8(3), 276-283. Retrieved from http://psycnet.apa.org/record/2015-42694-001

225 Human Rights Watch. Booted. Lack of Recourse for wrongfully discharged US military rape survivors. (2016). Retrieved from https://www.hrw.org/report/2016/05/19/booted/lack-recourse-wrongfully-discharged-us-military-rape-survivors

226 Department of Defense Inspector General, Evaluation of the Separation of Service Members Who Made a Report of Sexual Assault (2016). Retrieved from http://www.dodig.mil/pubs/

documents/DODIG-2016-088.pdf

227 Department of Defense Inspector General, Veterans Legal Clinic, Legal Services Center of Harvard Law School, Underserved: How the VA Wrongfully Excludes Veterans with Bad Paper (2016). Retrieved from https://www.swords-to-plowshares.org/sites/default/files/Underserved.pdf

228 Fischer, B. Son, men don't get raped. GQ Magazine August 2015. Retrieved from https://www.gq.com/long-form/male-military-rape

229 Department of Defense Annual Report on Sexual Assault in the Military Fiscal Year 2015 (2016). Retrieved from http://www.sapr.mil/public/docs/reports/FY15_Annual/FY15_Annual_Report_on_Sexual_Assault_in_the_Military.pdf

230 Department of Defense Annual Report on Sexual Assault in the Military Fiscal Year 2015 (2016). Retrieved from http://www.sapr.mil/public/docs/reports/FY15_Annual/FY15_Annual_Report_on_Sexual_Assault_in_the_Military.pdf

231 Northcut, T.B., & Kienow, A. (2014). The trauma trifecta of military sexual trauma: A case study illustrating the integration of mind and body in clinical work with survivors of MST. Clinical Social Work, 42, 247-259. Retrieved from https://link.springer.com/article/10.1007/s10615-014-0479-0

232 Valente, S. & Wright, C. (2007). Military Sexual Trauma: Violence and Sexual Abuse. Military Medicine, 172 (3), 259-265. Retrieved from http://militarymedicine.amsus.org/doi/pdf/10.7205/MILMED.172.3.259

233 Northcut, T.B., & Kienow, A. (2014). The trauma trifecta of military sexual trauma: A case study illustrating the integration of mind and body in clinical work with survivors of MST. Clinical Social Work, 42, 247-259. Retrieved from https://link.springer.com/article/10.1007/s10615-014-0479-0

234 U.S. Department of Veterans Affairs National Center for PTSD. (2015). Military Sexual Trauma. Retrieved from http://www.ptsd.va.gov/public/types/violence/military-sexual-trauma-general.asp

235 Fischer, B. Son, men don't get raped. GQ Magazine August 2015. Retrieved from https://www.gq.com/long-form/male-military-rape

236 Monteith LL, Bahraini NH, Matarazzo BB, Soberay KA, Smith CP. Perceptions of Institutional Betrayal Predict Suicidal Self-Directed Violence Among Veterans Exposed to Military Sexual Trauma. J Clin Psychol. 2016 Jul;72(7):743-55. Retrieved from http://onlinelibrary.wiley.com/doi/10.1002/jclp.22292/abstract

237 Schry, A.R., Hibberd, R., Wagner, H.R., Turchik, J.A., Kimbrel, N.A., Wong, M. and Strauss, J.L. Functional Correlates of Military Sexual Assault in Male Veterans. Psychological Services. (2015) Vol. 12, No. 4, 384-393. Retrieved from https://www.apa.org/pubs/journals/releases/ser-ser0000053.pdf

238 Kimerling, R.,, Makin-Byrd, K., Louzon, S., Ignacio, R.V. and McCarthy, J.F. Military Sexual Trauma and Suicide Mortality. American Journal of Preventive Medicine. June 2016. Vol. 50, Iss. 6, 684-691. Retrieved from http://www.sciencedirect.com/science/article/pii/S0749379715007035

239 Brignone E, Gundlapalli AV, Blais RK, Carter ME, Suo Y, Samore MH, Kimerling R, Fargo JD. Differential Risk for Homelessness Among US Male and Female Veterans With a Positive Screen

for Military Sexual Trauma. JAMA Psychiatry. 2016 Jun 1;73(6):582-9. Retrieved from http://jamanetwork.com/journals/jamapsychiatry/fullarticle/2515956

240 638 F.3d 1379 (Fed. Cir. 2011)

241 Wolters Kluwer UpToDate Medical Reference for Health Care Providers. Medical Care of the Returning Veteran. Literature review Dec 2019. https://www.uptodate.com/contents/medical-care-of-the-returning-veteran/print?search=traumatic%20brain%20injury%20military&source=search_result&selectedTitle=5~150&usage_type=default&display_rank=5

242 Wolters Kluwer UpToDate Medical Reference for Health Care Providers. Traumatic brain injury: Epidemiology, classification, and pathophysiology. Literature review Dec 2019. https://www.uptodate.com/contents/traumatic-brain-injury-epidemiology-classification-and-pathophysiology/print?search=traumatic%20brain%20injury%20military&source=search_result&selectedTitle=3~150&usage_type=default&display_rank=3

243 Wolters Kluwer UpToDate Medical Reference for Health Care Providers. Medical Care of the Returning Veteran. Literature review Dec 2019. https://www.uptodate.com/contents/medical-care-of-the-returning-veteran/print?search=traumatic%20brain%20injury%20military&source=search_result&selectedTitle=5~150&usage_type=default&display_rank=5

244 Wolters Kluwer UpToDate Medical Reference for Health Care Providers. Medical Care of the Returning Veteran. Literature review Dec 2019. https://www.uptodate.com/contents/medical-care-of-the-returning-veteran/print?search=traumatic%20brain%20injury%20military&source=search_result&selectedTitle=5~150&usage_type=default&display_rank=5

245 Wolters Kluwer UpToDate Medical Reference for Health Care Providers. Sequelae of mild traumatic brain injury (concussion) in adults. Literature review Dec 2019. https://www.uptodate.com/contents/sequelae-of-mild-traumatic-brain-injury?search=traumatic%20brain%20injury&source=search_result&selectedTitle=3~150&usage_type=default&display_rank=3

246 Hoge CW, Castro CA. Treatment of generalized war-related health concerns: placing TBI and PTSD in context. Walter Reed Army Institute of Research, Silver Spring, Maryland. JAMA. 2014 Oct;312(16):1685-6. PMID25335151

247 Andrews B, Brewin CR, Philpott R, Stewart L. Delayed-onset posttraumatic stress disorder: a systematic review of the evidence. Department of Psychology, Royal Holloway University of London, Egham, Surrey TW20 OEX, UK. Am J Psychiatry. 2007;164(9):1319. PMID17728415

248 Hoge CW, Auchterlonie JL, Milliken CS. Mental health problems, use of mental health services, and attrition from military service after returning from deployment to Iraq or Afghanistan. Division of Psychiatry and Neuroscience, Walter Reed Army Institute of Research, Washington, DC, USA. JAMA. 2006;295(9):1023. PMID16507803

249 Fonda JR, Fredman L, Brogly SB, McGlinchey RE, Milberg WP, Gradus JL. Traumatic Brain Injury and Attempted Suicide Among Veterans of the Wars in Iraq and Afghanistan. Am J Epidemiol. 2017;186(2):220. PMID28472407

250 Wilk JE, Bliese PD, Kim PY, et al. Relationship of combat experiences to alcohol misuse among U.S. soldiers returning from the Iraq war. Division of Psychiatry and Neuroscience, Walter Reed Army Institute of Research, U.S. Army Medical Research and Materiel Command, Silver Spring, MD 20910, US. Drug Alcohol Depend 2010; 108:115. PMID20060237

251 Spelman JF, Hunt SC, Seal KH, Burgo-Black AL. Post deployment care for returning combat veterans. VA Connecticut Health Care System, West Haven, CT 06511, US. J Gen Intern Med 2012; 27:1200. PMID 22648608

252 Schneiderman AI, Braver ER, Kang HK. Understanding sequelae of injury mechanisms and mild traumatic brain injury incurred during the conflicts in Iraq and Afghanistan: persistent postconcussive symptoms and posttraumatic stress disorder. War-Related Illness and Injury Study Center, Washington DC VA Medical Center, Washington, DC 20422, US. Am J Epidemiol 2008; 167:1446. PMID18424429

253 Kennedy RE, Livingston L, Riddick A, et al. Evaluation of the Neurobehavioral Functioning Inventory as a depression screening tool after traumatic brain injury. Department of Psychiatry, Virginia Commonwealth University, Richmond 23298, US. J Head Trauma Rehabil 2005; 20:512. PMID16304488

254 Seel RT, Kreutzer JS, Rosenthal M, et al. Depression after traumatic brain injury: a National Institute on Disability and Rehabilitation Research Model Systems multicenter investigation. Defense and Veterans Brain Injury Center, McGuire Veterans Administration Medical Center, Richmond, VA, US. Arch Phys Med Rehabil 2003; 84:177. PMID 12601647

255 Spelman JF, Hunt SC, Seal KH, Burgo-Black AL. Post deployment care for returning combat veterans. VA Connecticut Health Care System, West Haven, CT 06511, US. J Gen Intern Med 2012; 27:1200. PMID 22648608

256 Taylor BC, Hagel EM, Carlson KF, et al. Prevalence and costs of co-occurring traumatic brain injury with and without psychiatric disturbance and pain among Afghanistan and Iraq War Veteran V.A. users. Center for Chronic Disease Outcomes Research, Department of Veterans Affairs Health Care System, Minneapolis, MN 55417, US. Med Care 2012; 50:342. PMID22228249

257 Wolters Kluwer UpToDate Medical Reference for Health Care Providers. Sequelae of mild traumatic brain injury (concussion) in adults. Literature review Dec 2019. https://www.uptodate. com/contents/sequelae-of-mild-traumatic-brain-injury?search=traumatic%20brain%20 injury&source=search_result&selectedTitle=3~150&usage_type=default&display_rank=3

258 Wolters Kluwer UpToDate Medical Reference for Health Care Providers. Sleep-wake disorders in patients with traumatic brain injury. Literature review Dec 2019. https://www. uptodate.com/contents/sleep-wake-disorders-in-patients-with-traumatic-brain-injury/ print?search=traumatic%20brain%20injury%20military&source=search_result&selectedTitle=4 ~150&usage_type=default&display_rank=4

259 Yang CC, Tu YK, Hua MS, Huang SJ. The association between the postconcussion symptoms and clinical outcomes for patients with mild traumatic brain injury. Department of Psychology, National Taiwan University Hospital, Republic of China. J Trauma 2007; 62:657. PMID17414343

260 De Kruijk JR, Leffers P, Menheere PP, et al. Prediction of post-traumatic complaints after mild traumatic brain injury: early symptoms and biochemical markers. Department of Neurology, University Hospital Maastricht, Maastricht, Netherlands. J Neurol Neurosurg Psychiatry 2002; 73:727. PMID 12438478

261 McAllister TW, Flashman LA, Maerlender A, et al. Cognitive effects of one season of head impacts in a cohort of collegiate contact sport athletes. Department of Psychiatry, Dartmouth Medical School. Neurology 2012; 78:1777. PMID22592370

262 McKee AC, Cantu RC, Nowinski CJ, et al. Chronic traumatic encephalopathy in athletes: progressive tauopathy after repetitive head injury. Department of Neurology, Center for the Study of Traumatic Encephalopathy, Boston University School of Medicine, Boston, MA, US. J Neuropathol Exp Neurol 2009; 68:709. PMID 19535999

263 DeKosky ST, Blennow K, Ikonomovic MD, Gandy S. Acute and chronic traumatic encephalopathies: pathogenesis and biomarkers. Office of the Dean and Department of Neurology, University of Virginia School of Medicine, P. O. Box 800793, Charlottesville, VA 22908, US. Nat Rev Neurol 2013; 9:192. PMID 23558985

264 Wolters Kluwer UpToDate Medical Reference for Health Care Providers. Post-traumatic seizures and epilepsy. Literature review Dec 2019. https://www.uptodate.com/contents/post-traumatic-seizures-and-epilepsy?search=mild%20traumatic%20brain%20injury&topicRef=111925&source=see_link

265 McMillan TM, Teasdale GM, Weir CJ, Stewart E. Death after head injury: the 13 year outcome of a case control study. Psychological Medicine, Faculty of Medicine, University of Glasgow, Gartnavel Royal Hospital, 1055 Great Western Road, Glasgow G12 0XH, UK. J Neurol Neurosurg Psychiatry 2011; 82:931. PMID21282727

266 McMillan TM, Weir CJ, Wainman-Lefley J. Mortality and morbidity 15 years after hospital admission with mild head injury: a prospective case-controlled population study. Institute of Health and Wellbeing, MVLS, University of Glasgow, Glasgow, UK. J Neurol Neurosurg Psychiatry 2014; 85:1214. PMID 24623794

267 Wolters Kluwer UpToDate Medical Reference for Health Care Providers. Sequelae of mild traumatic brain injury (concussion) in adults. Literature review Dec 2019. https://www.uptodate.com/contents/sequelae-of-mild-traumatic-brain-injury?search=traumatic%20brain%20injury&source=search_result&selectedTitle=3~150&usage_type=default&display_rank=3

268 Goodman JC. Pathologic changes in mild head injury. Department of Pathology, Baylor College of Medicine, Houston, Texas 77030. Semin Neurol 1994; 14:19. PMID 8029556

269 McCrory P, Meeuwisse WH, Aubry M, et al. Consensus statement on concussion in sport: the 4th International Conference on Concussion in Sport held in Zurich, November 2012. The Florey Institute of Neuroscience and Mental Health, , Heidelberg, Victoria, Australia. Br J Sports Med 2013; 47:250. PMID23479479

270 Wilson S. (2018, January 25). John K. Lopez Disabled Veteran Business Enterprises awards for 2018. CalVet Connect. Retrieved from https://calvetconnectblog.com/2018/01/25/john-k-lopez-disabled-veteran-business-enterprises-awards-for-2018/

271 Cal. P.C.C. §10115

272 CalVet gets small business award, recognizes DVBE's. (2012, December). *CalVet Newsletter.* Retrieved from https://www.calvet.ca.gov/Documents/Newsletter%202012-12.pdf

273 Kerry floor statement on providing assistance to veteran-owned small businesses. (1999, August 5). U.S. Senate Committee on Small Business & Entrepreneurship. Retrieved from https://www.sbc.senate.gov/public/index.cfm/statements?ID=79BED882-5060-4184-9102-E1C1391A86A7

274 Veterans Entrepreneurship and Small Business Development Act Of 1999. (1999, June 29). U.S. House of Representatives. Rept. 106-206. Retrieved from https://www.congress.gov/106/crpt/hrpt206/CRPT-106hrpt206-pt1.pdf

275 13 C.F.R §125

276 Contracting with service-disabled veterans' businesses. (2005, January 12). Office of Government Contracting & Business Development. Retrieved from https://www.sba.gov/offices/headquarters/ogc_and_bd/resources/5526

277 Veteran-owned businesses and their owners (2017, April). SBA Office of Advocacy. Retrieved

from https://www.sba.gov/sites/default/files/advocacy/435-veteran-owned-businesses-report.pdf

278 Leesburg man sentenced for role in procurement fraud scheme affecting over $33 million in federal contracts. (2014, February 21). USDOJ. Retrieved from https://www.justice.gov/usao-edva/pr/leesburg-man-sentenced-role-procurement-fraud-scheme-affecting-over-33-million-federal

279 ThunderCat agrees to civil settlement for bid-rigging and kickback schemes. (2016, December 15). USDOJ. Retrieved from https://www.justice.gov/usao-edva/pr/thundercat-agrees-civil-settlement-bid-rigging-and-kickback-schemes

280 Defense contractor ADS Inc. agrees to pay $16 million to settle False Claims Act allegations concerning fraudulently obtained small business contracts. (2017, August 10). USDOJ. Retrieved from https://www.justice.gov/opa/pr/defense-contractor-ads-inc-agrees-pay-16-million-settle-false-claims-act-allegations

281 Government contractors found guilty in $11 million veteran set-aside fraud scheme. (2018, November 21). USDOJ. Retrieved from https://www.justice.gov/usao-sdca/pr/government-contractors-found-guilty-11-million-veteran-set-aside-fraud-scheme

282 The Hayner Hoyt Corporation to pay $5 million to resolve False Claims Act liability. (2016, March 14). USDOJ. Retrieved from http://www.justice.gov/opa/pr/hayner-hoyt-corporation-pay-5-million-resolve-false-claims-act-liability

283 Owner of sham 'veteran-owned' company sentenced for $100 million fraud. (2016, September 27). USDOJ. Retrieved from https://www.justice.gov/usao-ma/pr/owner-sham-veteran-owned-company-sentenced-100-million-fraud

284 Gilbane Building Company to pay $1.1 million to resolve false claims allegations. (2015, March 18). USDOJ. Retrieved from https://www.justice.gov/opa/pr/gilbane-building-company-pay-11-million-resolve-false-claims-allegations

285 Engineering firm agrees to pay over $5 million to settle False Claims Act allegations related to small business, veterans set-asides. (2018, December 21). USDOJ. Retrieved from https://www.justice.gov/usao-cdca/pr/engineering-firm-agrees-pay-over-5-million-settle-false-claims-act-allegations-related

286 Ownership and control of service-disabled veteran-owned small business concerns. (2018, September 28). *Federal Register* 83:189. Retrieved from https://www.gpo.gov/fdsys/pkg/FR-2018-09-28/pdf/2018-21112.pdf

287 13 C.F.R. $125.13(m)

288 Project announcement: Audit of DoD service-disabled veteran-owned small business contract awards. (2018, October 9). DoD OIG Project No. D2019-D000AX-0019.000. Retrieved from http://www.dodig.mil/reports.html/Article/1660184/project-announcement-audit-of-dod-service-disabled-veteran-owned-small-business/

289 DoD OIG audit: What SDVOSBs need to know. (2018, October 25). *Natl. Law Review.* Retrieved from https://www.natlawreview.com/article/dod-oig-audit-what-sdvosbs-need-to-know

290 31 U.S.C. §§3729 - 3733

291 31 U.S.C. §§3729-33

292 Culbertson D. (2016, November 10). A deep look at the data: how are veterans doing in today's workforce? Indeed.com. Retrieved from http://blog.indeed.com/2016/11/10/veterans-employment/

293 3M Company agrees to pay $9.1 million to resolve allegations that it supplied the United States with defective dual-ended combat arms earplugs. (2018, July 26). USDOJ. Retrieved from https://www.justice.gov/opa/pr/3m-company-agrees-pay-91-million-resolve-allegations-it-supplied-united-states-defective-dual

294 Vassallo SA (July 2004). Lewis H. Wright Memorial Lecture. ASA Newsletter. **68** (7): 9-10. Retrieved from https://web.archive.org/web/20140202213600/http://www.asahq.org/For-Members/Publications-and-Research/Periodicals/ASA-Newsletter/July-2004-ASA-Newsletter.aspx.

295 Sobel R. They Satisfy: The Cigarette in American Life. (1978) Garden City (NY): Anchor Press/Doubleday, p84.

296 Benedict C. Quartermaster Activities in World War I. (1919) America's Munitions 1917-1918, Government Printing Office, Washington, DC. US Army Quartermaster Museum. Retrieved from http://old.qmfound.com/americas_munitions.htm.

297 Menninger RW, Nemiah JC. American Psychiatry After World War II (1944-1994). American Psychiatric Pub. Nov. 1 2008. p23. ISBN 978-1-58562-825-4.

298 Menninger RW, Nemiah JC. American Psychiatry After World War II (1944-1994). American Psychiatric Pub. Nov. 1 2008. p23. ISBN 978-1-58562-825-4.

299 Zinberg NE. G.I.'s and O.J.'s in Vietnam. New York Times Magazine, December 5, 1971. Retrieved from http://www.nytimes.com/1971/12/05/archives/gis-and-ojs-in-vietnam-gis-and-ojs-in-vietnam.html

300 Robins LN. et al. (1977). Vietnam Veterans Three Years after Vietnam: How Our Study Changed Our View of Heroin. Retrieved from http://onlinelibrary.wiley.com/doi/10.1111/j.1521-0391.2010.00046.x/abstract

301 National Institute on Drug Abuse. Substance Abuse in the Military. March 2013. Retrieved from https://www.drugabuse.gov/publications/drugfacts/substance-abuse-in-military.

302 Martinez M. Opiates killed 8 Americans in Afghanistan, Army records show. April 23, 2012. CNN. Retrieved from http://www.cnn.com/2012/04/21/us/afghanistan-soldier-drug-overdoses/index.html.

303 Committee on Prevention, Diagnosis, Treatment, and Management of Substance Use Disorders in the U.S. Armed Forces. February 21, 2013. Substance Use Disorders in the U.S. Armed Forces. Retrieved from http://www.ncbi.nlm.nih.gov/books/NBK207276/

304 Alvarez L. Home from the war, many veterans battle substance abuse. New York Times, 8 July 2008. Retrieved from http://www.nytimes.com/2008/07/08/world/americas/08iht-vets.1.14322423.html?pagewanted=all&_r=0.

305 Department of Health and Human Services. The Health Consequences of Smoking—50 Years of Progress: A Report of the Surgeon General. 2014. Retrieved from http://www.surgeongeneral.gov/library/reports/50-years-of-progress/.

306 Hoggatt KJ, Lehavot K, Krenek M, Schweizer CA, Simpson T. Prevalence of substance misuse among US veterans in the general population. Am J Addict. 2017 Jun; 26(4):357-365. Retrieved from http://onlinelibrary.wiley.com/doi/10.1111/ajad.12534/full.

307 Brown DW. Smoking prevalence among US veterans. J Gen Intern Med 2010;25(2):147-9.

308 Klevens RM, Giovino GA, Peddicord JP, Nelson DE, Mowery P, Grummer-Strawn L. The association between veteran status and cigarette-smoking behaviors. Am J Prev Med

1995;11(4):245-50.

309 Department of Defense. 2011 Health Related Behaviors Survey of Active Duty Military Personnel. February 2013. Retrieved from http://prevent.org//data/files/actiontoquit/final%20 2011%20hrb%20active%20duty%20survey%20report-release.pdf.

310 DiNicola CA, Seltxer DM. Tobacco product usage in deployed male and female military personnel. Mil Med. 2010;175:xi.

311 Department of Veterans Affairs, Veterans Health Administration. 2015 Survey of Veteran Enrollees' Health and Use of Health Care. December 2015. Retrieved from https://www.va.gov/ HEALTHPOLICYPLANNING/SoE2015/2015_VHA_SoE_Full_Findings_Report.pdf

312 Beckham JC, Kirby AC, Feldman ME, Hertzberg MA, Moore SD, Crawford AL, et al. Prevalence and correlates of heavy smoking in Vietnam veterans with chronic posttraumatic stress disorder. Addict Behav 1997;22(5):637-47.

313 McFall M, Saxon AJ, Malte CA, Chow B, Bailey S, Baker DG, et al. Integrating tobacco cessation into mental health care for posttraumatic stress disorder: a randomized controlled trial. JAMA 2010;304(22):2485-93.

314 McLaughlin JK, Hrubsec Z, Blot WJ, Fraumeni JF Jr. Smoking and cancer mortality among US veterans: a 26-year follow-up. Int J Cancer. 1995;60(2):190-193. Retrieved from https://www. ncbi.nlm.nih.gov/pubmed/7829214

315 National Institute on Drug Abuse. (March 2013). DrugFacts: Substance Abuse in the Military. Retrieved from https://www.drugabuse.gov/publications/drugfacts/substance-abuse-in-military

316 Stahre MA, Brewer RD, Fonesca VP, Naimi TS. Binge drinking among U.S. active-duty military personnel. American Journal of Preventative Medicine 36(3): 208-217, 2009. Retrieved from https://www.ncbi.nlm.nih.gov/pubmed?cmd=search&term=19215846

317 Harwood HJ, Zhang Y, Dall TM, et al. Economic implications of reduced binge drinking among the military health system's TRICARE Prime plan beneficiaries. Military Medicine 174(7):728-736, 2009. Retrieved from https://www.ncbi.nlm.nih.gov/pubmed?cmd=search&term=19685845

318 Hoggatt KJ, Lehavot K, Krenek M, Schweizer CA, Simpson T. Prevalence of substance misuse among US veterans in the general population. Am J Addict. 2017 Jun; 26(4):357-365.

319 Milliken CS, Auchterlonie JL, Hoge CW. Longitudinal Assessment of Mental Health Problems Among Active and Reserve Component Soldiers Returning from the Iraq War. JAMA. 2007;298(18):2141-2148.

320 Jacobson IG, Ryan MAK, Hooper TI, et al. Alcohol Use and Alcohol-Related Problems Before and After Military Combat Deployment. JAMA. 2008;300(6):663-675.

321 Maguen S, Lucenko BA, Reger MA, et al. The reported impact of direct and indirect killing on mental health symptoms in Iraq War Veterans. Journal of Traumatic Stress 23(1):86-90, 2010.

322 Savarese VW, Suvak MK, King LA, King DW. Relationships among alcohol use, hyperarousal, and marital abuse and violence in Vietnam veterans. J Trauma Stress. 2001 Oct; 14(4):717-32.

323 National Institute on Drug Abuse. Substance Abuse among the Military, Veterans, and Their Families. Topics in Brief. (April 2011) retrieved from http://www.drugs.indiana.edu/repository/ veterans.pdf

324 U.S. Department of Defense Survey of Health Related Behaviors among Active Duty Military Personnel. 2008. Retrieved from http://www.tricare.mil/tma/studiesEval.aspx

325 U.S. Department of Defense, Inspector General. Assessment of DoD Wounded Warrior Matters -- Camp LeJeune (2012). Retrieved from http://www.dodig.mil/spo/Reports/DODIG-2012-067.pdf

326 National Council on Alcoholism and Drug Dependence. Alcoholism, Drug Dependence and Veterans. 28 June 2015. Retrieved from https://www.ncadd.org/about-addiction/drugs/veterans-and-drugs

327 Jeffery DD, May L, Luckey B, Balison BM, Klette KL. Use and abuse of prescribed opioids, central nervous system depressants, and stimulants among US active duty military personnel in FY 2010. Mil Med. 2014;179(10):1141-1148. Retrieved from https://www.ncbi.nlm.nih.gov/pubmed/25269133

328 Seal KH, Shi Y, Cohen G, et al. Association of mental health disorders with prescription opioids and high-risk opioid use in US veterans of Iraq and Afghanistan. JAMA. 2012;307(9):940-947. Retrieved from https://www.ncbi.nlm.nih.gov/pubmed/22396516

329 Brewin B. Army Warns Doctors Against Using Certain Drugs in PTSD Treatment. Nextgov April 25, 2012. Retrieved from http://www.nextgov.com/defense/2012/04/broken-warriors-test/55389/

330 Demidenko M, Dobscha S, Morasco B, et al. Suicidal ideation and suicidal self-directed violence following clinician-initiated prescription opioid discontinuation among long-term opioid users. *General Hospital Psychiatry*. July-August 2017;47:29-35. Retrieved from http://www.sciencedirect.com/science/article/pii/S0163834317301093

331 Kessler RC, Nock MK, Schoenbaum M. Mental Health and the Army. JAMA Psychiatry. 2014;71(8):967-968. Retrieved from http://jamanetwork.com/journals/jamapsychiatry/article-abstract/1895655.

332 NIH Medline Plus. PTSD: A Growing Epidemic. 2009. Retrieved from https://medlineplus.gov/magazine/issues/winter09/articles/winter09pg10-14.html

333 Seal KH, Shi Y, Cohen G, et al. Association of Mental Health Disorders With Prescription Opioids and High-Risk Opioid Use in US Veterans of Iraq and Afghanistan. JAMA. 2012;307(9):940-947. Retrieved from http://jama.jamanetwork.com/article.aspx?articleid=1105046

334 Bohnert ASB, Ilgen MA, Ignacio RV, McCarthy JF, Valenstein M, Blow FC. Risk of Death From Accidental Overdose Associated With Psychiatric and Substance Use Disorders. Am. J. Psychiatry. 2012;169(1):64-70. Retrieved from http://ajp.psychiatryonline.org/doi/full/10.1176/appi.ajp.2011.10101476#

335 Corrigan JD, Rust E, Lamb-Hart GL. The nature and extent of substance abuse problems among persons with traumatic brain injuries. Journal of Head Trauma Rehabilitation. 1995 10 (3), 29-45

336 Ommaya AK, Salazar AM, Dannenberg AL, Ommaya AK, Chervinsky AB, Schwab K. Outcome After Traumatic Brain Injury in the U.S. Military Medical System. J Trauma. 1996 Dec;41(6):972-5.

337 Bjork JM, Grant SJ. Does Traumatic Brain Injury Increase Risk for Substance Abuse? J Neurotrauma. 2009 Jul; 26(7): 1077-1082.

338 Yurgil KA, Barkauskas DA, Vasterling JJ, et al. Association between traumatic brain injury and risk of posttraumatic stress disorder in active-duty Marines. JAMA Psychiatry. 2014 Feb;71(2):149-57.

339 Hoge CW, McGurk D, Thomas JL, et al. Mild traumatic brain injury in U.S. soldiers returning from Iraq. New England Journal of Medicine 358(5):453-463, 2008.

340 Suris A, Lind L. Military sexual trauma: A review of prevalence and associated health consequences in veterans. Trauma, Violence & Abuse 9(4):250-269, 2008.

341 https://betobaccofree.hhs.gov/about-tobacco/facts-figures/index.html

342 https://www.cdc.gov/alcohol/fact-sheets/alcohol-use.htm

343 Sayer NA, Carlson KF, Frazier PA. Reintegration Challenges in U.S. Service Members and Veterans Following Combat Deployment. Soc. Issues Pol. Rev. 2014;8(1) 33-73. Retrieved from http://onlinelibrary.wiley.com/doi/10.1111/sipr.12001/abstract

344 Sayer NA, Carlson KF, Frazier PA. Reintegration Challenges in U.S. Service Members and Veterans Following Combat Deployment. Soc. Issues Pol. Rev. 2014;8(1) 33-73. Retrieved from http://onlinelibrary.wiley.com/doi/10.1111/sipr.12001/abstract

345 Bronson J, Carson EA, Noonan ME, Berzofsky M. Veterans in Prison and Jail, 2011-2012. RTI International. December 7, 2015. Retrieved from https://www.bjs.gov/index.cfm?ty=pbdetail&iid=5479

346 100,000 Homes Campaign. (2011, November). National Survey of Homeless Veterans in 100,000 Homes Campaign Communities. Retrieved from http://www.va.gov/homeless/docs/nationalsurveyofhomelessveterans_final.pdf

347 Substance Abuse and Mental Health Services Administration. (2014, January 7). Twenty-one Percent of Veterans in Substance Abuse Treatment Were Homeless. Retrieved from http://www.samhsa.gov/data/sites/default/files/spot121-homeless-veterans-2014.pdf

348 Back SE, McCauley JL, Korte KJ, et al. A double-blind randomized controlled pilot trial of N-acetylcysteine in veterans with PTSD and substance use disorders. J Clin Psychiatry. 2016;77(11):e1439-e1446. Retrieved from https://www.ncbi.nlm.nih.gov/pmc/articles/PMC5226873/

349 Batki SL, Pennington DL, Lasher B, et al. Topiramate treatment of alcohol use disorder in veterans with posttraumatic stress disorder: a randomized controlled pilot trial. Alcohol Clin Exp Res. 2014;38(8):2169-2177. Retrieved from https://www.ncbi.nlm.nih.gov/pmc/articles/PMC4146719/

350 Allen v. Principi, 237 F.3d 1368, 1370 (Fed. Cir. 2001)

351 38 C.F.R. §3.301(c)(2).

352 Kessler RC, Sonnega A, Bromet E, Hughes M, Nelson CB. Posttraumatic stress disorder in the National Comorbidity Survey. Arch Gen Psychiatry. 1995 Dec;52(12):1048-60.

353 McFall M, Cook J. PTSD and health risk behavior. Department of Veterans Affairs. Research Quarterly. 2006;17(4) Retrieved from https://www.ptsd.va.gov/professional/newsletters/research-quarterly/V17N4.pdf

354 2018 PIT estimate of veteran homelessness in the U.S. (2018, November). HUD. Retrieved from https://www.hudexchange.info/resource/5772/2018-pit-estimate-of-veteran-homelessness-in-the-us/

355 Trump administration announces decline in veteran homelessness. (2018, November 1). HUD. Retrieved from https://www.hud.gov/press/press_releases_media_advisories/HUD_No_18_132

356 Women veterans and homelessness. (2016, July). U.S. Department of Veterans Affairs National

Center on Homelessness Among Veterans. Retrieved from https://www.va.gov/HOMELESS/ nchav/docs/HERS-Womens-Proceedings.pdf

357 Homelessness in America: Focus on veterans. (2018, June). U.S. Interagency

Council on Homelessness. Retrieved from https://www.usich.gov/resources/uploads/asset_library/ Homelessness_in_America._Focus_on_Veterans.pdf

358 Tsai J, Rosenheck RA. (2015, July 31) Risk factors for homelessness among US veterans. *Epidemiol Rev.* 2015. 37: 177-195. Retrieved from https://www.ncbi.nlm.nih.gov/pmc/articles/ PMC4521393/

359 Official unemployment rate was 3.9 percent in December 2018; U-6 was 7.6 percent. (2019, January 9). Bureau of Labor Statistics. Retrieved from https://www.bls.gov/opub/ted/2019/ official-unemployment-rate-was-3-point-9-percent-in-december-2018-u-6-was-7-point-6-percent.htm?view_full

360 Employment situation of veterans—2018. (2019, March 21). Bureau of Labor Statistics. Retrieved from https://www.bls.gov/news.release/pdf/vet.pdf

361 Disability status: Census 2000 brief (2003, March). US Census Bureau. Retrieved from https:// www.census.gov/prod/2003pubs/c2kbr-17.pdf

362 Homelessness in America: Focus on veterans. (2018, June). U.S. Interagency

Council on Homelessness. Retrieved from https://www.usich.gov/resources/uploads/asset_library/ Homelessness_in_America._Focus_on_Veterans.pdf

363 Employment situation of veterans—2018. (2019, March 21). Bureau of Labor Statistics. Retrieved from https://www.bls.gov/news.release/pdf/vet.pdf

364 Tarr P. (2018, November 19). Homelessness and mental illness: A challenge to our society. *Brain & Behavior.* Retrieved from https://www.bbrfoundation.org/blog/homelessness-and-mental-illness-challenge-our-society

365 Kessler RC, Nock MK, Schoenbaum M. (2014, August). Mental Health and the Army. *JAMA Psychiatry.* 71(8):967-968. Retrieved from http://jamanetwork.com/journals/jamapsychiatry/ article-abstract/1895655.

366 Homelessness in America: Focus on veterans. (2018, June). U.S. Interagency

Council on Homelessness. Retrieved from https://www.usich.gov/resources/uploads/asset_library/ Homelessness_in_America._Focus_on_Veterans.pdf

367 Brignone E, Gundlapalli AV, et al. (2016, June) Differential risk for homelessness among US male and female

veterans with a positive screen for military sexual trauma. *JAMA Psychiatry.* 73(6):582-589 Retrieved from https://jamanetwork.com/journals/jamapsychiatry/fullarticle/2515956

368 Montgomery AE, Sorrentino AE, et al. (2018, April). Recent intimate partner violence and housing instability among women veterans. *Am. J. Prevent. Med.* 54(4) 584-590. Retrieved from https://www.ajpmonline.org/article/S0749-3797(18)30051-5/fulltext

369 Homelessness in America: Focus on veterans. (2018, June). U.S. Interagency

Council on Homelessness. Retrieved from https://www.usich.gov/resources/uploads/asset_library/ Homelessness_in_America._Focus_on_Veterans.pdf

370 Homelessness in America: Focus on veterans. (2018, June). U.S. Interagency

Council on Homelessness. Retrieved from https://www.usich.gov/resources/uploads/asset_library/ Homelessness_in_America._Focus_on_Veterans.pdf

371   Kaeble D, Cowhig M. (2018, April). Correctional populations in the United States, 2016. Bureau of Justice Statistics. Retrieved from https://www.bjs.gov/content/pub/pdf/cpus16.pdf

372   Bronson J, Carson EA, et al. (2015, December). Veterans in prison and jail, 2011-12. Bureau of Justice Statistics. Retrieved from https://www.bjs.gov/content/pub/pdf/vpj1112.pdf

373   Elbogen EB, Johnson SC, et al. (2012, December). Criminal justice involvement, trauma, and negative affect in Iraq and Afghanistan war era veterans. *J Consult Clin Psychol.* 80(6):1097-102. Retrieved from https://www.ncbi.nlm.nih.gov/pubmed/?term=10.1037 percent2Fa0029967

374   VA could improve management by establishing performance measures and fully assessing risks. (2016, April). U.S. General Accountability Office GAO-16-193. Retrieved from https://www.gao. gov/assets/680/676922.pdf

375   Breaking the cycle of veteran incarceration and homelessness: Emerging community practices. (2015, June). U.S. Interagency Council on Homelessness. Retrieved from https://www.usich.gov/ resources/uploads/asset_library/Justice_Involved_Veterans.pdf

376   Bronson J, Carson EA, et al. (2015, December). Veterans in prison and jail, 2011-12. Bureau of Justice Statistics. Retrieved from https://www.bjs.gov/content/pub/pdf/vpj1112.pdf

377   Recidivism among federal offenders: A comprehensive overview. (2016, March). U.S. Sentencing Commission. Retrieved from https://www.ussc.gov/sites/default/files/pdf/research-and-publications/research-publications/2016/recidivism_overview.pdf

378   Bronson J, Carson EA, et al. (2015, December). Veterans in prison and jail, 2011-12. Bureau of Justice Statistics. Retrieved from https://www.bjs.gov/content/pub/pdf/vpj1112.pdf

379   Canada KE, Peters C. (2017, June). 'They teach you how to weather the storm, but they don't teach you how to dance in the rain:' Veterans' perspectives on the pathways to criminal justice involvement. *J. Qual. Crim. Just. Criminol.* 5(1) 23-46. Retrieved from http://www.jqcjc.org/ documents/v5i1.pdf#page=29

380   Bronson J, Carson EA, et al. (2015, December). Veterans in prison and jail, 2011-12. Bureau of Justice Statistics. Retrieved from https://www.bjs.gov/content/pub/pdf/vpj1112.pdf

381   Enabling Collaborative Support to Reintegrate the Military Family. (2014, November). Office of the Chairman of the Joint Chiefs of Staff. Retrieved from https://www.jcs.mil/Portals/36/ Documents/CORe/141103_Enabling_Collaborative_Support.pdf

382   The state of the American veteran: The San Francisco veterans study. (2017, May). USC Suzanne Dworak-Peck School of Social Work Center for Innovation and Research on Veterans & Military Families. Retrieved from http://cir.usc.edu/publications/other-reports#8e74e7178ec1f94c8

383   Nussbaumer B. (2015, October 8). The military's transition programs are under-delivering support to service members. *Task & Purpose.* Retrieved from https://taskandpurpose.com/the-militarys-transition-programs-are-under-delivering-support-to-service-members

384   2018 veterans well-being survey. (2018, October). Edelman. Retrieved from https://www. edelman.com/sites/g/files/aatuss191/files/2018-10/2018-Edelman-Veterans-Well-being-Survey. pdf

385   DePastino T. (2003). Citizen hobo: How a century of homelessness shaped America. Chicago, IL: Univ. Chicago Press.

386 Homelessness in America: Hearing before the subcommittee on housing and urban affairs of the committee on banking, housing, and urban affairs. (1987, January 29). U.S. Committee on Banking, Housing, and Urban Affairs. Subcommittee on Housing and Urban Affairs. Retrieved from https://catalog.hathitrust.org/Record/007603683

387 Jansson BS. (2010). *Becoming an effective policy advocate.* Cengage Learning Inc. p. 72.

388 Howell K. (2014, December 3). Despite first lady's vow to end veteran homelessness, VA fails miserably. *Washington Times.* Retrieved from http://www.washingtontimes.com/news/2014/dec/3/despite-michelle-obamas-vow-to-end-veteran-homeles/?page=all#pagebreak

389 Trump administration announces decline in veteran homelessness. (2018, November 1). HUD. Retrieved from https://www.hud.gov/press/press_releases_media_advisories/HUD_No_18_132

390 2018 veterans well-being survey. (2018, October). Edelman. Retrieved from https://www.edelman.com/sites/g/files/aatuss191/files/2018-10/2018-Edelman-Veterans-Well-being-Survey.pdf

391 2018 veterans well-being survey. (2018, October). Edelman. Retrieved from https://www.edelman.com/sites/g/files/aatuss191/files/2018-10/2018-Edelman-Veterans-Well-being-Survey.pdf.

392 2018 veterans well-being survey. (2018, October). Edelman. Retrieved from https://www.edelman.com/sites/g/files/aatuss191/files/2018-10/2018-Edelman-Veterans-Well-being-Survey.pdf

393 Wax-Thibodeaux E. (2019, February 7). The parking lot suicides. *Washington Post.* Retrieved from https://www.washingtonpost.com/news/national/wp/2019/02/07/feature/the-parking-lot-suicides/

394 VA National Suicide Data Report 2005-2016 (2018, September). Office of Mental Health and Suicide Prevention. Retrieved from https://www.mentalhealth.va.gov/docs/data-sheets/OMHSP_National_Suicide_Data_Report_2005-2016_508.pdf

395 VA releases veteran suicide statistics by state. (2017, September 15). VA Press Release. Retrieved from https://www.va.gov/opa/pressrel/pressrelease.cfm?id=2951

396 Slack D. (2017, November 15). Vet set himself on fire after long VA waits, appointment cancellation, investigation finds. *USA Today.* Retrieved from https://www.usatoday.com/story/news/politics/2017/11/15/vet-set-himself-fire-after-long-va-waits-appointment-cancellation-investigation-finds/866834001/

397 Rebelo K. (2016, August 24). Veteran kills himself in parking lot of V.A. hospital on Long Island. *The New York Times.* Retrieved from https://www.nytimes.com/2016/08/25/nyregion/veteran-kills-himself-in-parking-lot-of-va-hospital-on-long-island.html

398 Wax-Thibodeaux E. (2019, February 7). The parking lot suicides. *Washington Post.* Retrieved from https://www.washingtonpost.com/news/national/wp/2019/02/07/feature/the-parking-lot-suicides/

399 Jaglois J. (2016, November 28). Man takes own life at Murfreesboro VA hospital. WKRN News. Retrieved from https://www.wkrn.com/news/man-takes-own-life-at-murfreesboro-va-hospital/1057580857

400 Review of mental health care provided prior to a veteran's death by suicide Minneapolis VA health care system Minnesota (2018, September 25). VAOIG Office of Healthcare Inspections. Report # 18-02875-305. Retrieved from https://www.va.gov/oig/pubs/VAOIG-18-02875-305.pdf

401 Wax-Thibodeaux E. (2019, February 7). The parking lot suicides. *Washington Post*. Retrieved from https://www.washingtonpost.com/news/national/wp/2019/02/07/feature/the-parking-lot-suicides/

402 Fitzgerald M. (2018, October 10). Phillip Crews killed himself in a VA waiting room, a 'parking lot suicide.' *Riverfront Times*. Retrieved from https://m.riverfronttimes.com/stlouis/phillip-crews-killed-himself-in-a-va-waiting-room-now-hes-a-parking-lot-suicide/Content?oid=25580100&showFullText=true

403 Altman H. (2018, December 17). Jim Turner, a retired Marine colonel, took his life at the Bay Pines VA campus. He was the 5th veteran to do so since 2013. *Tampa Bay Times*. Retrieved from https://www.tampabay.com/news/military/jim-turner-a-retired-marine-colonel-took-his-life-at-the-bay-pines-va-campus-he-was-the-5th-veteran-to-do-so-since-2013-20181217/

404 Shane L, Kime P. (2016, July 7). New VA study finds 20 veterans commit suicide each day. *Military Times*. Retrieved from https://www.militarytimes.com/veterans/2016/07/07/new-va-study-finds-20-veterans-commit-suicide-each-day/

405 Weiner J, Richmond TS, Conigliaro J, Wiebe DJ. (2011, May). Military veteran mortality following a survived suicide attempt. *BMC Public Health*. 11(1):374. Retrieved from https://www.ncbi.nlm.nih.gov/pubmed/21605448.

406 Improvements needed in suicide prevention media outreach campaign oversight and evaluation. (2018, November 15). U.S. Government Accountability Office. GAO-19-66. Retrieved from https://www.gao.gov/products/GAO-19-66

407 U.S. drug overdose deaths continue to rise; increase fueled by synthetic opioids. (2018, March 29). Centers for Disease Control and Prevention Press Release. Retrieved from https://www.cdc.gov/media/releases/2018/p0329-drug-overdose-deaths.html

408 Kristof N. (2012, April 14). A veteran's death, the nation's shame. *The New York Times*. Retrieved from https://www.nytimes.com/2012/04/15/opinion/sunday/kristof-a-veterans-death-the-nations-shame.html

409 VA National Suicide Data Report 2005-2016 (2018, September). Office of Mental Health and Suicide Prevention. Retrieved from https://www.mentalhealth.va.gov/docs/data-sheets/OMHSP_National_Suicide_Data_Report_2005-2016_508.pdf

410 VA National Suicide Data Report 2005-2016 (2018, September). Office of Mental Health and Suicide Prevention. Retrieved from https://www.mentalhealth.va.gov/docs/data-sheets/OMHSP_National_Suicide_Data_Report_2005-2016_508.pdf

411 VA National Suicide Data Report 2005-2016 (2018, September). Office of Mental Health and Suicide Prevention. Retrieved from https://www.mentalhealth.va.gov/docs/data-sheets/OMHSP_National_Suicide_Data_Report_2005-2016_508.pdf

412 VA National Suicide Data Report 2005-2016 (2018, September). Office of Mental Health and Suicide Prevention. Retrieved from https://www.mentalhealth.va.gov/docs/data-sheets/OMHSP_National_Suicide_Data_Report_2005-2016_508.pdf

413 VA National Suicide Data Report 2005-2016 (2018, September). Office of Mental Health and Suicide Prevention. Retrieved from https://www.mentalhealth.va.gov/docs/data-sheets/OMHSP_National_Suicide_Data_Report_2005-2016_508.pdf

414 VA National Suicide Data Report 2005-2016 (2018, September). Office of Mental Health and Suicide Prevention. Retrieved from https://www.mentalhealth.va.gov/docs/data-sheets/OMHSP_National_Suicide_Data_Report_2005-2016_508.pdf

415 Suicide: risk and protective factors. (2018, September 6). Centers for Disease Control and Prevention. Retrieved from https://www.cdc.gov/violenceprevention/suicide/riskprotectivefactors.html

416 Isometsa ET. (2001, November). Psychological autopsy studies-a review. *Eur Psychiatry.* 16(7):379-85. Retrieved from https://www.ncbi.nlm.nih.gov/pubmed/11728849

417 Kessler RC, Sonnega A, et al. (1995, December). Posttraumatic stress disorder in the national co-morbidity survey. *Archives of General Psychiatry.* 52:1048-1060. Retrieved from https://www.ncbi.nlm.nih.gov/pubmed/7492257

418 Reeves WC, Strine TW, et al. (2011, September 2). Mental illness surveillance among adults in the United States. *CDC Morbidity and Mortality Weekly Report.* 60(03);1-32. Retrieved from https://www.cdc.gov/mmwr/preview/mmwrhtml/su6003a1.htm?s_cid=su6003a1_w

419 Meadows SO, Engel CC, et al. (2018) Mental and emotional health among U.S. active-duty service members. *RAND Corporation.* Retrieved from https://www.rand.org/pubs/research_briefs/RB9955z3.html

420 McLaughlin KA, Costello EJ, et al. (2012, September). Socioeconomic status and adolescent mental disorders. *Am J Public Health.* 102(9): 1742-1750. Retrieved from https://www.ncbi.nlm.nih.gov/pmc/articles/PMC3482020/

421 Kane T. (2006, October 27). Who are the recruits? The demographic characteristics of U.S. military enlistment, 2003-2005. *The Heritage Foundation.* Retrieved from https://www.heritage.org/defense/report/who-are-the-recruits-the-demographic-characteristics-us-military-enlistment-2003

422 Lutz A. (2008). Who joins the military?: A look at race, class, and immigration status. *Syracuse University SURFACE.* Retrieved from https://surface.syr.edu/cgi/viewcontent.cgi?article=1002&context=soc

423 Lutz A. (2008). Who joins the military?: A look at race, class, and immigration status. *Syracuse University SURFACE.* Retrieved from https://surface.syr.edu/cgi/viewcontent.cgi?article=1002&context=soc

424 Broughman S, Rettig A, Peterson J. (2017, August 15). Characteristics of private schools in the United States: Results from the 2015-16 private school universe survey Council for American Private Education. National Center for Education Statistics. Retrieved from https://nces.ed.gov/pubsearch/pubsinfo.asp?pubid=2017073.

425 Actions needed to ensure post-traumatic stress disorder and traumatic brain injury are considered in misconduct separations. (2017 May). USGAO Report to Congressional Committees. GAO-17-260. Retrieved from http://www.gao.gov/assets/690/684608.pdf

426 Actions needed to ensure post-traumatic stress disorder and traumatic brain injury are considered in misconduct separations. (2017 May). USGAO Report to Congressional Committees. GAO-17-260. Retrieved from http://www.gao.gov/assets/690/684608.pdf

427 Mosti C, Coccaro EF. (2018, March 5). Mild traumatic brain injury and aggression, impulsivity, and history of other- and self-directed aggression. *J Neuropsychiatry Clin Neurosci.* 30(3):220-227. Retrieved from https://www.ncbi.nlm.nih.gov/pubmed/29505319

428 VA secretary announces intention to expand mental health care to former service members with other-than-honorable discharges and in crisis. (2017, March 8). VA Office of Public and Intergovernmental Affairs. Retrieved from https://www.va.gov/opa/pressrel/pressrelease.cfm?id=2867

429 Walsh S. (2018, October 18). VA struggles to reach other-than-honorable-discharge vets in need of help. *National Public Radio.* Retrieved from https://www.npr.org/2018/10/18/657789457/va-struggles-to-reach-other-than-honorable-discharge-vets-in-need-of-help

430 President Donald J. Trump signs Executive Order to improve mental health resources for veterans transitioning from active duty to civilian life. (2018, January 9). VA Office of Public and Intergovernmental Affairs. Retrieved from https://www.va.gov/opa/pressrel/pressrelease.cfm?id=3995

431 Department of Veterans Affairs - Budget in Brief 2019. Retrieved from https://www.va.gov/budget/docs/summary/fy2019VAbudgetInBrief.pdf

432 Care and benefits for veterans strengthened by $186.5 billion VA budget. (2017, May 23). VA Office of Public and Intergovernmental Affairs. Retrieved from https://www.va.gov/opa/pressrel/pressrelease.cfm?id=2909

433 Improvements needed in suicide prevention media outreach campaign oversight and evaluation. (2018, November 15). U.S. Government Accountability Office. GAO-19-66. Retrieved from https://www.gao.gov/products/GAO-19-66

434 Department of Veterans Affairs - Budget in Brief 2019. Retrieved from https://www.va.gov/budget/docs/summary/fy2019VAbudgetInBrief.pdf

435 National Health and Nutrition Examination Survey 2017–March 2020 Prepandemic data files. Retrieved December 4, 2022, from https://stacks.cdc.gov/view/cdc/106273

436 VA/DoD Clinical Practice Guideline for Screening and Management of Overweight and Obesity. Retrieved December 4, 2022, from https://www.healthquality.va.gov/guidelines/CD/obesity/

437 Robinson, K. M., Vander Weg, M., Laroche, H. H., Carrel, M., Wachsmuth, J., Kazembe, K., & Vaughan Sarrazin, M. (2022). Obesity treatment initiation, retention, and outcomes in the Veterans Affairs MOVE! program among rural and Urban Veterans. *Obesity Science & Practice.* doi:10.1002/osp4.622

438 Ídem

439 Breland, J. Y., Phibbs, C. S., Hoggatt, K. J., Washington, D. L., Lee, J., Haskell, S., . . . Frayne, S. M. (2017). The obesity epidemic in the Veterans Health Administration: Prevalence among key populations of women and Men Veterans. *Journal of General Internal Medicine, 32*(S1), 11-17. doi:10.1007/s11606-016-3962-1

440 Puhl, R. M., & Heuer, C. A. (2010). Obesity stigma: Important considerations for public health. *American Journal of Public Health, 100*(6), 1019-1028. doi:10.2105/ajph.2009.159491

441 People who are overweight get paid less, according to a new study. *Business Insider.* Retrieved December 4, 2022, from https://ca.finance.yahoo.com/news/people-overweight-paid-less-according-125100596.html

442 Nguyen, J. C., Killcross, A. S., & Jenkins, T. A. (2014). Obesity and cognitive decline: Role of inflammation and vascular changes. *Frontiers in Neuroscience, 8.* doi:10.3389/fnins.2014.00375

443 Ward, Z. J., Bleich, S. N., Long, M. W., & Gortmaker, S. L. (2021). Association of Body Mass index with health care expenditures in the United States by age and sex. *PLOS ONE, 16*(3). doi:10.1371/journal.pone.0247307

444 Novelly, T. (2022, September 28). Even more young Americans are unfit to serve, a new study finds. here's why. Retrieved December 4, 2022, from https://www.military.com/daily-news/2022/09/28/new-pentagon-study-shows-77-of-young-americans-are-ineligible-military-service.html

445 Demographics of the U.S. Military. (2020, July 13). Council on Foreign Relations.

446 National Health and Nutrition Examination Survey 2017–March 2020 Prepandemic data files. Retrieved December 4, 2022, from https://stacks.cdc.gov/view/cdc/106273

447 Bentley, R. A., Ormerod, P., & Ruck, D. J. (2018). Recent origin and evolution of obesity-income correlation across the United States. *Palgrave Communications, 4*(1). doi:10.1057/s41599-018-0201-x

448 Goto, R., Nianogo, R., Okubo, Y., & Inoue, K. (2022). Evaluation of obesity trends among US adolescents by socioeconomic status, 1999-2018. *JAMA Pediatrics, 176*(9), 937. doi:10.1001/jamapediatrics.2022.1838

449 Prevalence of obesity among adults, by household income and education - United States, 2011–2014. (2018, February 26). *Morbidity and Mortality Weekly Report (MMWR)*. Retrieved December 4, 2022, from https://www.cdc.gov/mmwr/volumes/66/wr/mm6650a1.htm?s_cid=mm6650a1_w

450 Demographics of the U.S. Military. (2020, July 13). Council on Foreign Relations.

451 Demographics of the U.S. Military. (2020, July 13). Council on Foreign Relations.

452 CDC - Behavioral Risk Factor Surveillance System. (2022, August 29). Retrieved December 5, 2022, from https://www.cdc.gov/brfss/index.html

453 Why is the U.S. military struggling to recruit Young Americans? *NBC News*. Retrieved December 5, 2022, from https://www.nbcnews.com/news/military/every-branch-us-military-struggling-meet-2022-recruiting-goals-officia-rcna35078

454 Falbe, J., Thompson, H. R., Becker, C. M., Rojas, N., McCulloch, C. E., & Madsen, K. A. (2016). Impact of the Berkeley Excise Tax on Sugar-Sweetened Beverage Consumption. *American journal of public health, 106*(10), 1865–1871. https://doi.org/10.2105/AJPH.2016.303362

455 *Larson v. McDonough*. 10 F.4th 1325 (Fed. Cir. 2021).

456 VA/DoD Clinical Practice Guideline for Screening and Management of Overweight and Obesity. Retrieved December 4, 2022, from https://www.healthquality.va.gov/guidelines/CD/obesity/

457 USDA - My Plate. Protein foods. Retrieved December 5, 2022, from https://www.myplate.gov/eat-healthy/protein-foods

458 USDA - Summary of business reports. Retrieved December 5, 2022, from https://www.rma.usda.gov/SummaryOfBusiness

459 Government support for real conservation, not CAFOs. Retrieved December 5, 2022, from https://news.yahoo.com/government-support-real-conservation-not-080012333.html

460 Dietary guidelines for Americans 2020-2025. Retrieved December 5, 2022, from https://www.dietaryguidelines.gov/resources/2020-2025-dietary-guidelines-online-materials

461 Juul, F., Parekh, N., Martinez-Steele, E., Monteiro, C. A., & Chang, V. W. (2021). Ultra-processed food consumption among US adults from 2001 to 2018. *The American Journal of Clinical Nutrition, 115*(1), 211-221. doi:10.1093/ajcn/nqab305

462 Elflein, J. (2022, July 26). Alzheimer's Medicare and Medicaid costs forecast 2022-2050. Retrieved December 5, 2022, from https://www.statista.com/statistics/643072/alzheimers-medicare-medicaid-care-costs-us/

463 Tsai, C., Pan, C., Chen, F., Huang, T., Tsai, M., & Chuang, C. (2019). Differences in neurocognitive performance and metabolic and inflammatory indices in male adults with obesity as a function of regular exercise. *Experimental Physiology, 104*(11), 1650-1660. doi:10.1113/ep087862

464 *Commissioner, I.N.S. v. Jean*, 110 S. Ct. 2316, 2321 (1990).

465 28 U.S.C.S. § 2412(d)(1)(A).

466 See McArthur Jones v. Derwinski and Karnas v. Derwinski, 2 Vet. App. 231 (1992).

467 *See* Federal Courts Administration Act of 1992, Pub. L. No. 102-572, tit. V, § 506, 106 Stat. 4513 (Oct. 29, 1992). Congress amended section 2412(d)(2)(F) to add the United States Court of Veterans Appeals (now Court of Appeals for Veterans Claims) to the definition of Courts authorized to make awards under the EAJA. *Id.*